Solutions and Tests For

Advanced Physics
in
Creation

by Dr. Jay L. Wile

Solutions and Tests for Advanced Physics in Creation

Published by
Apologia Educational Ministries, Inc.
1106 Meridian Plaza, Suite 220
Anderson, IN 46016
www.apologia.com

Manufactured in the United States of America
Third Printing October, 2009

ISBN: 978-1-932012-19-4

Printed by Courier, Inc., Kendallville, IN

Advanced Physics in Creation
Solutions and Tests

TABLE OF CONTENTS

Tests

Solutions to the Tests

TEACHER'S NOTES

Advanced Physics In Creation

Thank you for choosing *Advanced Physics In Creation.* I designed this modular course specifically to meet the needs of the homeschooling parent. I am very sensitive to the fact that most homeschooling parents do not know physics very well, if at all. As a result, they consider it nearly impossible to teach to their children. This course has several features that make it ideal for such a parent.

1. The course is written in a conversational style. Unlike many authors, I do not get wrapped up in the desire to write formally. As a result, the text is easy to read and the student feels more like he or she is *learning*, not just reading.

2. The course is completely self-contained. Each module includes the text of the lesson, experiments to perform, problems to work, questions to answer, and a test to take. The solutions to the problems and questions are fully explained, and the test answers are provided. The experiments are written in a careful, step-by-step manner that tells the student not only what he or she should be doing, but also what he or she should be observing.

3. Most importantly, this course is Christ-centered. In every way possible, I try to make the science of physics glorify God. One of the most important things that you and your student should get out of this course is a deeper appreciation for the wonder of God's creation!

I hope that you and your student enjoy taking this course as much as I have enjoyed writing it.

Pedagogy of the Text

(1) There are three types of exercises that the student is expected to complete: "on your own" problems, review questions, and practice problems.

- The **"on your own"** problems should be solved as the student reads the text. The act of working out these problems will cement in the student's mind the concepts he or she is trying to learn. The solutions to these problems are included as a part of the student's text. The student should feel free to use these solutions to help understand the problems.

- The **review questions** are conceptual in nature and should be answered after the student completes the module. They will help the student recall the important concepts from the reading. As your student's teacher, you can decide whether or not they can look at the solutions to these questions. They are located in this book.

- The **practice problems** should also be solved after the module has been completed, allowing the student to review the important quantitative skills from the module. As your student's teacher, you can decide whether or not they can look at the solutions to these problems. They are located in this book.

(2) In addition to the problems, there is also a test for each module in this book. **I strongly recommend that you administer each test once the student has completed the module and all associated exercises. The student should be allowed to have only a calculator, pencil, and paper while taking the test.** I understand that many homeschoolers do not like the idea of administering tests. However, if your student is planning to attend college, it is *absolutely* necessary that he or she become comfortable with taking tests!

(3) Any information that the student must memorize is centered in the text and put in boldface type. In addition, all definitions presented in the text need to be memorized. Finally, if an equation must be used to answer any "on your own" problem, practice problem, or review question, then it must be memorized for the test. In general these student exercises are meant as a study guide for the tests. Skills and knowledge necessary to complete these student exercises will be required for the test.

(4) Words that appear in bold-face type (centered or not) in the text are important terms that the student should know.

(5) The equations are numbered so that I can refer to them easily.

(6) When looking at the solutions to the students exercises and tests, you will notice that every solution contains an underlined section. That is the answer. The rest is simply an explanation of how to get the answer. For questions that require a sentence or paragraph as an answer, the student need not have *exactly* what is in the solution. The basic message of his or her answer, however, has to be the same as the basic message given in the solutions.

Experiments

The experiments in this course are designed to be done as the student is reading the text. I recommend that your student keep a notebook of these experiments. This notebook serves two purposes. First, as the student writes about the experiment in the notebook, he or she will be forced to think through all of the concepts that were explored in the experiment. This will help the student cement them into his or her mind. Second, certain colleges might actually ask for some evidence that your student did, indeed, have a laboratory component to his or her physics course. The notebook will not only provide such evidence but will also show the college administrator the quality of the physics instruction that you provided to your student. I recommend that you perform your experiments in the following way:

- When your student gets to the experiment during the reading, have him or her read through the experiment in its entirety. This will allow the student to gain a quick understanding of what her or she is to do.

- Once the student has read the experiment, he or she should then start a new page in his or her laboratory notebook. The first page should be used to write down all of the data taken during the experiments and perform any calculation explained in the experiment.

- When the student has finished the experiment, he or she should write a brief report in his or her notebook, right after the page where the data and calculations were written. The report should be a brief discussion of what was done and what was learned. The report should be written so that someone who had never read the experiment in the text could understand the basics of what was done and what was learned. It needn't be incredibly detailed, but it should be written clearly and with good grammar.

> **PLEASE OBSERVE COMMON SENSE SAFETY PRECAUTIONS. The experiments are no more dangerous than most normal, household activities. Remember, however, that the vast majority of accidents do happen in the home. Chemicals should never be ingested; hot beakers and flames should be regarded with care; and OSHA recommends that all physics experiments be performed while wearing some sort of eye protection such as safety glasses or goggles.**

Question/Answer Service

For all those who use my curriculum, I offer a question/answer service. If there is anything in the modules that you do not understand - from an esoteric concept to a solution for one of the problems - just contact me by any of the means listed on the **NEED HELP?** page located at the front of the student text.

Answers To The

Review Questions

ANSWERS TO THE REVIEW QUESTIONS FOR MODULE #1

1. The conversion relationship between meters and kilometers is as follows:

$$1 \text{ km} = 1,000 \text{ m}$$

However, to get the relationship between meters *squared* and kilometers *squared*, we must square both sides:

$$\underline{1 \text{ km}^2 = 1,000,000 \text{ m}^2}$$

2. The speeds given are the magnitudes of the vectors. Thus, vector **A** is more than twice as long (but not quite three times as long) as vector **B**. The angles are defined counterclockwise from the positive x-axis:

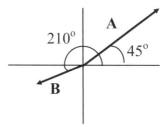

3. In scalar multiplication, you multiply the magnitude of the vector by the scalar. If the scalar is negative, the vector points in the opposite direction. You can point a vector in the opposite direction by just adding 180.0° to the angle. Thus, the new vector is <u>72 miles at 195 degrees</u>.

4. This vector has a positive x-component and a negative y-component. That means it is to the right of and below the origin. That is region <u>IV</u>.

5. The angles we report must be defined counterclockwise from the positive x-axis. The angle that comes from the equation does not always do that. What we must do to correct this depends on the region. This vector is in region III (left of and below the origin), so you <u>must add 180.0 to the result of the equation</u>.

6. The dot product is commutative. Thus, **A•B** = **B•A**. Therefore it is <u>34.2 m^2</u>.

7. <u>parallel</u>

8. <u>No work is being done</u>. Remember, $W = \mathbf{F \bullet x} = F \cdot x \cdot \cos\theta$. The cosine of 90 is 0.

9. The cross product is not commutative: **A** x **B** = -**B** x **A**. Thus, it is <u>-(45 m^2/sec^2)·**k**</u>.

10. Pointing the fingers of your right hand in the direction of **A** and curling along the arc of the angle between the vectors, your thumb points down at the paper. Thus, <u>the torque points back behind the plane of the paper</u>.

ANSWERS TO THE REVIEW QUESTIONS FOR MODULE #2

1. Since acceleration is simply the change in velocity divided by the time, and since the time was 1 second, we just have to imagine the vector that, when multiplied by 1 and added to the first vector, gives the second vector.

The dotted arrow is the acceleration vector.

2. <u>This is not true. A projectile traveling in two dimensions experiences constant acceleration (only gravity is accelerating the projectile, and it is constant). However, it does not travel in a straight line; it follows a parabolic trajectory.</u> If you remember circular motion from your first-year course, you will also remember that when the speed of an object moving in a circle is constant, its acceleration (the centripetal acceleration) is also constant. However, it is moving in a circle, not a straight line.

3. The only time instantaneous velocity and average velocity can be the same at all times is if the velocity does not change. Thus, this is a situation where <u>acceleration is zero</u>. This corresponds to a linear position versus time graph.

4. <u>The time measured by the second student will be smaller,</u> because his ball drops straight to the ground. The other student's ball first rises and then falls to the ground. <u>The acceleration of each ball is exactly the same,</u> because gravity accelerates all objects exactly the same near the surface of the earth.

5. <u>The second ball experiences greater air resistance initially.</u> They are identical, so C and A are the same for each ball. They are both traveling through the same air, so ρ is the same for each ball. However, the speed of the second ball is much higher initially, so it experiences greater air resistance. <u>The terminal velocities are the same for both balls.</u> This was sort of a trick question. Look at the equation for terminal velocity. The initial velocity (the only difference between the balls) is not in the equation. Thus, they have the same terminal velocity. The second ball will *reach* terminal velocity sooner than the first, but they will each have the same terminal velocity.

6. <u>You cannot conclude that the acceleration is zero. If the *velocity* is constant, the acceleration is zero. However, if velocity continually changes direction but does not change magnitude, the speed would be constant, but there would have to be acceleration because the *velocity* is changing.</u> One example is uniform circular motion. As an object travels around a circle at constant speed, its velocity is changing because its direction of motion changes. Thus, its acceleration is not zero.

7. The horizontal direction is easy. <u>In the horizontal direction, there is no acceleration vector</u>. The vertical dimension is influenced by gravity. The acceleration due to gravity always points down. However, in this situation, the vertical velocity of the projectile is initial pointed upward. Only after the projectile has reached its maximum height will the velocity begin to point downward. Thus, <u>the velocity vector and acceleration vector are pointed in opposite directions until the projectile reaches its maximum height. After that point, they are pointed in the same direction</u>.

8. If the projectile lands at the same height from which it was launched, the vertical component of the velocity will have the same magnitude but the opposite direction. The horizontal component of the velocity will be exactly the same. Think about what that means:

Initial: Final:

$$\theta = \tan^{-1} \frac{v_y}{v_x}$$

This means <u>the magnitude of the velocity will still be v, but its angle will be -θ</u>.

9. For parabolic motion to occur, the projectile must have no forces acting on it except gravity. It can have initial velocity, but no other forces can be accelerating it. Thus, there can be no acceleration in the horizontal dimension, and the only acceleration in the vertical dimension is gravity. Please note that the projectile doesn't have to travel a complete parabola to be considered in parabolic motion. Even if it ends at a different height than that from which it was launched (as in Example 2.6), it still follows a parabola while it is in the air. Thus, <u>(a) and (d) meet the criteria</u>. Both (b) and (c) have other forces acting on them (the plane's engines and the rocket's engines).

10. <u>They would reach the ground at the same time</u>. The only things that affect when they hit the ground are the initial velocity and acceleration in the vertical dimension. They are the *same* for both balls. The dropped ball has zero initial velocity in both dimensions. The thrown ball has a horizontal initial velocity, but no vertical initial velocity. Thus, both balls have zero initial velocity in the vertical dimension. They both are accelerated the same in that dimension by gravity, so the balls hit the ground at the same time.

ANSWERS TO THE REVIEW QUESTIONS FOR MODULE #3

1. <u>You were not in an inertial reference frame. The ball moved without a force acting on it.</u> <u>That means Newton's First Law does not apply in your reference frame</u>. The ball hung from the ceiling is actually called an "accelerometer." It detects acceleration because it moves seemingly of its own accord when the room accelerates.

2. Since the ball moved to the right, the room must have been accelerating ahead of it to the left. Thus, <u>the net force is pointed to the left</u>, because that's the way the room is accelerating.

3. <u>Yes, you were</u>. Once the ball begins hanging straight down again, Newton's First Law is valid, and you are therefore in an inertial reference frame.

4. <u>It would swing away from the center of the curve</u>. Remember, to stay on the curve, the car must experience centripetal acceleration. The ball will move in the car opposite of the acceleration, as discussed in the answer to problem 2. Since centripetal acceleration is pointed to the center of the curve, the ball would swing away from the center.

5. If the masses are moving at a constant velocity, then the acceleration is zero. Ignoring friction and the mass of the string and pulley, the only way that can happen is if <u>the masses are</u> <u>equal</u>.

6. a. <u>The reading would increase</u>. As the car accelerates, you must accelerate to keep up with it. The car provides the force of the acceleration, pushing you along. This is just like the situation in an elevator, where the weight of the person increases as the elevator accelerates upwards.

b. <u>The reading would go back to 20 pounds</u>. If the car is not accelerating, the situation is equivalent to being at rest, at least from the point of view of the force exerted by the seat.

c. <u>The reading would drop below 20 pounds</u>. As the car slows down, your body will lurch forward because it is still moving at the car's original velocity.

7. <u>The 75 kg skater applies a force to the 150 kg skater. In the absence of friction, the 150 kg</u> <u>skater will move in response to that force. However, in accordance with Newton's Third Law,</u> <u>the 150 kg skater applies an equal and opposite force to the 75 kg skater. She moves in reaction</u> <u>to that force</u>.

8. The forces must be equal but opposite. Thus, <u>the 150 kg skater will move in the opposite</u> <u>direction as compared to the 75 kg skater</u>.

9. <u>The acceleration of the 150 kg skater will be half that of the 75 kg skater</u>. They both experience an equal (but opposite) force. Since the mass of the 150 kg skater is twice that of the 75 kg skater, an equal force will give that skater only half the acceleration.

10. <u>During the kick, the action force is applied by the foot to the ball. The reaction force is</u> <u>applied by the ball to the foot. While in the air, the only force the ball experiences is the force of</u>

gravity pulling down on the ball. The reaction force is also that of gravity, but it is the ball pulling up on the earth.

ANSWERS TO THE REVIEW QUESTIONS FOR MODULE #4

1. <u>The centripetal force does no work</u>. Remember, the centripetal force is directed towards the center of the circle, along the radius. The radius is perpendicular to a tangent line drawn at the point of contact, so **F•x** is zero. You could also look at it in terms of energy. Constant speed means kinetic energy is constant. Thus, the centripetal force cannot do any work, as it would add or subtract from the energy.

2. Impulse changes momentum according to the relationship:

$$\mathbf{J} = \Delta\mathbf{p}$$

The ball initially had a momentum of +m·v, if we define motion to the wall as positive. After it bounced, its momentum is -m·v, because it is traveling in exactly the opposite direction. Thus, $\Delta\mathbf{p}$ = -m·v - (+m·v), or -2·m·v. Thus, the impulse is <u>-2·m·v</u>. You could say +2·m·v as well, but that means you define motion away from the wall as positive.

3. <u>The collision could be elastic</u>. To be sure, we would have to know whether or not energy was lost. <u>The collision could be inelastic</u>. In the real world, most such collisions are inelastic because of friction. <u>The collision could not be perfectly inelastic</u>, because the objects move separately.

4. The fact that there is less energy in the system after the collision as compared to before indicates that this is an <u>inelastic collision</u>. <u>Momentum was conserved because there are no net forces acting on the objects</u>.

5. <u>Energy is never conserved</u>. You should be able to determine that from the name itself. However, you can also think about what has to happen to make such a collision. The two objects must mesh together and stick. There *must* be friction, etc., in a situation like that, so energy cannot be conserved.

6. <u>Momentum will be conserved as long as there are no net external forces working on the objects</u>. The friction of them meshing together is a force *between* the objects, and that does not affect momentum conservation. Only *external* forces affect momentum conservation.

7. <u>Potential energy can be negative, and therefore total energy can be as well</u>. Potential energy can be negative because the definition of potential energy is relative. If you define the floor as the place of zero potential energy, for example, then all objects beneath the floor have negative potential energy. Only kinetic energy must be positive.

8. <u>The equation is valid only when the acceleration due to gravity is constant, and that is only true near the surface of the earth</u>. As you should have learned in your first-year course, when the elevation is no longer negligible compared to the distance to the center of the earth, the acceleration due to gravity is not constant.

9. Remember, power is work divided by time. If they each do the same work, then the difference in power must be related to the time. The lower the time, the higher the power. Thus, <u>the second machine does the work in half the time as compared to the first machine</u>.

10. If ball 4 were to move with twice the velocity, <u>the system would have *more energy* after the collision than before</u>, and that is not possible. Remember, energy depends on v^2. Two balls have twice the energy of one ball. However, one ball moving twice as fast would have 2^2, or 4 times the energy!

ANSWERS TO THE REVIEW QUESTIONS FOR MODULE #5

1. Remember, any system of objects can be replaced by its center of mass. In this system, the center of mass is not moving. Thus, even after the collision, the center of mass will still not move. This means that once the cars collide, <u>they will come to a dead stop</u>.

2. Since the two cars came to a dead stop, they must have had equal and opposite momenta. That way, the total momentum of the system was zero. Since the momenta had to be equal, <u>the more massive car traveled at half the speed of the less massive car</u>.

3. <u>Yes</u>, if a system is moving but not rotating, it is in static rotational equilibrium and not in static translational equilibrium. For example, a block falling under the influence of gravity is in static rotational equilibrium (not rotating) but not in static translational equilibrium.

4. If it is rolling down the ramp and not losing energy, it is being accelerated due to gravity. Thus, it has translational acceleration, and <u>it is not in dynamic translational equilibrium</u>. Since angular acceleration is simply a divided by R, it must have angular acceleration as well. Thus, <u>it is not in dynamic rotational equilibrium either</u>.

5. <u>Yes, it can be in either static or dynamic rotational equilibrium as long as the force is applied at the axis of rotation</u>. If the force is applied at the axis of rotation, the torque is zero, and the object will be in either static or dynamic rotational equilibrium.

6. According to Figure 5.4, a hollow sphere has a larger moment of inertia than a solid sphere. Thus, <u>the solid sphere will experience greater angular acceleration</u>.

7. <u>Yes, it could be experiencing a torque</u> as long as it was experiencing one or more other torques so that the sum of the torques is zero. As long as the sum of the torques is zero, the angular velocity will be constant.

8. <u>The angular velocities of the pennies will be the same</u>. They will rotate with the disk. Thus, they will make the same number of rotations each second, which means they will sweep out the same angle each second. <u>The penny closer to the center will have a smaller velocity than the one near the end</u>. Remember, velocity is angular velocity times the radius. Since the penny closer to the center has a smaller radius, it will have a smaller velocity.

9. If the penny close to the center slides near the edge of the disk, the radius of its motion increases. This will increase its moment of inertia. However, the total angular momentum ($I \cdot \omega$) of the system cannot change. Thus, <u>the angular velocity must decrease to offset the increasing moment of inertia of the penny</u>.

10. Rotational kinetic energy is $\frac{1}{2} \cdot I \cdot \omega^2$. The moment of inertia of a rod spinning about its center is 4 times smaller than that of a rod spinning about its end. Since energy depends on ω^2, however, that factor of 4 will result in only a factor of two increase in angular velocity. Thus, <u>the angular velocity of the rod rotating about its center is twice that of the rod rotating about its end</u>.

ANSWERS TO THE REVIEW QUESTIONS FOR MODULE #6

1. The total energy depends on the initial displacement from equilibrium, because initially, all energy is potential, and the potential energy, according to Equation (4.8), depends only on the spring constant and the initial displacement from equilibrium. Thus, the total energy is the same. The maximum kinetic energy occurs when there is no potential energy. At that point, then, the kinetic energy is the total energy. Since the total energy is the same, the maximum kinetic energy is the same. Remember, KE = ½·m·v². Thus, as mass increases, the speed achieved with the same kinetic energy decreases. Therefore, the maximum speed of the second system is lower by a factor of the square root of 2. Since both were initially displaced the same distance from equilibrium, the maximum displacement is the same.

2. Both systems have the same amount of total energy. However, since the mass of the second system is heavier, it generates a larger normal force, which means the frictional force is greatest in the second system. Since the frictional force is greater, and since
Work = f·x, friction will be able to work the energy out of the second system over a smaller distance. The second system travels the shorter distance before stopping.

3. The period is the time that the system takes to start at its initial position and return to its initial position. Thus, the mass travels A to get back to equilibrium; then it travels A to get to the other side; then it travels A to get back to equilibrium again; and finally it travels A to get back to its initial position. Thus, it travels a total distance of 4·A. By the same reasoning, the pendulum sweeps out an angle of 4·θ.

4. Potential energy cannot be negative in a mass/spring system. Equation (4.8) contains ½, which is positive, k, which is positive, and x², which is always positive.

5. Think about the period of a pendulum. According to Equation (6.11), it depends inversely on the square root of g. When the elevator accelerates, that affects the apparent gravitational acceleration, as discussed in Example (3.3). If the elevator accelerates upwards, the elevator's acceleration effectively adds to the gravitational acceleration. If the elevator accelerates downwards, the acceleration effectively takes away from the gravitational acceleration. When the elevator does not accelerate, the apparent gravitational acceleration is the same as when the elevator is stationary.

a. This is the same as if the elevator were stationary. Thus, the two periods are the same.

b. When the elevator accelerates upwards, the effective gravitational acceleration is greater. Thus, the period of the pendulum in the elevator accelerating upwards is lower than the period of the pendulum when the elevator is stationary.

c. In free fall, there is no apparent gravitational acceleration, as the elevator is accelerating at the acceleration due to gravity. Thus, it is like g = 0. When that happens, the period is infinite. Thus, the pendulum stops swinging when the elevator falls freely.

6. <u>Either one is a simple pendulum and the other is a physical pendulum, or they are both physical pendulums made from different shapes.</u> Remember, the period of a *simple* pendulum depends only on L and g. The period of a physical pendulum also depends on I, which depends on shape.

7. According to Equation (6.19), the speed of a wave on a string depends on the square root of the tension. If nothing else is changed, then, <u>the tension must increase by a factor of 4</u> so that its square root increases by a factor of 2.

8. According to Equation (6.13), frequency and wavelength are inversely proportional to one another. Thus, if frequency increases by a factor of 2, <u>wavelength decreases by a factor of 2.</u> The speed is affected ONLY by the tension of the string and the linear mass density of the string. Thus, <u>the speed does not change.</u>

9. <u>The linear mass density of the new string is higher than that of the old string.</u> The reflected wave is inverted if the wave travels slower in the new medium. Waves travel slower if the linear mass density is higher.

10. <u>The generated waves are destructively interfering with one another.</u> Destructive interference reduces the oscillations. If the destructive interference is perfect, there are no oscillations at all.

ANSWERS TO THE REVIEW QUESTIONS FOR MODULE #7

1. <u>The frequencies and wavelengths of both waves are the same</u>. After all, reflection does not change the speed of sound in air or the wavelength of the wave being reflected. Since the wave travels more quickly in brick than in air, the reflected wave is not inverted. Thus, <u>the phase angles are the same as well</u>.

2. Remember, when a wave hits a new medium, part of the wave is reflected and part travels through the new medium. Thus, part of the wave will be traveling in the brick. Sound travels more quickly in solids than in gases or liquids, so the speed of the wave increases. However, the frequency cannot change, as the waves hit the brick at a given frequency, and that frequency drives the wave in the brick. Since the speed changes and frequency does not, the wavelength *increases* to offset the increase in speed, according to Equation (6.13). Thus, <u>the frequencies of both waves are the same, but the wavelength of the wave inside the brick is longer than that of the wave in the air</u>. There is no change in phase when a wave enters a new medium, so <u>the phase angles are the same</u>.

3. <u>Sound travels more quickly in helium than in air</u>. If the pitch goes up, sound must be traveling faster, according to Equation (6.13).

4. <u>She could strike the glass with a utensil and listen to the pitch at which the glass rings</u>. That's its fundamental harmonic, so if she sings at that pitch, she will shake the glass with resonance.

5. <u>The boy is hearing beats produced by the sound that is coming from her and the reflection of the sound off of the wall</u>. When the sound reaches the wall, it bounces off of the wall. Thus, the wall is an "observer" of the girl's scream. However, the girl is running towards the wall. As a result, it "hears" the scream Doppler shifted because the source is moving towards it. This means that when the scream reflects off of the wall, it is Doppler-shifted to a higher frequency. This higher frequency wave interferes with the wave that is reaching the boy straight from the girl's mouth, and beats are produced.

6. For total internal reflection to occur, Snell's Law must be impossible to solve. That will happen when the angle of incidence meets the requirements of Equation (7.10). If $n_2 < n_1$, however, Equation (7.10) cannot be solved for certain angles, because sine is *never* greater than one. Thus, <u>the light should originate in the top piece of plastic so that $n_2 < n_1$</u>.

7. <u>The observed depth is less than the true depth</u>. Remember, your eyes assume that the light has been moving in a straight line, so they extrapolate backwards. When the light coming from the object leaves the water, it is bent away from the perpendicular. When your eyes extrapolate the line back, they see the object at a more shallow depth.

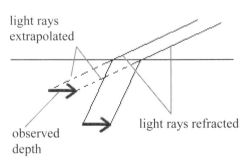

8. Here is a diagram that explains the effect.

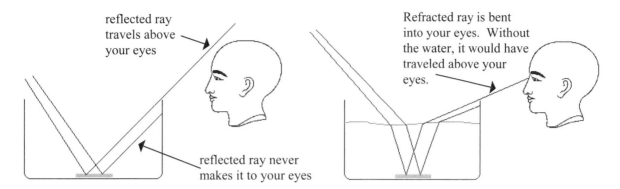

reflected ray travels above your eyes

reflected ray never makes it to your eyes

Refracted ray is bent into your eyes. Without the water, it would have traveled above your eyes.

Because the light rays are either stopped by the bowl or travel above your eyes, no light reflected off the quarter makes it into your eyes. Thus, you do not see it.

Because the light rays are refracted coming out of the water, the light rays that normally would have traveled above your eyes are bent towards your eyes. You now see the quarter.

9. The distance between the bright lines would increase. After all, the farther the screen is away, the longer the light rays travel and the more they can spread out. Thus, the interference pattern will be spread out as well.

10. You would use diverging lenses. Notice the problem. The light rays are bent too strongly. To get the image on the retina, then, the light rays have to be bent less. We can't do that, but we can spread the light rays out before they get to the eye's lens. That way, the lens has to bend the light more than normal just to get the image on the retina. Thus, by spreading the light rays out, the diverging lens will push the image back, making it possible for the image to focus on the retina.

ANSWERS TO THE REVIEW QUESTIONS FOR MODULE #8

1. Mass never changes, as you learned in your first-year course. Thus, the mass is m. The weight, however, is simply a measure of gravity's pull. If the object is raised to an altitude of R_e (the radius of the earth), that means its distance from the center of the earth is $2 \cdot R_e$. This means the distance in Equation (8.3) doubles, which means gravitational force goes down by a factor of 4. Thus, the weight is w/4.

2. $F = f$. Remember, gravitational force is mutual, so each exerts an equal force on the other.

3. The first object will exert 16 times the gravitational force on the new object. To counteract that, it will need to be placed farther from the first object. Since the gravitational force varies as distance squared, however, you need to place it four times farther away from the first object as compared to the distance to the second object. Thus, place it a distance of (4/5)·x away from the first object.

4. Gravitational acceleration depends on Equation (8.3). With 1/10 the mass, the gravitational acceleration will be 1/10 as large. With 1/5 the radius, the gravitational acceleration will be $(5)^2$ times larger. Thus, the gravitational acceleration will be 2.5 times that of earth.

5. Kepler's Third Law says T^2/a^3 is constant for all planets. Thus, if a decreases by 0.387, T^2 will also have to decrease by $(0.387)^3$ in order to keep T^2/a^3 constant. Thus, the orbital period for Mercury is 0.241 that of earth (whose period is 365.25 days), or 88.0 days.

6. The earth would be closest to the sun when it is going fastest and farthest from the sun when it is going slowest.

7. Remember, you can ignore the shell of mass around you, as discussed in the module. Thus, the gravitational force is zero and never changes as long as the mass stays inside the hollow sphere.

8. No, they are not approaching each other at 1.6c, because information cannot be transferred faster than the speed of light. Basically, the speed of light is the universal speed limit. They are approaching each other at near the speed of light, not above. If you study more relativity, you will learn equations that can be used to calculate their relative speed.

9. Light would be approaching the second space ship at c and traveling away from the other space ship at c. That must be the case if the laws of physics work in moving reference frames.

10. There would only be two forces in Creation, because according to general relativity, gravity is not a force. It is a consequence of how matter and energy curve spacetime.

ANSWERS TO THE REVIEW QUESTIONS FOR MODULE #9

1. <u>As the temperature increases, the speed with which the molecules strike the container increases.</u> This increases the force with which they hit the container. Since the surface area stays the same (because volume is constant), the pressure goes up.

2. <u>A phase change occurred.</u> Remember, during a phase change, the temperature cannot change. Since heat was being added continually, the time during which temperature does not change must be during a phase change.

3. <u>The temperature of the surroundings would increase.</u> Remember, there is energy associated with a phase change. When ice melts, energy must be absorbed. It stands to reason, then, that when water freezes, energy must be released. Why? The water molecules move a lot more in the liquid state than in the solid state. Thus, to freeze, the water molecules must give up energy. That energy is absorbed by the surroundings, heating them up.

4. <u>A substance exerts the least pressure in the solid phase.</u> After all, pressure is the force with which the molecules strike the container divided by the surface area. Since molecules in the solid phase move the least, they strike the container with the least force.

5. If the sides are divided by two, the volume ($side^3$) decreases by a factor of 8. If n and T are the same, then the ideal gas law says that the product of P and V must stay the same. Thus, if volume decreases by a factor of 8, <u>pressure increases by a factor of 8</u>. You might have been tempted to say a factor of 4 here, because the surface area decreased by a factor of 4. However, a smaller volume means *more* collisions in the container, which means more force applied to the container.

6. A mole is 6.02×10^{23} molecules. Thus, there are <u>831 moles</u> in the sample.

7. Temperature is proportional to the average speed squared. Thus, <u>the average speed increases by a factor of $\sqrt{2}$</u> .

8. According to the ideal gas law, if V and n are the same, then pressure is directly proportional to temperature. Thus, <u>the pressure increases by a factor of 2</u>.

9. <u>You should keep the pressure constant</u>, because C_p is greater than C_v.

10. The distribution with the highest average speed represents the highest temperature. Thus, the answer is <u>graph (a)</u>.

ANSWERS TO THE REVIEW QUESTIONS FOR MODULE #10

1. The Zeroth Law of Thermodynamics - If object A is in thermal equilibrium with object C, and if object B is in thermal equilibrium with object C, objects A and B are in thermal equilibrium with each other.

The First Law of Thermodynamics - Energy cannot be created or destroyed. It can only change form.

The Second Law of Thermodynamics - The entropy of the universe must always either increase or remain the same. It can never decrease.

The Third Law of Thermodynamics - It is impossible to reach a temperature of 0 K in a finite number of cooling steps.

2. a. The First Law of Thermodynamics forbids this. If the mass and energy are greater after the reaction than before, this means energy was created, which is not allowed.

b. The Zeroth Law of Thermodynamics forbids this. In order for the person to get warmer, energy must be transferred to him. If it is cool outside, energy will be transferred *from* him to the outside, according to the zeroth law.

c. The Second Law of Thermodynamics forbids this. The first law would allow this, because the ball could absorb energy from the hot pavement. Since the pavement is warmer than the ball, the zeroth law would allow the energy to be absorbed. However, the second law will not allow this, because the energy of rolling would be more ordered than the thermal energy, resulting in a decrease in entropy. The surroundings cannot offset this decrease, either, as the pavement would cool down, lowering *its* entropy as well.

3. The temperature will increase. $\Delta U = q - W$, and in this situation, $q = 0$. If the gas is compressed, work is negative. Thus, ΔU is positive, and temperature will therefore increase.

4. W = -1000 J. If the process is reversed, ΔU, q, and W all change signs.

5. The temperature decreases. $\Delta U = q - W$. In adiabatic processes, $q = 0$. As the gas expands, W is positive, so ΔU is negative. Thus, temperature decreases.

6. If the gas is isothermally compressed, then $\Delta U = 0$. Thus, q = W. You might be inclined, therefore, to say that q = 500 J, but it does not. To compress a gas, you must work *on* the gas, which means W is *negative*. Thus, W = -500 J. This means that q = -500 J. Since q is negative, the system *lost* heat. Thus, heat went into the surroundings, so the temperature of the surroundings increased. You can also think this through physically. Typically, a gas is warmed when it is compressed (remember the experiment). However, if the gas stayed at the same temperature (isothermal), that means it must have lost heat to the surrounding. Thus, q is negative and the temperature of the surroundings increased.

7. <u>This is not possible</u>. If it expands isothermally, $\Delta U = 0$. If it expands adiabatically $q = 0$. Since $\Delta U = q - W$, in a process that was *both* isothermal and adiabatic, W would have to be 0. The only way that can happen is if the gas neither expands nor contracts.

8. <u>This is possible</u>. If the gas expands isobarically, it just means we can use Equation (10.4) to calculate W. However, it puts no constraints on the value of W. If it expands adiabatically, $q = 0$. Thus, in an expansion that is both isobaric and adiabatic, $\Delta U = -W = -P \cdot \Delta V$. This tells us that as the gas expands, it will cool.

9. If the entropy decreases, q must be negative. Remember, the change in entropy is equal to q divided by T (in Kelvin). Since a Kelvin temperature can never be negative (or zero), if ΔS is negative, q must be negative. However, the temperature of the gas increased. Thus, ΔU is positive. Since $\Delta U = q - W$, the only way ΔU can be positive and q can be negative is if <u>W is negative</u>. Also, to be compliant with the Second Law of Thermodynamics, if the ΔS of the system (the gas) is negative, then the ΔS of the surroundings must be positive. Thus, <u>the entropy of the surroundings increased</u>.

10. <u>A Carnot engine is the most efficient heat engine possible</u>. First, a gas undergoes an <u>isothermal compression</u>. Second, the gas goes through an <u>adiabatic compression</u>. Third, the gas undergoes an <u>isothermal expansion</u>. Finally, an <u>adiabatic expansion</u> occurs in order to get the gas back to its original state so the process can start all over again.

ANSWERS TO THE REVIEW QUESTIONS FOR MODULE #11

1. According to Equation (11.1), the electrostatic force is directly proportional to the charges and inversely proportional to the square of the distance between them. If the distance is increased by a factor of 4, then, the force will decrease by a factor of 4^2, or 16. If one charge is doubled, the force will double. If the other charge is doubled as well, the force will double again. Thus, the increases in the charge increased the force by a total of a factor of 4. However, the increase in distance decreased the force by a factor of 16. In the end, then, the force decreased by a factor of 4.

2. The two charges will attract one another. Thus, the one that is free to move will begin to move towards the fixed particle. Since the force continues to act as time goes on, the particle that is free to move will continue to experience acceleration directed towards the fixed particle. Thus, the velocity will continue to increase. The closer the moving particle gets to the fixed particle, the stronger the electrostatic force. Thus, the force will continue to increase, which means the acceleration will increase as well.

3. The two negative charges will repel one another. Thus, the one that is free to move will begin to move away from the fixed particle. Since the force continues to act as time goes on, the particle that is free to move will continue to experience acceleration directed away from the fixed particle. Thus, the velocity will continue to increase. However, the farther the charged particle moves away, the weaker the electrostatic force. Thus, the force will continue to decrease, which means the acceleration will decrease.

4. Since $\mathbf{F} = q \cdot \mathbf{E}$, we know that the particle with 3 times the charge will experience 3 times the force. The signs of the charges are switched as well, however. This means the positive charge will experience a force in the exact opposite direction. Thus, the new force is $-3 \cdot \mathbf{F}$. You must have the negative in your answer!

5. Since the negative charge is twice as large as the other, it must have twice as many lines going into it as the positive charge has going out of it:

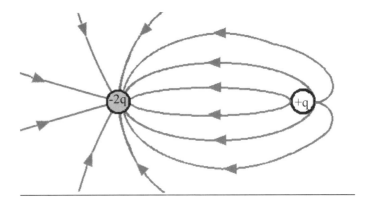

6. On the left of the charge labeled "-2q," the negative charge pulls a positive particle towards it and the positive charge pushes in the opposite direction. However, since the positive charge is weaker, its electric field will always be weaker than the electric field of the negative charge in that region. Thus, the electric field is not zero in that region. In between the two charges, the negative charge pulls a positive charge towards it and the positive charge pushes a positive charge in the same direction. Thus, the fields add, and the electric field is not zero. However, to the right of the positive charge, the charges once again pull in opposite directions. Since the negative charge is larger in magnitude than the positive charge, it is possible that to the right of the positive charge, the increased distance between the negative charge will offset the increased magnitude of the negative charge, and the total electric field will be zero. Thus, <u>it is possible to have a zero electric field somewhere to the right of the positive charge</u>.

7. <u>All particles are positively charged</u>. We know this because electric field lines are pointed away from all of the charges.

8. <u>Particle "b" has a charge of "2q," and particle "c" has a charge of "q/2."</u> You get this by counting the lines coming out of the charges. The more lines, the more the charge.

9. <u>The order is 1, 3, 2</u>. You can determine the strength of the field by the density of the lines. The density is least at 1 and greatest at 2.

10. <u>F_g is smaller than F_c</u>. It is actually *significantly smaller*, as gravity is an incredibly weak force compared to the electrostatic force. You can see this in the constants. The equations are very similar:

$$F_c = \frac{k \cdot q_1 \cdot q_2}{r^2} \text{ and } F_g = \frac{G \cdot m_1 \cdot m_2}{r^2}$$

Since the charges are 1 C and the masses are 1 kg (both the standard units), and since the r's are the same, the only difference between the two forces is given by their constants.

$$k = 8.99 \times 10^9 \; \frac{N \cdot m^2}{C^2}, \text{ while } G = 6.67 \times 10^{-11} \; \frac{N \cdot m^2}{kg^2}$$

The gravitational force, then, is some 10^{20} times weaker than the electrostatic force!

ANSWERS TO THE REVIEW QUESTIONS FOR MODULE #12

1. <u>No, the electric field is not necessarily zero.</u> Consider two opposite charges that are separated in space. If you add up the potentials at the point midway between them, you will find that they add to zero. However, the electric field is definitely not zero.

2. <u>No, the electric potential is not necessarily zero.</u> Consider two like charges that are separated in space. The electric field midway between them is zero. However, if you add up the electric potential at that point, it is definitely not zero.

3. <u>The negative charge will accelerate towards a higher potential.</u> Remember, $\Delta U = q \cdot \Delta V$. Since the particle is gaining kinetic energy (by accelerating), its potential energy must decrease. Thus ΔU is negative. Well, q is negative as well. Thus, ΔV must be positive. That means the ending potential must be higher than the beginning potential.

4. Since $\Delta U = -W$, a negative value for work means that the positive particle's potential energy increases. When particles move the way they want to move in an electric field, their potential energy decreases. Thus, the particle is moving opposite the way it would normally move. Since positive particles move in the direction of the electric field, <u>this particle is moving opposite the electric field</u>.

5. <u>Particles (a) and (c) are at equal potentials.</u> Remember, the electric potential tells how much the particles can be pushed. Since the electric field is pointing up, positive particles will be pushed up and negative particles will be pushed down. Thus, the vertical position is an indicator of potential.

6. Remember, based on the argument in question #3, negative charges accelerate towards *higher* potentials. Thus, <u>particle d is at the highest potential</u>.

7. <u>Yes, it is.</u> Only (a) and (c) are at equal potentials. However, *potential energy* is $q \cdot V$. Thus, if particle (d) had a lower charge than (a) and (c), and if particle (b) had a higher charge than (a) and (c), it would be possible for them all to have the same potential energy.

8. Based on Equation (12.8), the physicist could <u>increase the size of the plates</u> and/or <u>decrease the distance between the plates</u>. Finally, the physicist could <u>put a dielectric with a large dielectric constant in between the plates</u>, because dielectrics increase capacitance by an amount based on their dielectric constant.

9. Based on Equation (12.9), if the capacitance stays the same, then charge is directly proportional to the potential difference. A 9.0-Volt battery has $9.0/1.5 = 6.0$ times the potential difference, so <u>$Q = (6.0) \cdot q$</u>.

10. According to Equation (12.14), when capacitance stays the same, the energy stored in a capacitor increases as the square of the potential difference. Thus, <u>$E = (36) \cdot e$</u>.

ANSWERS TO THE REVIEW QUESTIONS FOR MODULE #13

1. In Table 13.1, the resistivity of lead is 2.06 x 10^{-7} Ω·m, while the resistivity of iron is 9.71 x 10^{-8} Ω·m. This means lead is 2.12 times more resistive than is iron, and therefore the lead conductor will have 2.12 times less current than the iron conductor. The ratio of the current in lead to the current in iron, then, is 1/2.12 , or 0.471.

2. Since there is less current in the lead conductor, we must find some way to reduce the resistance of the lead. The larger the area, the lower the resistance. Thus, we must increase the cross-sectional area of the lead conductor to 2.12 times the cross-sectional area of the iron conductor.

3. Light bulb #2 is in series with light bulb #1. Thus, light bulb #1 will go out as well. None of the other light bulbs will go out, however, because there is still a complete circuit from the battery, through light bulbs #3 and #4, back to the battery through light bulbs #5 and #6.

4. If light bulb #5 or light bulb #6 were to go out, the entire circuit would go dark, because there would be no path for electricity to get to the negative side of the battery.

5. You have to be careful here. We know that $P = I \cdot V$, but we also know that $P = I^2 \cdot R$. You might be tempted to say that the power output triples, since P is proportional to R. However, you are forgetting that when R is changed, I changes as well. If the resistance triples, I goes down by a factor of 3 (Ohm's Law). Thus, I is reduced by 3 and V is the same. Based on $P = I \cdot V$, then, power decreases by a factor of 3, so the new power output is P/3. You get the same result with $P = I^2 \cdot R$, of course. When I drops by a factor of 3, that causes a factor of 9 drop in P, but R increased by a factor of three. Thus, the net result is still that power decreases by a factor of 3.

6. The potential will increase. Remember, the battery delivers less than its rated voltage because of internal resistance. If the resistance of the circuit is higher, the current will be lower. Thus, the voltage drop over the internal resistance will be lower, and the battery will deliver a potential closer to that for which it is rated.

7. When S1 is closed, the first capacitor will charge until the potential difference is 9.0 V. Then, current will stop flowing. When S1 is opened, the capacitor will hold the charge it was given. When S2 is then closed, current will flow from the first capacitor to the second. Since the capacitors are in parallel, they must end up with the same potential. Thus, charge will flow until each carries 4.5 V of potential. At that point, current will stop flowing again.

8. Based on Ohm's Law, the new current will be triple the old current, or 3·I.

9. You would place the resistor in series with the resistor that is already there. That will increase the resistance, which will decrease the current.

10. You would place the resistor in parallel with the resistor that is already there. That will decrease the total resistance, which will increase the current.

ANSWERS TO THE REVIEW QUESTIONS FOR MODULE #14

1. <u>Yes, it is possible.</u> <u>If the charged particle's velocity forms an angle of 0 or 180 degrees with the magnetic field</u>, the cross product of the velocity and magnetic field is zero, and no force is experienced.

2. <u>It is not possible.</u> Because the force is the result of a cross product between the velocity and the magnetic field, it is always perpendicular to *both*. Thus, the force is perpendicular to the velocity. Since the only work done is by the component of the force that is *parallel* to the displacement [see Equation (1.8)], no work can be done by the magnetic field.

3. The direction of the magnetic force depends on **v** x **B** and the charge of the particle. Since this is a negatively-charged particle, it experiences a force opposite of the cross product. Thus, the cross product points up. If you point the thumb of your right hand up (the result of the cross product), which way must you point your fingers so that when they curl to the left, your thumb stays up? They must point <u>into the paper</u>.

4. There is no need for calculation here. Look at the situation:

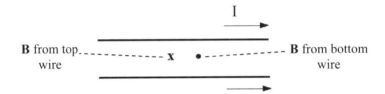

The right hand rule says that in the region between the wires, the top wire's magnetic field goes into the page. The same rule says that the magnetic field from the bottom wire comes out of the page. Thus, they are opposite. Since the wires carry the same current and the point midway between is the same distance from each, they produce equal and opposite magnetic fields. Thus, the total magnetic field is <u>zero</u>.

5. <u>The potential difference will quickly disappear.</u> When the conductor stops, there will no longer be a force on the electrons. Thus, they will travel to the positive side of the conductor, canceling the potential difference.

6. As the north pole pushes into the loop, the magnetic field lines point right and the flux increases. The current, therefore, must produce a magnetic field that points to the left inside the loop. Thus, the current flows as indicated in the drawing to the right.

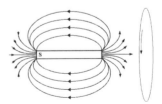

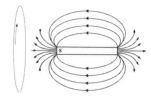

However, once the magnet passes through the loop, the magnetic field lines still point to the right, but the flux decreases as the magnet moves farther away. Thus, the current's magnetic field must oppose that decrease by pointing to the right inside the loop. The only way that can happen is if the current switches direction, as shown to the right. Thus, the current changes direction because the change in flux alters once the magnet gets through the loop.

7. The current would decrease to zero, since the magnetic flux must *change* in order to produce an emf. If the magnet was stationary, there would be a constant flux and thus no emf.

8. The charged particles have opposite charges, because the magnetic field deflected them in opposite directions.

9. The cyclotron's magnetic field *cannot* speed up a charged particle. Remember, the magnetic field can do no work on the charged particle, because the force it exerts is perpendicular to the motion. A cyclotron uses electric fields to accelerate charged particles. The magnetic field simply causes the charged particle to move in a circle with a constant period.

10. a. The current will keep changing direction, because the flux changes in one direction as the magnet is pushed into the loop, and it changes in the other direction as the magnet is pulled out. Thus, this will produce alternating current.

b. As the frequency increases, the time it takes to push the magnet in and out decreases. This means the flux changes more quickly, which means an increase in emf. An increase in emf means the current will increase as well.

ANSWERS TO THE REVIEW QUESTIONS FOR MODULE #15

1. <u>Statement (b) is more correct</u>. Although statement (a) is correct, physicists do not think that the wave/particle duality is unique to light. They think that matter has wavelike properties as well, even though matter comes in particles. As stated in the text, there is experimental evidence for this.

2. a. <u>Classical physics could explain this</u>. The light provides energy to the electrons, which allow them to escape the hold that the metal has on them. This is pure Newtonian physics.

b. <u>Classical physics could not explain this</u>. In classical physics, the intensity of the wave should govern how much energy is transferred to the electrons.

c. <u>Classical physics could not explain this</u>. In classical physics, the electrons could, given enough time, "soak up" enough energy from the light regardless of its frequency.

d. <u>Classical physics could not explain this</u>. In classical physics, the intensity of the wave should govern how much energy is transferred to the electrons.

e. <u>Classical physics could not explain this</u>. In classical physics, the electrons would have to take time to absorb the energy before they could get enough to be released.

3. Einstein assumed that <u>light came in small electromagnetic bundles (particles) called photons</u>.

4. A baseball has wavelike properties, but the <u>wavelength is just too small to be noticeable</u>. As Equation (15.3) tells us, however, as the mass gets very small, the wavelength becomes bigger and can be noticeable, as is the case with small particles like electrons.

5. <u>Bohr made the quantum assumption that electrons are restricted to be in certain orbits and nowhere in between</u>.

6. <u>He used no justification other than the fact that the results of the assumption were able to explain the data</u>. To this day, we have no justification for the quantum assumption other than the fact that models which use it are successful at explaining the data.

7. <u>We have no idea</u>. This is one of the reasons that the quantum assumption makes no sense. Literally, the Bohr model requires that the electrons "blip" from one orbit to another. Even the quantum mechanical model requires this odd situation. Look at the lobes on p-orbitals, d-orbitals, etc. A given p-orbital, for example, has two lobes. The electron can *never* be in the space between the lobes, but it can be found in *either* lobe. Thus, the electron can "blip" from lobe to lobe within an orbital!

8. <u>No</u>. If an atom emits no *visible* light when excited, it is most likely emitting light that is not in the visible spectrum.

9. The electron can jump directly from orbit #3 to orbit #1, and that would emit light of one energy. But it can also move from orbit #3 to orbit #2 and then from orbit #2 to orbit #1, and that would require emission of 2 different energies of light. That's 3 different energies and therefore 3 different wavelengths total.

10. In atomic emission spectroscopy, scientists look at the light emitted by excited atoms while in atomic absorption spectroscopy, scientists examine the light absorbed by atoms in the process of being excited.

ANSWERS TO THE REVIEW QUESTIONS FOR MODULE #16

1. <u>Binding energy is the energy that comes from the mass deficit of a nucleus. It is used to provide energy for pion exchange, which holds the nucleus together.</u>

2. The most stable nucleus is ^{56}Fe, because it has more binding energy per nucleon than all other nuclei in Creation.

3. <u>The strong nuclear force is caused by the exchange of pions between the nucleons of a nucleus. It acts over a short range because the pions are short-lived particles.</u>

4. To be stable, a nucleus must be in the valley of stable nuclei in Figure 16.2. If you determine the number of neutrons and protons in each nucleus:

^{14}N is stable, because 7 protons and 7 neutrons puts it in the valley.

^{88}Ru is not stable, because 44 protons and 44 neutrons puts it below the valley.

^{118}Sn is stable, because 50 protons and 68 neutrons puts it in the valley.

^{50}Ca is not stable, because 20 protons and 30 neutrons puts it above the valley.

5. Alpha particles are ^{4}He nuclei emitted by a radioactive isotope. Gamma rays are high energy light particles emitted by radioactive isotopes, and beta particles are electrons emitted by radioactive isotopes. <u>Gamma rays can pass through the most matter, alpha particles pass through the least matter.</u>

6. <u>Positron emission and electron capture</u> are artificial forms of radioactivity.

7. When a positron and an electron collide, <u>they destroy each other, producing a gamma ray. This process is called annihilation.</u>

8. <u>Although X-rays and smoke detectors expose you to radiation, the levels are so small that the risk is significantly less than that of not getting X-rays or using smoke detectors.</u>

9. <u>In fusion, two small nuclei make a larger nucleus. In fission, a large nucleus splits into smaller nuclei. Isotopes with mass numbers less than 56 tend to undergo fusion, while those with mass numbers larger than 56 tend to undergo fission.</u>

10. <u>We do not use nuclear fusion for energy simply because we have not mastered the technology yet.</u> Right now, too much energy is wasted getting the nuclei to fuse.

Solutions To The

Practice Problems

SOLUTIONS TO THE PRACTICE PROBLEMS FOR MODULE #1

1. You are given the conversion relationship between meters and feet. To get the conversion relationship between sec^2 and $hour^2$, we have to square the relationship between hours and seconds:

$$1 \text{ hour} = 3600 \text{ sec}$$

$$1 \text{ hour}^2 = 1.296 \times 10^7 \text{ sec}^2$$

Now we have all we need to do the conversion:

$$\frac{845 \text{ ft}}{1 \text{ hr}^2} \times \frac{1 \text{ m}}{3.281 \text{ ft}} \times \frac{1 \text{ hr}^2}{1.296 \times 10^7 \text{ sec}^2} = \underline{1.99 \times 10^{-5} \frac{\text{m}}{\text{sec}^2}}$$

2. We know the relationship between kg and g as well as the one between m and cm. However, to get the relationship between sec^2 and $minutes^2$, we must square the relationship between seconds and minutes:

$$1 \text{ minute} = 60 \text{ sec}$$

$$1 \text{ minute}^2 = 3600 \text{ sec}^2$$

Now we have all we need to do the conversion:

$$\frac{15.1 \text{ kg} \cdot \text{m}}{1 \text{ sec}^2} \times \frac{1,000 \text{ g}}{1 \text{ kg}} \times \frac{1 \text{ cm}}{0.01 \text{ m}} \times \frac{3,600 \text{ sec}^2}{1 \text{ minute}^2} = \underline{5.44 \times 10^9 \frac{\text{g} \cdot \text{cm}}{\text{minute}^2}}$$

3. This problem simply uses the equations given in Figure 1.2:

$$\text{Magnitude} = \sqrt{v_x^2 + v_y^2} = \sqrt{(13 \frac{\text{m}}{\text{sec}})^2 + (-11 \frac{\text{m}}{\text{sec}})^2} = 17 \frac{\text{m}}{\text{sec}}$$

To get the angle, we start with this equation:

$$\theta = \tan^{-1}(\frac{v_y}{v_x}) = \tan^{-1}(\frac{-11 \frac{\text{m}}{\text{sec}}}{13 \frac{\text{m}}{\text{sec}}}) = -4.0 \times 10^{1 \ \circ}$$

This vector, however is in region IV, because it has a positive x-component and a negative y-component. Thus, we must add 360.0 degrees to it. The answer, then, is 3.20×10^2 degrees. Thus, the vector is <u>17 m/sec at 3.20×10^2 degrees</u>. Notice that we must use scientific notation here, since the zero in the ones place is significant, by the significant figures rule of addition.

4. First, we have to add the vectors graphically by placing the tail of the second onto the head of the first:

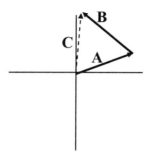

The dotted arrow (vector **C**) gives the sum. Now we do it mathematically. To do that, I need to get the components of each vector:

$$A_x = (2.2 \; \frac{m}{sec}) \cdot \cos(35.0°) = 1.8 \; \frac{m}{sec}$$

$$A_y = (2.2 \; \frac{m}{sec}) \cdot \sin(35.0°) = 1.3 \; \frac{m}{sec}$$

$$B_x = (3.4 \; \frac{m}{sec}) \cdot \cos(120.0°) = -1.7 \; \frac{m}{sec}$$

$$B_y = (3.4 \; \frac{m}{sec}) \cdot \sin(120.0°) = 2.9 \; \frac{m}{sec}$$

Now that we have the individual components, we can add them together.

$$C_x = A_x + B_x = 1.8 \; \frac{m}{sec} + -1.7 \; \frac{m}{sec} = 0.1 \; \frac{m}{sec}$$

$$C_y = A_y + B_y = 1.3 \; \frac{m}{sec} + 2.9 \; \frac{m}{sec} = 4.2 \; \frac{m}{sec}$$

Now that we have the components to our answer, we can get the magnitude and direction of the sum.

$$\text{Magnitude} = \sqrt{C_x^{\,2} + C_y^{\,2}} = \sqrt{(0.1 \; \frac{m}{sec})^2 + (4.2 \; \frac{m}{sec})^2} = 4.2 \; \frac{m}{sec}$$

$$\theta = \tan^{-1}(\frac{C_y}{C_x}) = \tan^{-1}(\frac{4.2\,\frac{m}{sec}}{0.1\,\frac{m}{sec}}) = 90°$$

This vector is in region I, so the angle is correct as given. Thus, the sum is <u>4.2 m/sec at 90°</u>.

5. To add vectors, we just add the components. To subtract them, we just subtract the components:

$$\mathbf{A} + \mathbf{B} = (A_x + B_x)\cdot\mathbf{i} + (A_y + B_y)\cdot\mathbf{j} = (1.5\text{ miles} + 1.8\text{ miles})\cdot\mathbf{i} + (7.1\text{ miles} - 2.2\text{miles})\cdot\mathbf{j}$$

$$\underline{\mathbf{A} + \mathbf{B} = (3.3\text{ miles})\cdot\mathbf{i} + (4.9\text{ miles})\cdot\mathbf{j}}$$

$$\mathbf{A} - \mathbf{B} = (A_x - B_x)\cdot\mathbf{i} + (A_y - B_y)\cdot\mathbf{j} = (1.5\text{ miles} - 1.8\text{ miles})\cdot\mathbf{i} + (7.1\text{ miles} + 2.2\text{miles})\cdot\mathbf{j}$$

$$\underline{\mathbf{A} - \mathbf{B} = (-0.3\text{ miles})\cdot\mathbf{i} + (9.3\text{ miles})\cdot\mathbf{j}}$$

6. In scalar multiplication, you just multiply the components by the scalar:

$$\underline{-5\cdot\mathbf{C} = (-60.0\text{ m})\cdot\mathbf{i} + (-65.0\text{ m})\cdot\mathbf{j}}$$

7. This is a simple application of Equation (1.8):

$$W = \mathbf{F} \bullet \mathbf{x} = (1.5\text{ N})\cdot(-5.2\text{ m}) + (-4.3\text{ N})\cdot(1.1\text{ m}) = -12.5\text{ N·m} = \underline{-12.5\text{ J}}$$

The negative sign simply means that the force was oriented against the displacement. Thus, kinetic energy was removed from the object. In other words, the force was used to slow down the object.

8. Work is the dot product of **F**•**x**. Thus,

$$W = F\cdot x\cdot\cos\theta$$

$$W = (18\text{ N})\cdot(3.4\text{ m})\cdot\cos(35.1°)$$

$$W = \underline{5.0\text{x}10^1\text{ J}}$$

Once again, I had to use scientific notation here because the zero is significant.

9. We know that torque is the cross product of **r** and **F**. The only thing that makes this problem hard is that it uses three-dimensional vectors, so we have to use the more difficult cross product formula:

$$\mathbf{r} \times \mathbf{F} = (r_y \cdot F_z - r_z \cdot F_y) \cdot \mathbf{i} + (r_z \cdot F_x - r_x \cdot F_z) \cdot \mathbf{j} + (r_x \cdot F_y - r_y \cdot F_x) \cdot \mathbf{k}$$

$$\mathbf{r} \times \mathbf{F} = [(0.25 \text{ m}) \cdot (43 \text{ N}) - (0.22 \text{ m}) \cdot (-34 \text{ N})] \cdot \mathbf{i} + [(0.22 \text{ m}) \cdot (-55 \text{ N}) - (0.23 \text{ m}) \cdot (43 \text{ N})] \cdot \mathbf{j} +$$
$$[(0.23 \text{ m}) \cdot (-34 \text{ N}) - (0.25 \text{ m}) \cdot (-55 \text{ N})] \cdot \mathbf{k}$$

$$\mathbf{r} \times \mathbf{F} = \underline{(18 \text{ N·m}) \cdot \mathbf{i} - (22 \text{ N·m}) \cdot \mathbf{j} + (6 \text{ N·m}) \cdot \mathbf{k}}$$

10. This deals only with magnitudes and an angle. Thus, we will use Equation (1.9):

$$|\mathbf{r} \times \mathbf{F}| = A \cdot B \cdot \sin\theta = (0.50 \text{ m}) \cdot (15 \text{ N}) \cdot \sin(65°) = \underline{6.8 \text{ N·m}}$$

The way to change the torque without increasing F or changing r is to change θ. Since the magnitude of the torque depends on the sine of θ, the closer θ is to 90, the larger the torque. Thus, he could increase the torque by applying the force at a larger angle relative to the crank. For maximum torque, the angle should be 90 degrees.

SOLUTIONS TO THE PRACTICE PROBLEMS FOR MODULE #2

1. a. Speed is the magnitude of the velocity. Thus, the greatest slope (positive or negative) will indicate the greatest speed. <u>From t = 8.0 to t=10.0 seconds</u>, the slope is 2 m/sec, which is larger than the other slopes.

b. The object stops when the velocity (the slope) is zero. This happens <u>from t = 3.0 to t = 4.0 seconds and once again at t = 8.0 seconds.</u>

c. The object changes direction when the slope changes sign. This happens at <u>t = 4.0 seconds and t = 8.0 seconds.</u>

d. To do this, we need to calculate the slope at different times. Since the graph is made up only of straight lines, that's not so hard.

From t = 0.0 to t = 3.0 seconds, the slope is 1.0 m/sec.
From t = 3.0 to t = 4.0 seconds, the slope is 0.
From t = 4.0 to t = 8.0 seconds, the slope is -1.5 m/sec.
From t = 8.0 to t = 10.0 seconds, the slope is 2.0 m/sec.

That results in the following graph:

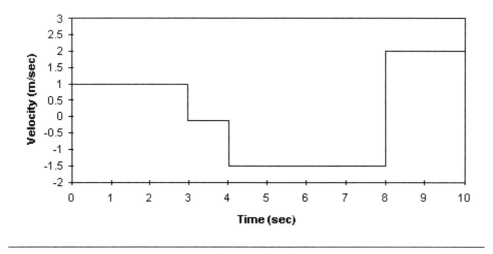

2. a. The object speeds up when acceleration and velocity are pointed in the same direction and acceleration is not zero. Thus, acceleration and velocity have the same sign. This <u>happens from t = 0.0 to t = 3.0 seconds</u> when velocity and slope are both negative, <u>from t = 6.0 seconds to t = 8.0 seconds</u> when velocity and slope are both positive, and from <u>t = 9.5 seconds to t = 10.0 seconds</u> when velocity and slope are both negative.

b. This is a question designed to make sure you are paying attention. The object is at rest when v = 0. Thus, you need not look at slope here. According to the graph, the velocity is at zero at <u>t = 0.0 seconds, t = 6.0 seconds, and t = 9.5 seconds.</u>

c. Once again, we need to determine slope. This is easy, however, since the graph is made of straight lines.

From t = 0.0 to t = 3.0 seconds, the slope is -1.0 m/sec^2.
From t = 3.0 to t = 4.0 seconds, the slope is 0.
From t = 4.0 to t = 8.0 seconds, the slope is 1.5 m/sec^2.
From t = 8.0 to t = 10.0 seconds, the slope is -2.0 m/sec^2.

That results in the following graph:

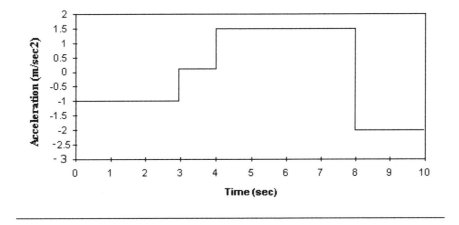

3. The easiest way to do this is to realize that the first part of the problem tells you all you need to know to calculate the distance halfway down.

$$x = v_0 t + \frac{1}{2} a t^2$$

$$x = (0) \cdot t + \frac{1}{2} \cdot (-9.81 \frac{m}{sec^2}) \cdot (1.5 \, sec)^2 = -11 \, m$$

Since the downward direction is negative, that just means the rock traveled 11 m downwards. Since that's half the distance, the total displacement will be -22 m when the rock reaches the ground. Thus, the total time to reach the ground can now be calculated:

$$x = v_o t + \frac{1}{2}at^2$$

$$-22 \text{ m} = (0) \cdot t + \frac{1}{2} \cdot (-9.81 \frac{m}{\sec^2}) \cdot t^2$$

$$t = \sqrt{\frac{2 \cdot (-22 \text{ m})}{-9.81 \frac{m}{\sec^2}}} = \underline{2.1 \text{ sec}}$$

Note that the total time is not 3.0 seconds. Some students think that they can just double the time it takes to travel halfway, and that will be the time it takes for the entire trip. However, that reasoning assumes that the velocity stays *constant*. In free fall, the velocity continually gets more negative until terminal velocity is reached.

4. For the first half of the trip, the object is speeding up. At the end of 25 seconds, however, the acceleration changes, opposing the velocity that was built up over the previous 25 seconds.

a. You can plug through the math if you like, but the answer should be obvious. The velocity gained by the positive acceleration over 25 seconds will be completely canceled out by the velocity lost by the negative acceleration over the next 25 seconds. The final velocity, then, will be $\underline{0}$.

b. The maximum speed will be that attained right before the acceleration changes, because once the acceleration changes, the object begins to slow:

$$v = v_o + at$$

$$v = 0 + (2.0 \frac{m}{\sec^2}) \cdot (25 \text{ sec}) = \underline{5.0 \times 10^1 \frac{m}{\sec}}$$

c. Many students are inclined to think the answer is zero here, but it is not. If acceleration were 2.0 m/sec for 25 seconds and then -2.0 m/sec for 25 seconds, the total displacement would be zero. But in this situation, the object never actually turns around. During the second period, it is slowing down, but it never changes direction. Thus, the object never gets back to the place that it started. In fact, it moves in one direction the entire time.

Since our equations are good only for situations involving constant acceleration, we must split this up into two problems. In the first time period, the initial velocity is zero and the acceleration is 2.0 m/sec². Thus, the distance traveled is:

$$x = v_o t + \frac{1}{2}at^2$$

$$x = (0)\cdot(25\sec) + \frac{1}{2}\cdot(2.0\,\frac{m}{\sec^2})\cdot(25\sec)^2 = 630\,m$$

During the first time period, then, the object moved 630 m in the positive direction. During the second time period, it had an initial velocity from all of the acceleration done in the first time period. In part (b), we determined that it was 5.0×10^1 m/sec. The acceleration during the second time period was -2.0 m/sec^2.

$$x = v_o t + \frac{1}{2}at^2$$

$$x = (5.0 \times 10^1\,\frac{m}{\sec})\cdot(25\sec) + \frac{1}{2}\cdot(-2.0\,\frac{m}{\sec^2})\cdot(25\sec)^2 = 630\,m$$

The total displacement, then, was 1260 m. Note that the object traveled the same distance during each time period. That makes sense, since the motion in time period two was just a mirror image of the motion in time period 1. In the first time period, the object started from rest and ended up traveling at a velocity of 50 m/sec. In the second time period, it started at 50 m/sec and ended up at rest.

5. We do not know the speed of either biker. However, we do know that biker 1 travels twice as quickly as biker 2. This means:

$$v_1 = -2\cdot v_2$$

The only other thing that we know is that the difference in their positions (the distance between them) is 9401 m.

$$x_2 - x_1 = 9401\ m$$

That's all we need to solve the problem. After all, we know:

$$x_1 = v_{o_1}t + \frac{1}{2}a_1 t^2$$

$$x_1 = v_{o_1}t + \frac{1}{2}\cdot(0)\cdot t^2$$

$$x_1 = v_{o_1}t$$

Similarly.

$$x_2 = v_{o2}t$$

Thus,

$$v_{o2} \cdot t - v_{o1}t = 9401 \ m$$

We know that the time is 30.0 minutes (1.80×10^3 sec) and that $v_1 = -2 \cdot v_2$. We can therefore substitute those into our equation:

$$v_{o2} \cdot (1.80 \times 10^3 \ sec) + 2v_{o2} \cdot (1.80 \times 10^3 \ sec) = 9401 \ m$$

$$v_{o2} = \frac{9401 \ m}{3 \cdot (1.80 \times 10^3 \ sec)} = 1.74 \frac{m}{sec}$$

The speed of the second biker, then is 1.74 m/sec, while the speed of the first biker is 3.48 m/sec.

Some students might wonder why I *subtracted* the positions to get 9401 m rather than added them. Remember, x is *position*, not distance. If we were not dealing with direction, then adding would have been fine. However, when you have two *positions* (which include direction and therefore have positive and negative signs), the distance between those positions is calculated by *subtraction*. Think of the number line. The distance between -2 and 2 is not 0, it is 4, because you calculate distance between positions by subtraction.

6. In this problem, we know the acceleration (-32.2 ft/sec^2), the initial velocity (5.0 ft/sec) and the displacement (-15.0 ft). The displacement is negative because the ball lands *below* the place where it was released. Thus, calculating the final velocity is just an application of Equation (2.4).

$$v^2 = v_0^2 + 2ax$$

$$v^2 = (5.0\frac{ft}{sec})^2 + 2 \cdot (-32.2\frac{ft}{sec^2}) \cdot (-15.0 \ ft)$$

$$v = \sqrt{25\frac{ft^2}{sec^2} + 966\frac{ft^2}{sec^2}} = \pm 31\frac{ft}{sec}$$

Since the ball is moving downward as it impacts the ground the velocity is -31 ft/sec, or 31 ft/sec downward.

7. This problem can use the range equation, since the gun is being fired on level ground. You do not have to use it, but it makes the problem easier, so why not? If you look at the range equation, you will see that range is maximized when $\theta = 45.0$. That's because $2\cdot\theta$ is 90.0, which gives you a sine of 1. That's the maximum value sine can take. The fact that an angle of 45.0 degrees gives you the maximum range of a projectile should make sense, and you should have learned that in your first-year course. Given that fact, the maximum range can be used to calculate the initial velocity:

$$R = \frac{(v_o^2)\cdot\sin(2\theta)}{g}$$

$$500.0 \text{ m} = \frac{(v_o^2)\cdot\sin(90.0)}{(9.81 \frac{m}{sec^2})}$$

$$v_o = \sqrt{(500.0 \text{ m})\cdot(9.81 \frac{m}{sec^2})} = 70.0 \frac{m}{sec}$$

I did not give the acceleration due to gravity a negative sign, and I did not worry about the negative root in the answer because the range equation *does not* deal with vectors (notice there are no bold-faced letters in it). It deals only with magnitudes.

Now that we have the initial velocity, calculating the range at 30.0 degrees is a snap:

$$R = \frac{(v_o^2)\cdot\sin(2\theta)}{g}$$

$$R = \frac{(70.0 \frac{m}{sec})^2 \cdot \sin(60.0)}{(9.81 \frac{m}{sec^2})} = \underline{433 \text{ m}}$$

8. The projectile must travel 2500.0 m horizontally to hit the target. The first thing we need to know, however, is how long it will be in the air. Let's go to the vertical dimension to find that out. In the vertical dimension, the acceleration is -9.81 m/sec^2 and the initial velocity is zero. It is zero because the cannon is fired horizontally off of the cliff.

$$\mathbf{x} \ = \ \mathbf{v}_o t \ + \ \frac{1}{2}\mathbf{a}t^2$$

$$-500.0 \ \text{m} = (0) \cdot (t) + \frac{1}{2} \cdot (-9.81 \ \frac{\text{m}}{\text{sec}^2}) \cdot t^2$$

$$t = \sqrt{\frac{-2 \cdot 500.0 \, \text{m}}{-9.81 \ \frac{\text{m}}{\text{sec}^2}}} = 10.1 \ \text{sec}$$

Thus, the projectile must have traveled 2500.0 m in the horizontal dimension in 10.1 sec. In this case, the initial velocity is completely in the horizontal dimension, because the cannon shoots horizontally.

$$\mathbf{x} \ = \ \mathbf{v}_o t \ + \ \frac{1}{2}\mathbf{a}t^2$$

$$2500.0 \ \text{m} = (\mathbf{v}_o) \cdot (10.1 \ \text{sec}) + \frac{1}{2} \cdot (0) \cdot (10.1 \ \text{sec})^2$$

$$\mathbf{v}_o = \frac{2500.0 \, \text{m}}{10.1 \ \text{sec}} = 248 \ \frac{\text{m}}{\text{sec}}$$

The cannon must fire the projectile at 248 m/sec in order to hit the ship.

9. This problem is much like the previous one (of course), but it requires you to be comfortable dealing with variables instead of numbers. We could solve this either way, but I actually want to start in the horizontal dimension because the absence of acceleration in that dimension makes the mathematics easier. In the horizontal dimension, the initial velocity is (300 m/sec)·cosθ

$$2500.0 \ \text{m} \ = \ (300.0 \ \frac{\text{m}}{\text{sec}}) \cdot \cos\theta \cdot t \ + \ \frac{1}{2} \cdot (0) \cdot t^2$$

$$t = \frac{8.333 \ \text{sec}}{\cos\theta}$$

When the projectile has traveled for that amount of time, it is 2500.0 m from the cliff. At that same time, it must be -500.0 m from its initial vertical position. Thus:

$$-500.0 \text{ m} = (300.0 \frac{\text{m}}{\text{sec}}) \cdot \sin\theta \cdot (\frac{8.333 \text{ sec}}{\cos\theta}) + \frac{1}{2} \cdot (-9.81 \frac{\text{m}}{\text{sec}^2}) \cdot (\frac{8.333 \text{ sec}}{\cos\theta})^2$$

$$-500.0 \text{ m} = (2.500 \times 10^3 \text{ m}) \cdot (\frac{\sin\theta}{\cos\theta}) - (341 \text{ m}) \cdot (\frac{1}{\cos^2\theta})$$

Now we can use the three identities discussed in the text:

$$-500.0 \text{ m} = (2.500 \times 10^3 \text{ m}) \cdot \tan\theta - (341 \text{ m}) \cdot (1 + \tan^2\theta)$$

$$(341 \text{ m}) \cdot \tan^2\theta - (2.500 \times 10^3 \text{ m}) \cdot \tan\theta - 159 \text{ m} = 0$$

Now we can use the quadratic formula to solve for $\tan\theta$:

$$\tan\theta = \frac{2.500 \times 10^3 \text{ m} \pm \sqrt{(2.500 \times 10^3 \text{ m})^2 + 4 \cdot (341 \text{ m}) \cdot (159 \text{ m})}}{2 \cdot (341 \text{ m})} = \frac{2.500 \times 10^3 \text{ m} \pm 2543 \text{ m}}{682 \text{ m}}$$

This gives us two possible answers.

$$\tan\theta = \frac{-43}{682} \qquad \tan\theta = \frac{5043}{682}$$

$$\text{or}$$

$$\theta = -3.6° \qquad \theta = 82.3°$$

Either one of those angles will work. Thus, the cannon aims <u>down at an angle of 3.6 degrees or up at an angle of 82.3 degrees</u>.

10. This is another problem in which you need to be comfortable with using variables. We do not know the initial speed, but we know θ. The math is easiest if we start in the horizontal dimension. In that dimension, the initial velocity is $v_o \cdot \cos(30.0)$.

$$300.0 \text{ ft} = (v_o) \cdot \cos(30.0) \cdot t + \frac{1}{2} \cdot (0) \cdot t^2$$

$$t = \frac{346 \text{ ft}}{v_o}$$

Now we can go to the vertical dimension, where the initial velocity is $v_o \cdot \sin(30.0)$.

$$50.0 \text{ ft} = (v_e \cdot \sin(30.0)) \cdot (\frac{346 \text{ ft}}{v_e}) + \frac{1}{2} \cdot (-32.2 \frac{\text{ft}}{\text{sec}^2}) \cdot (\frac{346 \text{ ft}}{v_o})^2$$

$$50.0 \text{ ft} = 173 \text{ ft} - (1.93 \times 10^6 \frac{\text{ft}^3}{\text{sec}^2}) \cdot (\frac{1}{v_o^{\,2}})$$

$$v_o = \sqrt{\frac{1.93 \times 10^6 \frac{\text{ft}^3}{\text{sec}^2}}{123 \text{ ft}}} = \sqrt{15700 \frac{\text{ft}^2}{\text{sec}^2}} = \underline{125 \frac{\text{ft}}{\text{sec}}}$$

SOLUTIONS TO THE PRACTICE PROBLEMS FOR MODULE #3

1. In this problem, the mass is attached only to the third string. Thus, gravity pulls down on the mass, and the third string pulls up on the mass. Since there is no acceleration in the vertical dimension, the forces must sum to zero:

$$T_3 - m \cdot g = 0$$

$$T_3 = m \cdot g = 981 \text{ N}$$

Now we can look at the point where the three strings connect. Once again, the sum of the forces must be zero. However, this is now a two-dimensional problem, so we will have to split things up in the horizontal and vertical dimensions. Let's start with the vertical dimension. The first string is horizontal, so the tension in that string has no vertical component. Therefore:

$$T_2 \cdot \sin(40.0) - T_3 = 0$$

$$T_2 \cdot \sin(40.0) - 981 \text{ N} = 0$$

$$T_2 = 1530 \text{ N}$$

Now we can move to the horizontal dimension, where both strings have a component. I will define motion to the right as positive:

$$T_2 \cdot \cos(40.0) - T_1 = 0$$

$$(1530 \text{ N}) \cdot \cos(40.0) - T_1 = 0$$

$$T_1 = 1170 \text{ N}$$

The tensions are <u>1170 N, 1530 N, and 981 N</u>.

2. The easiest mass to start with in this problem is m_1. It has two forces acting on it: the tension in the string and the weight of the mass. Those sum up as:

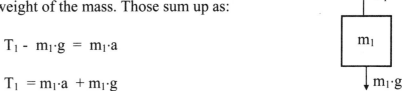

$$T_1 - m_1 \cdot g = m_1 \cdot a$$

$$T_1 = m_1 \cdot a + m_1 \cdot g$$

That gives us an equation for the tension in the first string. Now we can go to the second mass. It has three forces acting on it. The tension in the first string is pulling it up, its weight is pulling it down, and the tension in the second string is also pulling it down. In working with m_1, we defined upward motions as positive and downward motion as negative, because we subtracted weight from tension. However, as m_1 travels down, m_2 travels up. Thus, for m_2, upward motion is negative. As a result, the forces sum as follows:

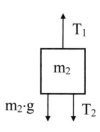

$$T_2 + m_2 \cdot g - T_1 = m_2 \cdot a$$

Substituting the equation we have for T_1:

$$T_2 + m_2 \cdot g - m_1 \cdot a - m_1 \cdot g = m_2 \cdot a$$

$$T_2 = m_1 \cdot a + m_2 \cdot a + m_1 \cdot g - m_2 \cdot g$$

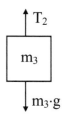

This gives us an equation for T_2. Now we can look at the last mass. It has two forces working on it: the tension in the second string and its weight. Once again, upward motion for this mass is negative, because downward motion for m_1 is negative.

$$m_3 \cdot g - T_2 = m_3 \cdot a$$

Plugging in the equation for T_2:

$$m_3 \cdot g - m_1 \cdot a - m_2 \cdot a - m_1 \cdot g + m_2 \cdot g = m_3 \cdot a$$

$$a = \frac{m_3 \cdot g - m_1 \cdot g + m_2 \cdot g}{m_1 + m_2 + m_3} = 0.892 \ \frac{m}{sec^2}$$

Notice that the acceleration is positive, indicating that m_1 travels up while m_2 and m_3 travel down. Now that we have the acceleration, we can plug it into our tension equations to get the tension in each string:

$$T_1 = m_1 \cdot a + m_1 \cdot g = \underline{535 \ N}$$

$$T_2 = m_1 \cdot a + m_2 \cdot a + m_1 \cdot g - m_2 \cdot g = \underline{268 \ N}$$

3. Since someone grasps m_1 and pulls it down, the force diagram for m_1 changes. Also, since we want this machine to move with a constant velocity, that means the sum of the forces must be zero :

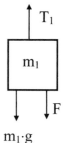

$$T_1 - m_1 \cdot g - F = 0$$

$$T_1 = m_1 \cdot g + F$$

Now think about it. The *other side* of the machine *did not change*. Thus, the forces acting on the other two objects are the same. They just sum to zero this time. Thus, the sum of the forces for m_2 is:

$$T_2 + m_2 \cdot g - T_1 = 0$$

Substituting in our equation for T_1:

$$T_2 + m_2 \cdot g - m_1 \cdot g - F = 0$$

$$T_2 = -m_2 \cdot g + m_1 \cdot g + F$$

The sum of the forces equation for m_3 is

$$m_3 \cdot g - T_2 = 0$$

Substituting in our equation for T_2:

$$m_3 \cdot g + m_2 \cdot g - m_1 \cdot g - F = 0$$

$$F = m_3 \cdot g + m_2 \cdot g - m_1 \cdot g = \underline{98.1 \text{ N}}$$

4. This problem could be made easier by adding m_1 and m_2 together and treating them as one mass. That would give you the right answer. However, since I wrote the book, I know that the *next* problem asks for all of the forces on m_1. To get that, I will have to do the problem the long way, so I might as well do that now!

The third mass is the easiest to deal with, so I will start with it. It has two forces: the tension in the string and the weight. Defining downward motion as negative gives us:

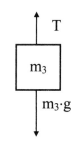

$$T - m_3 \cdot g = m_3 \cdot a$$

$$T = m_3 \cdot a + m_3 \cdot g$$

The second mass has three forces acting on it parallel to the incline. The first mass is pushing on it (we will call the force "P"), friction is opposing the motion, and the component of its weight parallel to the incline pulls it down the incline. Since we are dealing with friction, we also have to look at the dimension perpendicular to the incline to get the normal force. Those perpendicular forces tell us that $F_{normal} = m_2 \cdot g \cdot \cos\theta$, which means $F_{friction} = \mu_k \cdot m_2 \cdot g \cdot \cos\theta = 24.1$ N. Before we add the parallel forces, we have to think about direction. Since

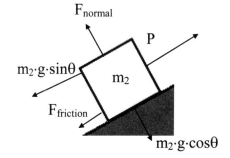

m_3 moving down is negative, that means motion up the incline is negative. That gives us the following sum of forces parallel to the incline:

$$m_2 \cdot g \cdot \sin\theta + F_{friction} - P = m_2 \cdot a$$

We actually know everything in this equation except P, so we can solve for it. Please note that because I said motion downwards for m_3 is negative, that means motions upwards for m_1 is negative. Thus, acceleration is -1.00 m/sec².

$$P = m_2 \cdot g \cdot \sin\theta + F_{friction} - m_2 \cdot a = 123.5 \text{ N}$$

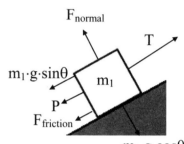

Now we can move on to m_1. The forces perpendicular to the incline tell us that $F_{normal} = m_1 \cdot g \cdot \cos\theta$, which means $F_{friction} = \mu_k \cdot m_1 \cdot g \cdot \cos\theta = 80.4$ N. With this information, we can now look at the parallel dimension. There, we find four forces. The tension in the string pulls the mass up the incline (negative motion); friction opposes that motion; there is a component of the weight parallel to the incline; and m_2 pushes back on m_1 with a force equal and opposite of P, as demanded by Newton's Third Law. Thus, the forces sum as follows:

$$m_1 \cdot g \cdot \sin\theta + F_{friction} + P - T = m_1 \cdot a$$

We can plug in the equation for T that we derived when analyzing m_3, and then everything else we know:

$$m_1 \cdot g \cdot \sin\theta + F_{friction} + P - m_3 \cdot a - m_3 \cdot g = m_1 \cdot a$$

$$(50.0\,\text{kg}) \cdot (9.81\frac{m}{sec^2}) \cdot \sin(35.0) + 80.4\,\text{N} + 123.5\,\text{N} - m_3 \cdot (-1.00\frac{m}{sec^2}) - m_3 \cdot (9.81\frac{m}{sec^2}) = (50.0\,\text{kg}) \cdot (-1.00\frac{m}{sec^2})$$

$$m_3 = \frac{(50.0\,\text{kg}) \cdot (9.81\frac{m}{sec^2}) \cdot \sin(35.0) + 80.4\,\text{N} + 123.5\,\text{N} + 50.0\,\text{N}}{8.81\,\frac{m}{sec^2}} = \underline{60.7 \text{ kg}}$$

Notice that I had to plug in a negative value for a. After all, the acceleration is negative.

5. Now that I did the hard work in problem #4, the answer to this one is easy:

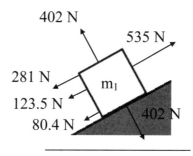

6. Let's look at the forces affecting the point at which the man grips the rope with his hand. At that point, the force with which the man pulls is directed downward, and the tension in the string is directed upward. Since we want the person and chair to rise at a constant velocity, the sum of these two forces must be zero.

$$T - F = 0$$

$$T = F$$

The tension, then, equals the force with which the man pulls down. Okay, now let's look at the man. This is where you might have trouble. There are *three* forces acting on the man and chair. First, the tension in the string is pulling up where it is attached to the chair. Second, the weight of the man and chair pulls down. However, there is a third force. Remember, the man is grasping the rope. Thus, as he pulls down on the rope, the rope pulls up on him. As a result, the tension on the rope pulls him up *again*, this time at the point where his hands grasp the rope! The sum of the forces, then, is:

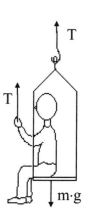

$$m \cdot g - T - T = 0$$

$$2T = m \cdot g$$

$$T = 613 \text{ N}$$

Since the tension is equal to the force, <u>the force required is 613 N</u>. Note that the weight of the man and the chair together is 1,226 N. However, the bosun's chair allows him to apply half of that force in lifting the chair. Now please realize that the *pulley is doing nothing to reduce the force that is needed*. A single pulley gives you no mechanical advantage. It simply changes the direction of the force. However, the man is essentially using his strength twice: once to lift himself up on the rope, and then once again where the rope attaches to the chair. Since the force is being used twice, you only need half as much of it.

7. Let's start with the weight. It has two forces acting on it: tension and its weight. Since the weight is supposed to move with constant velocity, those forces add to zero:

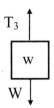

$$T_3 - W = 0$$

$$T_3 = W$$

Now let's look at the lower pulley. It has three forces acting on it. T_2 acts on it twice (once on either side of the pulley), pulling it up. T_3 pulls it down. Once again, these forces must sum to zero:

$$T_2 + T_2 - T_3 = 0$$

Since we know $T_3 = W$, and since that's what we must have in our final equation:

$$T_2 + T_2 - W = 0$$

$$T_2 = \frac{W}{2}$$

Now let's look at the point at which the rope is grasped on the other side of the pulley. Remember, upward motion of the weight is positive, which means downward motion on this side is positive. At the point where the rope is grasped, there are two forces: the tension in the rope (T_2) and the force. Thus:

$$F - T_2 = 0$$

$$F = T_2$$

Since we know that $T_2 = W/2$, we know that the <u>force required is half that of the weight</u>. This problem demonstrates what you should have learned in seventh grade when you covered simple machines: multiple pulleys give you a mechanical advantage. Two pulleys make the force half of what is necessary with one pulley. Three pulleys make the force one-third as much as one pulley.

8. Notice that we did not have to analyze the top pulley in the solution to problem 7. You could have, but you did not need to. However, I am making you do that analysis now. This pulley is stationary. Thus, even if the weight was accelerating, the sum of the forces on this pulley would have to be 0.

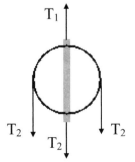

$$T_1 - T_2 - T_2 - T_2 = 0$$

$$T_1 = 3 \cdot T_2$$

Since we found before that T_2 was half of the weight, then T_1 is 3W/2.

9. You could go through the whole analysis again, but it is not necessary. Think about what happens with the bosun's chair. Because the person is pulling on the rope, there is an extra force pulling him up (the tension on the string that he is holding). Thus, not only does T_2 pull up twice as a result of the pulley that is connected to W, but T_2 pulls up again where the person on the chair holds the rope. Thus, T_2 pulls up three times. This means the tension need only be one-third of the weight. Thus, the force with which he pulls needs only be W/3.

10. In this one, you must be *very* careful to identify every force working on each block. Let's start with the 10.0 kg block. Gravity pulls down on the block and, in response, the 50.0 kg block pushes up with an equal and opposite normal force. The tension of the rope pulls the block to the left, and friction pulls it to the right. The normal force is equal to the weight of the block (there is no vertical motion), and since the μ_k between the blocks is 0.250, the frictional force is 24.5 N. The horizontal forces must sum to zero, since this block does not move:

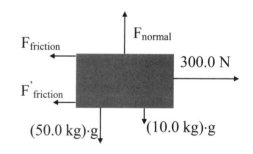

$$F_{friction} - T = 0$$

$$T = 24.5 \text{ N}$$

That answers the second part of the question. To answer the first part of the question, we have to look at the 50.0 kg block. This is where you have to really think about all of the forces. First, let's get the obvious ones. The 300.0 N force pulls the block to the right. Its weight pulls it down. The floor exerts a normal force up, and the friction between the floor and the ground opposes the motion. We will call that $F'_{friction}$, because this friction is different than the friction which exists between the blocks. There are still two forces to consider, however. First, the 10.0 kg block pushes down on this block with its weight. Thus, that is another downward force. Also, the friction between the blocks opposes motion. That's another force to the left. That's all of the forces. Now we are ready to look at the different dimensions. The vertical dimension will tell us what we need to know about $F'_{friction}$:

$$F_{normal} - (50.0 \text{ kg}) \cdot g - (10.0 \text{ kg}) \cdot g = 0$$

$$F_{normal} = 589 \text{ N}$$

Since μ_k between the block and the floor is 0.350, $F'_{friction} = 206$ N. We already know the other frictional force. It was calculated before. Remember, forces work in pairs according to Newton's Third Law. Thus, the frictional force we calculated before was pointed to the right, and now we are working with the equal and opposite force, which pulls to the left. Now we can sum up the forces in the horizontal dimension:

$$300.0 \text{ N } - F'_{friction} - F_{friction} = (50.0 \text{ kg})\cdot a$$

$$300.0 \text{ N } - 206 \text{ N } - 24.5 \text{ N } = (50.0 \text{ kg})\cdot a$$

$$\underline{a = 1.4 \text{ m/sec}^2}$$

SOLUTIONS TO THE PRACTICE PROBLEMS FOR MODULE #4

1. The skier has all potential and no kinetic energy at the top of the hill. Thus:

$$TE = PE + KE = m \cdot g \cdot h + 0$$

At the bottom of the hill, all of that energy is kinetic. Thus:

$$m \cdot g \cdot h = PE + KE = 0 + \frac{1}{2} \cdot m \cdot v^2$$

$$\cancel{m} \cdot g \cdot h = \frac{1}{2} \cdot \cancel{m} \cdot v^2$$

$$v = \sqrt{2 \cdot g \cdot h} = \sqrt{2 \cdot (9.81 \, \frac{m}{sec^2}) \cdot (150 \ m)} = \underline{54 \, \frac{m}{sec}}$$

2. In order for the skier to come to a halt, friction must work to remove all of the kinetic energy. To get an expression for kinetic energy, let's determine the initial potential energy:

$$PE = m \cdot g \cdot h = m \cdot (9.81 \, \frac{m}{sec^2}) \cdot (150 \ m) = 1{,}500 \cdot m \ J$$

We don't know the mass, so we will just leave it as "m." Since that all becomes kinetic energy at the bottom of the hill, friction must do -1,500·m J worth of work to dissipate all of that energy. The force with which friction works is:

$$f = \mu_k \cdot F_n = \mu_k \cdot m \cdot g = (0.550) \cdot (m) \cdot (9.81 \, \frac{m}{sec^2}) = 5.40 \cdot m \ N$$

Friction opposes motion, so the angle between force and displacement is 180.0 degrees. We know the work that must be done, we know the frictional force, and we know the angle. Thus:

$$W = f \cdot x \cdot \cos \theta$$

$$-1{,}500 \cdot \cancel{m} \, J = (5.40 \cdot \cancel{m} \ N) \cdot x \cdot \cos(180.0)$$

$$x = \underline{280 m}$$

3. In this problem, you have to be comfortable working with variables and no numbers. The potential energy of the rock at the top of the cliff is m·g·h, and that is also the total energy, since kinetic energy is zero. Halfway down, half of that energy will be converted to kinetic energy. Thus, KE = ½·m·g·h. Thus, at the halfway point:

$$KE = \frac{1}{2} \cdot m \cdot v_{halfway}^2$$

$$\frac{1}{2} \cdot m \cdot g \cdot h = \frac{1}{2} \cdot m \cdot v_{halfway}^2$$

$$v_{halfway} = \sqrt{g \cdot h}$$

At the bottom, all of the potential energy has been converted to kinetic energy, so KE = m·g·h. Thus:

$$KE = \frac{1}{2} \cdot m \cdot v_{bottom}^2$$

$$m \cdot g \cdot h = \frac{1}{2} \cdot m \cdot v_{bottom}^2$$

$$v_{bottom} = \sqrt{2 \cdot g \cdot h}$$

To answer the question, then, we can just compute the ratio:

$$\frac{v_{halfway}}{v_{bottom}} = \frac{\sqrt{g \cdot h}}{\sqrt{2 \cdot g \cdot h}}$$

$$\underline{v_{halfway} = \frac{1}{\sqrt{2}} \cdot v_{bottom}}$$

4. If the mass starts at rest, then its only energy is potential energy, and we can use Equation (4.4) to determine an expression for it:

$$PE = m \cdot g \cdot h = (m) \cdot \left(9.81 \frac{m}{sec^2}\right) \cdot (1.00 \text{ m}) = 9.81 \cdot m \text{ J}$$

If there were no friction, the box would reach the bottom of the ramp. However, friction works against the motion, taking energy away. To calculate that work, we first have to determine the frictional force:

$$F_{friction} = \mu_k \cdot F_{normal} = \mu_k \cdot m \cdot g \cdot \cos\theta = (0.150) \cdot (m) \cdot (9.81\frac{m}{sec^2}) \cdot \cos(45.0) = 1.04 \cdot m \text{ N}$$

That force works along the ramp. To get the distance over which it works, we use trigonometry:

$$\sin(45.0) = \frac{1.00 \text{ m}}{\text{hypotenuse}}$$

$$\text{hypotenuse} = \frac{1.00 \text{ m}}{\sin(45.0)} = 1.41 \text{ m}$$

The force works against the motion, so the angle between the force and the displacement is 180.0°. Thus, to get the work:

$$W = F \cdot x \cdot \cos\theta = (1.04 \cdot m \text{ N}) \cdot (1.41 \text{ m}) \cdot \cos(180.0) = -1.47 \cdot m \text{ J}$$

The total energy of the box at the bottom of the ramp, then, is:

$$TE = 9.81 \cdot m \text{ J} + -1.47 \cdot m \text{ J} = 8.34 \text{ m J}$$

Once the box reaches the bottom, there is no more friction so no more energy will be lost. As it travels up the loop, it will gain potential energy and thus lose kinetic energy.

$$TE = PE + KE$$

$$TE = m \cdot g \cdot h + \frac{1}{2} \cdot m \cdot v^2$$

$$8.34 \cdot \cancel{m} \text{ J} = (\cancel{m}) \cdot (9.81\frac{m}{sec^2}) \cdot (0.300 \text{ m}) + \frac{1}{2} \cdot (\cancel{m}) \cdot v^2$$

$$\underline{v = 3.29\frac{m}{sec}}$$

5. a. At t=8.0 seconds, the velocity is constant. Thus, there is no acceleration. The motor must be supplying just enough force to overcome friction. At t = 5.0 seconds, the toy is accelerating. Thus, the motor is supplying more than just enough force to overcome friction. That means the force is greater at 5.0 seconds.

b. When velocity and force are constant, $P = F \cdot v$. At each time, there is no acceleration, so the force is the same each time - it is equal to the frictional force. Thus, <u>more power is being exerted at 9.0 seconds</u>.

6. When the charged particle is far from the fixed charge, it has essentially no potential energy. As it gets close to the fixed charge, it gains potential energy. At 0.500 m away, the potential energy is:

$$PE = q \cdot V$$

$$V = \frac{k \cdot Q}{r}$$

$$PE = \frac{k \cdot Q \cdot q}{r} = \frac{(8.99 \times 10^9 \ \frac{N \cdot m^2}{C^2}) \cdot (0.00250 \ C) \cdot (0.00150 \ C)}{(0.500 \ m)} = 6.74 \times 10^4 \ J$$

Initially, the charged particle had no energy. Now, it has a total energy of 6.74×10^4 J. That means something must have worked on the object with 6.74×10^4 J of work. If it took ten minutes, the average power was:

$$P = \frac{W}{t} = \frac{6.74 \times 10^4 \ J}{6.00 \times 10^2 \ seconds} = \underline{112 \ Watts}$$

7. The ball's momentum changed from zero to:

$$\mathbf{p} = m \cdot \mathbf{v} = (5.0 \ kg) \cdot (3.5 \ \frac{m}{sec}) = 18 \ \frac{kg \cdot m}{sec}$$

The momentum changed because the force applied an impulse:

$$\mathbf{J} = \Delta \mathbf{p}$$

Well, we also know that

$$\mathbf{J} = \mathbf{F} \cdot \Delta t$$

Thus

$$\mathbf{J} = \Delta \mathbf{p}$$

$$\mathbf{F} \cdot \Delta t = 18 \ \frac{kg \cdot m}{sec}$$

$$(55 \text{ N}) \cdot \Delta t = 18 \frac{\text{kg} \cdot \text{m}}{\text{sec}}$$

$$\Delta t = \underline{0.33 \text{ sec}}$$

8. a. Energy is put into the system by pushing the mass attached to the spring towards the wall. As a result, the mass/spring system has the following potential energy:

$$U_{spring} = \frac{1}{2} \cdot k \cdot x^2$$

$$U_{spring} = \frac{1}{2} \cdot (15.1 \frac{\text{N}}{\text{m}}) \cdot (0.500 \text{ m})^2 = 1.89 \text{ J}$$

When the mass is released, the potential energy will be converted into kinetic energy, until all of the potential energy has been converted. That will happen at the equilibrium position. At that point, the masses will collide. We had better determine the velocity of the 10.0 kg mass at that point:

$$KE = \frac{1}{2} \cdot m \cdot v^2$$

$$1.89 \text{ J} = \frac{1}{2} \cdot (10.0 \text{ kg}) \cdot (v)^2$$

$$v = 0.615 \frac{\text{m}}{\text{sec}}$$

First, let's conserve momentum:

$$m_1 \cdot v_{1i} + m_2 \cdot v_{2i} = m_1 \cdot v_{1f} + m_2 \cdot v_{2f}$$

$$(10.0 \text{ kg}) \cdot (0.615 \frac{\text{m}}{\text{sec}}) = (10.0 \text{ kg}) \cdot v_{1f} + (15.0 \text{ kg}) \cdot v_{2f}$$

$$v_{1f} = \frac{6.15 \frac{\text{kg} \cdot \text{m}}{\text{sec}} - (15.0 \text{ kg}) \cdot v_{2f}}{10.0 \text{ kg}} = 0.615 \frac{\text{m}}{\text{sec}} - (1.50) \cdot v_{2f}$$

Next, let's conserve energy:

$$\frac{1}{2} \cdot m_1 \cdot v_{1i}^2 + \frac{1}{2} \cdot m_2 \cdot v_{2i}^2 = \frac{1}{2} \cdot m_1 \cdot v_{1f}^2 + \frac{1}{2} \cdot m_2 \cdot v_{2f}^2$$

$$(10.0 \text{ kg}) \cdot (0.615 \frac{m}{sec})^2 = (10.0 \text{ kg}) \cdot v_{1f}^2 + (15.0 \text{ kg}) \cdot v_{2f}^2$$

Plugging our expression for v_{1f} in this equation:

$$(10.0 \text{ kg}) \cdot (0.615 \frac{m}{sec})^2 = (10.0 \text{ kg}) \cdot (0.615 \frac{m}{sec} - (1.50) \cdot v_{2f})^2 + (15.0 \text{ kg}) \cdot v_{2f}^2$$

$$3.78 \text{ J} = 3.78 \text{ J} - 18.5 \frac{kg}{m \cdot sec} \cdot v_{2f} + (22.5 \text{ kg}) \cdot v_{2f}^2 + (15.0 \text{ kg}) \cdot v_{2f}^2$$

$$(37.5 \text{ kg}) \cdot v_{2f}^2 - 18.5 \frac{kg}{m \cdot sec} \cdot v_{2f} = 0$$

$$v_{2f} \cdot [(37.5 \text{ kg}) \cdot v_{2f} - 18.5 \frac{kg}{m \cdot sec}] = 0$$

$$v_{2f} = 0, 0.493$$

Since the initial velocity of the 15.0 kg mass was zero, the other solution, $v_{2f} = 0.493$ m/sec, must be the correct one. With this velocity, the 15.0 kg mass has a kinetic energy of:

$$KE = \frac{1}{2} \cdot m \cdot v^2$$

$$KE = \frac{1}{2} \cdot (15.0 \text{ kg}) \cdot (0.493 \frac{m}{sec})^2$$

$$KE = 1.82 \text{ J}$$

For the mass to come to rest, friction must do -1.82 J worth of work.

$$W = \mu_k \cdot m \cdot g \cdot x \cdot \cos\theta$$

$$-1.82 \text{ J} = (0.250) \cdot (15.0 \text{ kg}) \cdot (9.81 \frac{m}{sec^2}) \cdot x \cdot \cos(180.0)$$

$$x = 0.0495 \text{ m}$$

The 15.0 kg mass, then, moves <u>4.95 cm</u> before it comes to a stop.

b. In (a), we determined that the 15.0 kg mass had a velocity of 0.493 m/sec. We also had an equation to relate the velocities of the two masses. Thus:

$$\mathbf{v}_{1f} = 0.615\frac{m}{sec} - (1.50)\cdot \mathbf{v}_{2f} = -0.125$$

The negative just means it is moving in the opposite direction as the 15.0 kg mass, but that makes sense. This mass experiences no friction, so it will compress the spring until all of its kinetic energy is used. The kinetic energy is:

$$KE = \frac{1}{2}\cdot m\cdot v^2$$

$$KE = \frac{1}{2}\cdot (10.0\ kg)\cdot (-0.125\frac{m}{sec})^2$$

$$KE = 0.0781\ J$$

That will all get converted to potential energy.

$$U_{spring} = \frac{1}{2}\cdot k\cdot x^2$$

$$0.0781\ J = \frac{1}{2}\cdot (15.1\frac{N}{m})\cdot x^2$$

$$x = 0.102\ m$$

The mass will compress the spring <u>10.2 cm</u>.

9. When the pendulum raises to a height of "h," it has a potential energy of

$$PE = (M+m)\cdot g\cdot h$$

How did it get that potential energy? Well, as a result of the collision, the system had kinetic energy. All of that kinetic energy got converted to potential energy. Thus, right after the collision, the kinetic energy of the system would have been $(M+m)\cdot g\cdot h$. That means:

$$KE = \frac{1}{2} \cdot (M + m) \cdot v^2$$

$$(M + m) \cdot g \cdot h = \frac{1}{2} \cdot (M + m) \cdot v^2$$

$$v = \sqrt{2 \cdot g \cdot h}$$

That's the velocity of the system after the collision. That means the momentum of the system after the collision is:

$$p = m \cdot v = (M + m) \cdot \sqrt{2 \cdot g \cdot h}$$

That has to be the momentum *before* the collision as well. Before the collision, however, the only thing moving was the bullet. Thus:

$$(M + m) \cdot \sqrt{2 \cdot g \cdot h} = m \cdot v$$

$$v = \frac{(M + m) \cdot \sqrt{2 \cdot g \cdot h}}{m}$$

b. <u>You cannot do that, because it assumes that the collision is elastic and thus no energy is lost. However, this is a perfectly inelastic collision, and energy will be lost</u>.

10. Let's draw what happened:

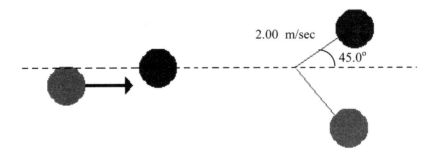

Since this is an elastic collision, we also know that the other angle is 45.0°, because the angles must add up to 90.0 degrees in this situation. Properly defined, of course, the angle is really 315.0°. If we conserve momentum in the y-dimension, we can determine the speed of the other mass.

$$m_1 \cdot v_{1i} \cdot \sin\theta_{1i} + m_2 \cdot v_{2i} \cdot \sin\theta_{2i} = m_1 \cdot v_{1f} \cdot \sin\theta_{1f} + m_2 \cdot v_{2f} \cdot \sin\theta_{2f}$$

$$(0) \cdot \sin\theta_{1i} + v_{2i} \cdot \sin(0.00) = (2.00 \text{ m / sec}) \cdot \sin(45.0) + v_{2f} \cdot \sin(315.0)$$

$$v_{2f} = 2.00 \text{ m / sec}$$

Now if we look at the x-dimension, we can determine the initial speed of ball 2. Recognizing that the masses cancel:

$$v_{1i} \cdot \cos\theta_{1i} + v_{2i} \cdot \cos\theta_{2i} = v_{1f} \cdot \cos\theta_{1f} + v_{2f} \cdot \cos\theta_{2f}$$

$$(0) \cdot \cos\theta_{1i} + (v_{2i}) \cdot \cos(0.00) = (2.00\frac{\text{m}}{\text{sec}}) \cdot \cos(45.0) + (2.00\frac{\text{m}}{\text{sec}}) \cdot \cos(315.0)$$

$$v_{2i} = 2.83 \frac{\text{m}}{\text{sec}}$$

SOLUTIONS TO THE PRACTICE PROBLEMS FOR MODULE #5

1. The setup is shown to the right. Each meter stick is (of course) 1.000 m long (a meter stick can be read to tenths of a cm). In my drawing, the metal meter stick which is twice as heavy is on the bottom, but it could be anywhere. Since an extended object can be replaced by its center of mass, and since meter sticks are uniform, the picture to the right changes to the picture on the left. In that picture, there are three masses, one of which is twice as heavy as the others. The geometry is a bit tricky, but it can be done. Let's treat the lower, left-hand corner of the triangle as the origin. If that's the case, the mass labeled "2m" is 0.5000 m to the right of the origin and 0.0000 m above it. What about the mass labeled "m" on the left leg? In an equilateral triangle, all three angles are 60.0°. Thus, its horizontal position is $(0.5000 \text{ m}) \cdot \cos(60.0) = 0.2500$ m to the right of the origin. Its vertical position is $(0.5000 \text{ m}) \cdot \sin(60.0) = 0.4330$ m above the origin. The mass on the right is also 0.4330 m above the origin. What is its horizontal position, however? The best way to think about that is to look at the corner on the bottom right. That corner is 1.000 m to the right of the origin. The mass is $(0.5000 \text{ m}) \cdot \cos(60.0) = 0.25000$ m to the left of that point. Thus, its horizontal position is 0.7500 m. That gives us three points:

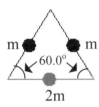

m: x = 0.2500 m, y = 0.4330 m
m: x = 0.7500 m, y = 0.4330 m
2m: x = 0.5000 m, y = 0.0000 m

Now we can calculate the center of mass:

$$X_{cm} = \frac{m_1 \cdot x_1 + m_2 \cdot x_2 + m_3 \cdot x_3 \dots m_n \cdot x_n}{m_1 + m_2 + m_3 \dots m_n}$$

$$X_{cm} = \frac{\cancel{m} \cdot (0.2500 \text{ m}) + \cancel{m} \cdot (0.7500 \text{ m}) + 2\cancel{m} \cdot (0.5000 \text{ m})}{\cancel{m} + \cancel{m} + 2\cancel{m}} = 0.5000 \text{ m}$$

$$Y_{cm} = \frac{m_1 \cdot y_1 + m_2 \cdot y_2 + m_3 \cdot y_3 \dots m_n \cdot y_n}{m_1 + m_2 + m_3 \dots m_n}$$

$$Y_{cm} = \frac{\cancel{m} \cdot (0.4330 \text{ m}) + \cancel{m} \cdot (0.4330 \text{ m}) + 2\cancel{m} \cdot (0.000 \text{ m})}{\cancel{m} + \cancel{m} + 2\cancel{m}} = 0.2165 \text{ m}$$

The center of mass, then, is 0.2165 m directly above the center of the metal meter stick.

2. The rod is 2.50 m long. Thus, its center of mass is 1.25 m from the wall. The mass of the rod (50.0 kg), then, can be assumed to be all right there. The 100.0 kg mass is also there, so there is a total of 150.0 kg pulling down on the rod 1.25 m from the wall. The string is pulling up on the stick 2.50 m from the wall at a properly-defined angle of 150.0°. Since I have defined the angle properly, I do not need to worry about assigning a positive or negative sign to the tension. Trigonometry will take care of that. If we sum up the torques on the stick using the end stuck to the wall as the axis of rotation, we get:

$$- (150.0 \text{ kg}) \cdot (9.81 \frac{\text{m}}{\text{sec}^2}) \cdot (1.25 \text{ m}) + T \cdot \sin(150.0) \cdot (2.50 \text{ m}) = 0$$

$$T = \underline{1470 \text{ N}}$$

That's the tension in the string. To get the force exerted by the wall, we have to sum up the forces in each dimension. In the x-dimension:

$$F_{wx} + (1470 \text{ N}) \cdot \cos(150.0) = 0$$

$$F_{wx} = 1270 \text{ N}$$

In the y-dimension:

$$F_{wy} + (1470 \text{ N}) \cdot \sin(150.0) - (150.0 \text{ kg}) \cdot (9.81 \frac{\text{m}}{\text{sec}^2}) = 0$$

$$F_{wy} = 737 \text{ N}$$

Turning those components into magnitude and direction, we get that the wall exerts a 1470 N force at an angle of 30.1°.

3. a. Remember, the torque is given by **r** x **F**, which is most easily evaluated with Equation (5.2). The angle in Equation (5.2), however, is the angle between the force and the radius. The force is gravity, and it pulls straight down. Thus, we have the following picture:

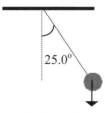

Since the angle is relative to the vertical, and since the gravitational force acts vertically, the angle between the force and the radius is 25.0°. The torque, then, is easy to calculate:

$$\tau = r \cdot F \cdot \sin\theta = (0.550 \text{ m}) \cdot (0.0500 \text{ kg}) \cdot (9.81 \frac{\text{m}}{\text{sec}^2}) \cdot \sin(25.0) = \underline{0.114 \text{ N} \cdot \text{m}}$$

Since the angle will decrease once the bob is released and the largest it will ever get is 25.0°, that is the maximum torque.

b. The angular acceleration is given by:

$$\tau = I \cdot \alpha$$

Since this is a mass rotating around a fixed point, its moment of inertia, according to Figure 5.4, is $M \cdot R^2$. Thus,

$$0.114 \ \text{N·m} = (0.0500 \ \text{kg}) \cdot (0.550 \ \text{m})^2 \cdot \alpha$$

$$\alpha = 7.54 \ \frac{\text{rad}}{\text{sec}^2}$$

c. <u>The minimum torque will be 0</u>, and that will occur when the string is at its vertical hanging position. At that point, the angle between the radius and the gravitational force is 0, and the sine of 0 is 0.

4. Let's start with the grand piano. In order to get it to move up at a constant rate, the sum of the forces must be zero. The only two forces are the weight of the piano and the tension in the string. Defining up as positive, we get :

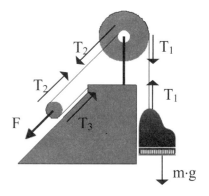

$$T_1 - m \cdot g = 0$$

$$T_1 = 1960 \ \text{N}$$

That's T_1. If the grand piano moves with constant velocity, the large pulley will move with a constant angular velocity, which means the angular acceleration will be zero. That means the sum of the torques is zero. T_1 pulls down at the outer radius (1.00 m), and T_2 pulls left (at the inner radius (0.250 m). If clockwise rotation is considered positive, then T_1 makes a positive torque and T_2 makes a negative torque:

$$T_1 \cdot (1.00 \ \text{m}) - T_2 \cdot (0.250 \ \text{m}) = 0$$

$$(1960 \ \text{N}) \cdot (1.00 \ \text{m}) - T_2 \cdot (0.250 \ \text{m}) = 0$$

$$T_2 = 7840 \ \text{N}$$

The force, F, supplies no torque, because it is applied at the center. Thus, to keep the small pulley rotating at a constant angular velocity, the torques supplied by those two tensions must be the same. If clockwise motion is positive, then T_2 makes a positive torque and T_3 makes a negative torque:

$$T_2 \cdot r - T_3 \cdot r = 0$$

$$T_3 = T_2 = 7840$$

Now we can finally figure out F. If the small pulley is moving at constant speed, the sum of the forces must be zero. F is positive because it makes the piano rise:

$$F - T_2 - T_3 = 0$$

$$F - 7840 \text{ N} - 7840 \text{ N} = 0$$

$$\underline{F = 15{,}680 \text{ N}}$$

Notice that this force is *significantly greater* than the weight of the grand piano (1960 N). Thus, this block and tackle *did not* make the job easier.

b. The piano mover was close. However, to get this system to actually make things easier, <u>the piano should be attached to the inner radius of the large pulley.</u> If the guy did that, the force needed would be only 980 N. Of course, even then, the small pulley hinders the job. If he were just to attach the piano to the inner radius and pull on a rope attached to the outer radius, he would only have to exert 490 N of force!

5. Since we know the acceleration and the mass, we can figure out the tension in the string. Summing up the forces on the mass:

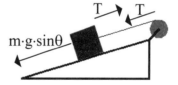

$$T - m \cdot g \cdot \sin\theta = m \cdot a$$

$$T - (10.0 \text{ kg}) \cdot (9.81 \frac{m}{sec^2}) \cdot \sin(25.0) = (10.0 \text{ kg}) \cdot (-3.75 \frac{m}{sec^2})$$

$$T = 4.0 \text{ N}$$

Note that the acceleration is negative because we defined motion down the ramp as negative. The tension exerts a torque on the wheel. That torque is equal to the moment of inertia times the angular acceleration. You actually know the angular acceleration. If the mass is accelerating at 3.75 m/sec^2, then so is the string. Thus, the outer edge of the wheel is accelerating at 3.75 m/sec^2. That means the angular acceleration is 3.75 m/sec^2 divided by R:

$$\tau = I \cdot \alpha$$

$$T \cdot R = \frac{1}{2} \cdot M \cdot R^2 \cdot (\frac{3.75}{R} \frac{m}{sec^2})$$

$$M = \frac{2 \cdot T}{3.75 \, \frac{m}{sec^2}} = \frac{2 \cdot (4.0 \text{ N})}{3.75 \, \frac{m}{sec^2}} = \underline{2.1 \text{ kg}}$$

6. This is a simple application of Equation (5.8). The force applies a torque. The moment of inertia can be found in Figure 5.4. Thus, Equation (5.8) becomes:

$$F \cdot R = I \cdot \alpha$$

$$F \cdot R = \frac{2}{5} \cdot M \cdot R^2 \cdot \alpha$$

$$(55.0 \text{ N}) \cdot (0.0600 \text{ m}) = \frac{2}{5} \cdot (0.2500 \text{ kg}) \cdot (0.0600 \text{ m})^2 \cdot \alpha$$

$$\alpha = \underline{9170 \, \frac{rad}{sec^2}}$$

7. In one revolution, the top sweeps out an angle of 2π. Thus, the top is sweeping out 10.0π radians every second. That's an angular velocity of 31.4 rad/sec. The angular momentum, then, is:

$$L = I \cdot \omega$$

$$L = \frac{2}{5} \cdot M \cdot R^2 \cdot \omega = \frac{2}{5} \cdot (0.2500 \text{ kg}) \cdot (0.0600 \text{ m})^2 \cdot (31.4 \, \frac{rad}{sec}) = \underline{0.0113 \, \frac{kg \cdot m^2}{sec}}$$

To determine angular momentum, you use the right hand rule. Pointing your right hand along the radius of the sphere (from the central axis out) and then curling your fingers in the direction of motion, your thumb points <u>down</u>.

8. You can use forces and torques to figure this out, but energy concepts make the job easier. Whenever a problem asks about speed instead of acceleration, try to use energy concepts. When the system starts out, its total energy is just the potential energy in the large mass ($m_2 \cdot g \cdot h = 601$ J). When the system starts to move, the small mass gains potential energy. At the very end, the small mass will be as high as the heavy mass was ($m_1 \cdot g \cdot h = 240$ J), each mass has translational kinetic energy ($\frac{1}{2} \cdot m_1 \cdot v^2 + \frac{1}{2} \cdot m_2 \cdot v^2$), and the pulley has rotational kinetic energy ($\frac{1}{2} \cdot I \cdot \omega^2$). Ignoring losses due to friction, the total energy at the beginning must equal the total energy at the end:

$$601 \text{ J} = 240 \text{ J} + \tfrac{1}{2} \cdot m_1 \cdot v^2 + \tfrac{1}{2} \cdot m_2 \cdot v^2 + \tfrac{1}{2} \cdot I \cdot \omega^2$$

$$361 \text{ J} = \frac{1}{2} \cdot (25.0 \text{ kg} + 10.0 \text{ kg}) \cdot v^2 + \frac{1}{2} \cdot [\frac{1}{2} \cdot (5.00 \text{ kg}) \cdot (0.750 \text{ m})^2] \cdot [\frac{v}{(0.750 \text{ m})}]^2$$

$$361 \text{ J} = (17.5 \text{ kg}) \cdot v^2 + 1.25 \cdot v^2$$

$$v = 4.38 \frac{\text{m}}{\text{sec}}$$

9. The ball starts out with a potential energy of m·g·h. That's its total energy. As it rolls down the incline, it picks up translational kinetic energy ($\frac{1}{2} \cdot m_2 \cdot v^2$) and rotational kinetic energy ($\frac{1}{2} \cdot I \cdot \omega^2$). When it rolls up the loop, it also gains potential energy, so it loses translational and rotational kinetic energy. At the top of the loop:

$$m \cdot g \cdot (0.750 \text{ m}) = m \cdot g \cdot (0.500 \text{ m}) + \frac{1}{2} \cdot m \cdot v^2 + \frac{1}{2} (\frac{2}{5} \cdot m \cdot R^2) \cdot (\frac{v}{R})^2$$

$$g \cdot (0.250 \text{ m}) = (\frac{1}{2} + \frac{1}{5}) \cdot v^2$$

$$v = 1.87 \frac{\text{m}}{\text{sec}}$$

10. The angular momentum ($I \cdot \omega$) must be conserved. With the disk spinning, the moment of inertia is $\frac{1}{2} \cdot M \cdot R^2$. It is spinning at 10.0 revolutions per minute, which is 20.0π radians per minute, or 1.05 rad/sec. When the ball of clay drops on the disk, the disk's moment of inertia is the same, but the ball of clay (a mass rotating about a fixed point) adds an additional moment of inertia of $m \cdot r^2$ where m is the mass of the clay and r is the radius at which the mass landed. Thus, the angular momentum equation becomes:

$$\frac{1}{2} \cdot (25.0 \text{ kg}) \cdot (1.00 \text{ m})^2 \cdot (1.05 \frac{\text{rad}}{\text{sec}}) = \frac{1}{2} \cdot (25.0 \text{ kg}) \cdot (1.00 \text{ m})^2 \cdot \omega + (2.50 \text{ kg}) \cdot (0.750 \text{ m})^2 \cdot \omega$$

$$\omega = 0.944 \frac{\text{rad}}{\text{sec}}$$

Since each revolution sweeps out an angle of $2 \cdot \pi$ rads, we can convert from rads/sec to revs/sec:

$$\frac{0.944 \text{ rads}}{\text{sec}} \times \frac{1 \text{ rev}}{2 \cdot \pi \text{ rads}} = 0.150 \frac{\text{rev}}{\text{sec}} \text{ or } 9.01 \frac{\text{rev}}{\text{min}}$$

SOLUTIONS TO THE PRACTICE PROBLEMS FOR MODULE #6

1. As the hint states, when the mass is displaced, the springs will each stretch different lengths because the spring constants are different. Let's call x_1 the distance that the first spring stretches and x_2 the distance the second spring stretches. The total displacement of the mass is the sum of those two:

$$\mathbf{x} = \mathbf{x_1} + \mathbf{x_2}$$

How can we find x_1 and x_2? Well, the force exerted by the spring is given by Hooke's Law. For the two springs, that law works out to:

$$\mathbf{F} = -k_1 \cdot \mathbf{x_1}$$

$$\mathbf{F} = -k_2 \cdot \mathbf{x_2}$$

Note that the force is the same for each spring, because only one force is used to displace the mass. That force acts on both springs. I can solve for $\mathbf{x_1}$ and $\mathbf{x_2}$ in the equations above and substitute those expressions into the first equation to get:

$$\mathbf{x} = \frac{-\mathbf{F}}{k_1} + \frac{-\mathbf{F}}{k_2}$$

Now I can solve for $\mathbf{F}$:

$$\mathbf{x} = -\mathbf{F} \cdot \left(\frac{1}{k_1} + \frac{1}{k_2}\right)$$

$$\mathbf{F} = -\frac{1}{\left(\dfrac{1}{k_1} + \dfrac{1}{k_2}\right)} \cdot \mathbf{x}$$

Notice what this is. This is Hooke's law again. Thus, the effective spring constant of this two-spring system is:

$$k_{effective} = \frac{1}{\left(\dfrac{1}{k_1} + \dfrac{1}{k_2}\right)} = \frac{1}{\left(\dfrac{1}{112\,\dfrac{N}{m}} + \dfrac{1}{235\,\dfrac{N}{m}}\right)} = 75.9\,\frac{N}{m}$$

Now that we know the effective spring constant, the period is a snap:

$$T = 2\pi\sqrt{\frac{m}{k}} = 2\pi\sqrt{\frac{15.0\ kg}{75.9\,\dfrac{N}{m}}} = \underline{2.79\ sec}$$

2. Remember, the total energy of a mass/spring system is determined by the initial potential energy, which depends on the displacement distance squared, according to Equation (4.8). Thus, if it is initially displaced to a distance of A, its total energy is:

$$TE = KE + PE = 0 + \frac{1}{2} \cdot k \cdot A^2 = \frac{1}{2} \cdot k \cdot A^2$$

When the mass is at ½ the total distance, its displacement is ½·A. Thus, its potential energy is:

$$U_{spring} = \frac{1}{2} \cdot k \cdot (\frac{1}{2} \cdot A)^2 = \frac{1}{8} \cdot k \cdot A^2$$

That's ¼ of the total energy. Thus, ¾ of the energy must be kinetic. Many people want to say that the mass has half of the total energy as kinetic energy and half of the total energy as potential energy when it is at the halfway point. That would be true if potential energy were linearly proportional to the displacement (as it is in free fall). However, since the potential energy depends on the square of the displacement, it drops off very quickly. The system loses most of its potential energy very early.

3. Remember, the displacement of a mass/spring system is given by:

$$x = A \cdot \cos(\omega \cdot t + \delta)$$

The equation tells us that:

a. The amplitude is 10.0 cm.

b. We know that ω = 11.5 rads/sec. We also know by Equation (6.5) that:

$$\omega = \frac{2\pi}{T}$$

Thus

$$11.5 \frac{rads}{sec} = \frac{2\pi}{T}$$

$$T = 0.546 \ sec$$

Note that radians are dropped because we don't need them any more.

c. Since we know the period and mass, we can determine the spring constant:

$$T = 2\pi\sqrt{\frac{m}{k}}$$

$$0.546 \text{ sec} = 2\pi\sqrt{\frac{(4.5 \text{ kg})}{k}}$$

$$k = \frac{(2\pi)^2 \cdot (4.5 \text{ kg})}{(0.546 \text{ sec})^2} = 6.0 \times 10^2 \frac{\text{kg}}{\text{sec}^2} = \underline{6.0 \times 10^2 \frac{\text{N}}{\text{m}}}$$

d. At time = 0:

$$x = (10.0 \text{ cm}) \cdot \cos\left[\frac{\pi}{2}\right] = 0$$

Thus, <u>time zero must have been defined as the time that the mass reached its equilibrium position</u>.

e. Remember, the displacement, velocity, and acceleration of this system all have similar equations. Displacement has the form given at the start of this solution. Thus, A = 10.0 cm, ω = 11.5 rads/sec, and $\delta = \pi/2$. The velocity is given by:

$$v = -\omega A \cdot \sin(\omega t + \delta)$$

Plugging in the numbers (including the time given) gives us:

$$v = -(11.5 \frac{\text{rads}}{\text{sec}}) \cdot (10.0 \text{ cm}) \cdot \sin([11.5 \frac{\text{rads}}{\text{sec}}] \cdot [5.00 \text{ sec}] + \frac{\pi}{2}) = \underline{-64.0 \frac{\text{cm}}{\text{sec}}}$$

The negative tells us the direction of the velocity.

4. The maximum speed and acceleration can be calculated by looking at the total energy of the system and the force exerted at the amplitude, but it can also be determined by the equations for **v** and **a**. We already know that:

$$v = -(11.5 \frac{\text{rads}}{\text{sec}}) \cdot (10.0 \text{ cm}) \cdot \sin([11.5 \frac{\text{rads}}{\text{sec}}] \cdot [t] + \frac{\pi}{2})$$

This equation reaches its maximum when sin = -1. Thus:

$$v_{max} = (11.5 \frac{\text{rads}}{\text{sec}}) \cdot (10.0 \text{ cm}) = \underline{115 \frac{\text{cm}}{\text{sec}}} \text{ or } \underline{1.15 \frac{\text{m}}{\text{sec}}}$$

The acceleration is given by:

$$\mathbf{a} = -\omega^2 A \cdot \cos(\omega t + \delta)$$

Which will be at its maximum when cos = -1. Thus:

$$\mathbf{a}_{max} = (11.5 \frac{rads}{sec})^2 \cdot (10.0 \ cm) = 1,320 \ \frac{cm}{sec^2} \ or \ 13.2 \ \frac{m}{sec^2}$$

The maximum velocity occurs when the mass is at its equilibrium position, while the maximum acceleration occurs when the mass is at its maximum displacement.

5. a. The frequency of the oscillation depends only on the mass and spring constant. The original frequency was:

$$f_{before} = \frac{1}{T} = \frac{1}{2\pi} \sqrt{\frac{k}{m}}$$

The mass is now $M + \frac{1}{4} \cdot M$, so that changes the frequency as follows:

$$f_{after} = \frac{1}{2\pi} \sqrt{\frac{k}{\frac{5}{4} \cdot M}}$$

The ratio is:

$$\frac{f_{before}}{f_{after}} = \frac{\frac{1}{2\pi} \sqrt{\frac{k}{m}}}{\frac{1}{2\pi} \sqrt{\frac{k}{\frac{5}{4} \cdot m}}} = \sqrt{\frac{5}{4}}$$

b. You might be tempted to think that this does not change, but as noted, this is a perfectly inelastic collision. In these collisions, energy is *lost*. Thus, we first need to figure out the total energy after the mass is added. We are at ½ the maximum displacement. As you already determined earlier, that means ¾ of the energy is kinetic and ¼ is potential. If the original amplitude was A, the kinetic energy and potential energy right before the collision are:

$$U_{before} = \frac{1}{8} \cdot k \cdot A^2$$

$$KE_{before} = \frac{3}{8} \cdot k \cdot A^2$$

The potential energy will be unaffected, as the collision deals only with kinetic energy. Since this is a perfectly inelastic collision, we know momentum is conserved:

$$\cancel{M} \cdot v_{before} = \frac{5}{4} \cdot \cancel{M} \cdot v_{after}$$

$$v_{after} = \frac{4}{5} \cdot v_{before}$$

Since $KE = \frac{1}{2} \cdot m \cdot v^2$:

$$KE_{after} = \frac{1}{2} \cdot (\frac{5}{4} \cdot M) \cdot (\frac{4}{5} \cdot v_{before})^2 = \frac{4}{5} \cdot \left[\frac{1}{2} \cdot M \cdot v_{before}{}^2 \right] = \frac{4}{5} \cdot KE_{before}$$

So, after the collision, the potential and kinetic energies are:

$$U_{after} = \frac{1}{8} \cdot k \cdot A^2$$

$$KE_{after} = \frac{4}{5} \cdot \left[\frac{3}{8} \cdot k \cdot A^2 \right] = \frac{3}{10} \cdot k \cdot A^2$$

That makes the total energy:

$$TE_{after} = \frac{1}{8} \cdot k \cdot A^2 + \frac{3}{10} \cdot k \cdot A^2 = \frac{17}{40} \cdot k \cdot A^2$$

The new amplitude will be determined by the position at which there is no kinetic energy but only potential energy. Thus, the total energy is all potential:

$$\frac{1}{2} \cdot k \cdot x^2 = \frac{17}{40} \cdot k \cdot A^2$$

$$x^2 = \frac{17}{20} \cdot A^2$$

$$x = \sqrt{\frac{17}{20}} \cdot A$$

That's the new amplitude. Thus, the ratio of the two is:

$$\frac{A_{before}}{A_{after}} = \frac{A}{\sqrt{\frac{17}{20}} \cdot A} = \sqrt{\frac{20}{17}}$$

The amplitude before, then, was about 1.08 times larger before the collision. Please note that this a difficult problem. Don't worry if you were stumped by it.

c. It would not change the answer to (a), because the frequency depends only on the mass and the spring constant. However, it would change the answer to (b). Think about it. In the solution to (b), the potential energy didn't change. Only the kinetic energy changed. At $x = A$, there is no kinetic energy. Thus, momentum is zero, and the fact that the collision is perfectly inelastic no longer affects the energy. Thus, if the mass was added right when the block was at the amplitude, the amplitude would stay the same.

6. The period of a simple pendulum is:

$$T = 2\pi \cdot \sqrt{\frac{L}{g}}$$

The period of a physical pendulum whose moment of inertia was given is:

$$T = 2\pi \cdot \sqrt{\frac{I}{m \cdot g \cdot d}} = 2\pi \cdot \sqrt{\frac{\frac{1}{3} \cdot m \cdot L^2}{m \cdot g \cdot \frac{1}{2} L}} = 2\pi \cdot \sqrt{\frac{\frac{2}{3} L}{g}}$$

Remember, "d" is the distance from the pivot point to the center of mass of the rod. Thus, $d = \frac{1}{2} \cdot L$ for a uniform rod pivoting on one end. The ratio of the two is:

$$\frac{T_{simple}}{T_{physical}} = \frac{2\pi \cdot \sqrt{\dfrac{L}{g}}}{2\pi \cdot \sqrt{\dfrac{2}{3}\dfrac{L}{g}}} = \sqrt{\dfrac{3}{2}}$$

The simple pendulum, then, has a period about 1.22 times longer than that of this physical pendulum.

7. Since we know the wavelength, we can get the frequency with Equation (6.13) if we can figure out the speed. That comes from Equation (6.19)

$$v = \sqrt{\dfrac{T}{\mu}} = \sqrt{\dfrac{85.0 \text{ N}}{\dfrac{0.750 \text{ kg}}{4.00 \text{ m}}}} = 21.3 \ \dfrac{m}{sec}$$

Now we can get the frequency:

$$f = \dfrac{v}{\lambda} = \dfrac{21.3 \ \dfrac{m}{sec}}{0.450 \ m} = \underline{47.3 \text{ Hz}}$$

8. a. The positive sign means that the wave is traveling in the negative direction. Thus, <u>it is moving to the left.</u>

b. According to the definition of the wave equation, the amplitude is <u>0.111 m</u>.

c. The speed, according to the definition of the wave equation, is 35.0 m/sec. That allows us to calculate the linear mass density:

$$v = \sqrt{\dfrac{T}{\mu}}$$

$$35.0 \ \dfrac{m}{sec} = \sqrt{\dfrac{341 \text{ N}}{\mu}}$$

$$\mu = \dfrac{341 \text{ N}}{(35.0 \ \dfrac{m}{sec})^2} = \dfrac{341 \ \dfrac{kg \cdot m}{sec^2}}{1225 \ \dfrac{m^2}{sec^2}} = \underline{0.278 \ \dfrac{kg}{m}}$$

9. Since the wave has 4 nodes, it is the third harmonic. Thus, we can get the wavelength:

$$\lambda = \frac{2 \cdot L}{n} = \frac{2 \cdot (5.50 \text{ m})}{3} = \underline{3.67 \text{ m}}$$

Now we can determine the frequency. Since the speed of a wave depends only on the medium, we were given the speed of this wave as well.

$$f = \frac{v}{\lambda} = \frac{45.0 \frac{\cancel{m}}{\sec}}{3.67 \cancel{m}} = \underline{12.3 \text{ Hz}}$$

10. We could determine the length of the rope if we knew the wavelength, because "fundamental resonant frequency" means n= 1, and Equation (6.21) relates the wavelength and the length of the rope. However, right now, we have only the frequency. If we can get the speed, however, we can get the wavelength:

$$v = \sqrt{\frac{T}{\mu}}$$

$$v = \sqrt{\frac{45.0 \text{ N}}{0.350 \frac{\text{kg}}{\text{m}}}} = 11.3 \frac{\text{m}}{\sec}$$

Now we can get wavelength:

$$f = \frac{v}{\lambda}$$

$$\lambda = \frac{v}{f} = \frac{11.3 \frac{\text{m}}{\cancel{\sec}}}{1.13 \frac{1}{\cancel{\sec}}} = \underline{10.0 \text{ m}}$$

Now we can get the length of the rope:

$$\lambda = \frac{2 \cdot L}{n}$$

$$10.0 \text{ m} = \frac{2 \cdot L}{1}$$

$$L = \underline{5.00 \text{ m}}$$

SOLUTIONS TO THE PRACTICE PROBLEMS FOR MODULE #7

1. If the person is only 1 meter away, he is 100 times closer than the man who is hearing the music at 40 dB. Since the intensity of a sound wave decreases with the square of the distance traveled, a person 100 times closer will hear the sound wave with an intensity of 100^2, or 10^4. Each unit on the bel scale represents a factor of 10 in intensity, so the loudness will be 4 bels, or 40 decibels higher. Thus, the music will have a loudness of <u>80 dB</u>, which is the approximate loudness of a pneumatic drill!

2. At 20.0 °C, sound has a speed in air of:

$$v = (331.5 + 0.606 \cdot T) \frac{m}{sec} = (331.5 + 0.606 \cdot 20.0) \frac{m}{sec} = 343.6 \frac{m}{sec}$$

If the sound took 0.55 seconds to return, it made a total trip of:

$$distance = 343.6 \frac{m}{sec} \times 0.55 \; sec = 190 \; m$$

Of course, that's the TOTAL trip, which means the sound left the bat, hit the obstacle, and came back. Thus, the obstacle is <u>95 meters away from the bat</u>.

3. A tube that is open on both ends can support the following standing waves:

$$\lambda = \frac{2 \cdot L}{n} \qquad n = 1, 2, 3, \ldots$$

The fundamental frequency indicates that n = 1. Thus, the wavelength is

$$\lambda = \frac{2 \cdot (0.250 \; m)}{1} = 0.500 \; m$$

To get the frequency, we need to know the speed of the waves:

$$v = (331.5 + 0.606 \cdot T) \frac{m}{sec} = (331.5 + 0.610 \cdot 25.0) \frac{m}{sec} = 346.7 \frac{m}{sec}$$

Now we can get the frequency:

$$f = \frac{v}{\lambda} = \frac{346.7 \; \frac{m}{sec}}{0.500 \; m} = \underline{693 \; Hz}$$

4. Beats will occur because of slight differences in frequency. To determine the frequency of the new tube, we have to go through the steps we did before. However, this tube is closed on one end, so the wavelength equation is different.

$$\lambda = \frac{4 \cdot L}{n} \qquad n = 1, 3, 5 \ldots$$

The fundamental frequency indicates that n = 1. Thus, the wavelength is

$$\lambda = \frac{4 \cdot (0.128 \text{ m})}{1} = 0.512 \text{ m}$$

To get the frequency, we need to know the speed of the waves:

$$v = (331.5 + 0.606 \cdot T) \frac{m}{sec} = (331.5 + 0.606 \cdot 25.0) \frac{m}{sec} = 346.7 \frac{m}{sec}$$

Now we can get the frequency:

$$f = \frac{v}{\lambda} = \frac{346.7 \frac{\cancel{m}}{sec}}{0.512 \cancel{m}} = 677 \text{ Hz}$$

The beat frequency is the absolute value of the difference between the two, or 16 Hz.

5. The Doppler shift equation is:

$$f_{observed} = \left(\frac{v_{sound} \pm v_{observer}}{v_{sound} \pm v_{source}} \right) \cdot f_{true}$$

Since the observer (the radar gun) is not moving, $v_{observer} = 0$. The source (the car) is moving towards the observer, so we must use a minus sign in the denominator of the fraction in order to increase the observed frequency as compared to the true frequency.

$$f_{observed} = \left(\frac{v_{sound}}{v_{sound} - v_{source}} \right) \cdot f_{true}$$

$$f_{observed} = \left(\frac{2.998 \times 10^8 \frac{\cancel{m}}{\cancel{sec}}}{2.998 \times 10^8 \frac{\cancel{m}}{\cancel{sec}} - 23.0 \frac{\cancel{m}}{\cancel{sec}}} \right) \cdot f_{true}$$

$$\frac{f_{observed}}{f_{true}} = \left(\frac{2.998 \times 10^8 \ \frac{m}{sec}}{2.998 \times 10^8 \ \frac{m}{sec} - 23.0 \ \frac{m}{sec}} \right)$$

If you try to just plug this in your calculator, you will get an answer of 1, because 23.0 is so small compared to 2.998×10^8. However, you can do some algebra so that you get around the limits of your calculator. For example, if you multiply the fraction by 1, but you choose your expression for "1" carefully, you get:

$$\frac{f_{observed}}{f_{true}} = \left(\frac{2.998 \times 10^8 \ \frac{m}{sec}}{2.998 \times 10^8 \ \frac{m}{sec} - 23.0 \ \frac{m}{sec}} \right) \cdot \frac{1 / 2.998 \times 10^8 \ \frac{m}{sec}}{1 / 2.998 \times 10^8 \ \frac{m}{sec}}$$

$$\frac{f_{observed}}{f_{true}} = \frac{1}{1 - \frac{23.0}{2.998 \times 10^8}} = \frac{1}{1 - 7.67 \ x 10^{-8}}$$

Since the 1's here are exact (because we are dividing a number by itself, which is one way you define "1") you can subtract 7.67×10^{-8} from one.

$$\frac{f_{observed}}{f_{true}} = \frac{1}{1 - 7.67 \ x 10^{-8}} = \frac{1}{0.9999999233} = 1.000000077$$

The observed frequency, then, is shifted by factor of only 1.000000077. Even though this is a *tiny* shift, modern radar equipment can detect it. I would never expect you to do an algebra trick like this on a test, but it is important for you to flex your algebra muscles every now and again in the practice problems!

6. In this experiment, constructive interference occurs when the waves "line up" with one another. This occurs in between the slits, because the light travels an equal distance from each slit. Thus, the light waves overlap perfectly. If the light travels different distances, the waves will only line up if the difference in the distance traveled is equal to λ. Thus, each bright spot away from the center is the point at which the difference in distance traveled is an integral multiple of λ. Since the question asks about the first bright spot above the central maximum, the light from one slit traveled a distance of λ farther than the light from the other slit. The next bright spot up would be the spot at which light from one slit traveled $2 \cdot \lambda$ farther than light from the other slit.

7. This problem requires you to realize that the fisherman does not see the flashlight at first because of total internal reflection. When the angle that the light must make to hit the fisherman's eyes is larger than the angle at which total internal reflection occurs, the fisherman will not see the light. However, as the fisherman approaches the light, the angle decreases, eventually allowing the fisherman to see refracted light. Thus, we first need to calculate that angle. Total internal reflection occurs when Equation (7.10) is satisfied.

$$\sin\theta_1 \geq \frac{n_2}{n_1}$$

$$\sin\theta_1 \geq \frac{1.0}{1.4}$$

$$\theta_1 \geq 46°$$

This tells us that as long as the light makes a $46°$ or greater angle with the perpendicular, light cannot be refracted, and the fisherman will not see it. Thus, the fisherman will see it when he gets close enough so that the angle is just under $46°$. Well, think of the geometry involved:

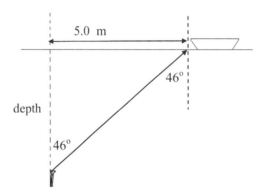

What does this tell us? It gives us the following relationship:

$$\tan(46°) = \frac{5.0 \text{ m}}{\text{depth}}$$

$$\text{depth} = 4.8 \text{ m}$$

You should be able to do this kind of geometric reasoning. Since the angle of the light relative to the boat changes as the boat moves towards the flashlight, you should have recognized that the boat's horizontal distance from the flashlight could be related to the angle that the light makes with the perpendicular. That relationship, then, gave you the depth.

8. As stated in the course, the higher the energy, the slower the light travels in a dense medium. Thus, when it passes through the prism, violet light (which has the most energy - remember

ROY G. BIV) will travel most slowly. According to Equation (7.9), then, it will have the *highest* index of refraction. Thus, when it enters the prism, it will be bent farthest *towards* the normal. Then, on the other side, it will be bent farthest *away from* the normal. Red light, on the other hand, travels fastest in the prism. Thus, its index of refraction is lowest, and it will be bent towards the normal less on its way in and away from the normal less on its way out:

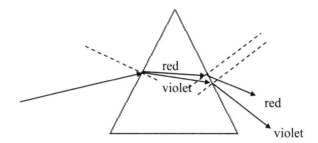

Thus, red will be on the top, and violet will be on the bottom.

9. For this problem, we must use the mirror equation. We know the object and image distance and must determine the focal length, which will give us the radius of curvature. Since the image is on the opposite side of the mirror, the image distance is negative according to the rules.

$$\frac{1}{7.5\text{cm}} + \frac{1}{-5.0\text{cm}} = \frac{1}{f}$$

$$f = -15 \text{ cm}$$

This makes sense, since convex mirrors have negative focal lengths. That's only *half* of the radius of curvature, however. Thus, the radius of curvature is 3.0×10^1 cm. The fact that the image is on the other side of the mirror indicates that the image is virtual. To get the size and whether it is upright or inverted, we use the magnification equation:

$$m = -\frac{s_i}{s_o} = -\frac{-5.0 \text{ cm}}{7.5 \text{ cm}} = 0.67$$

The image is upright and is 1.0×10^1 cm tall.

10. Since you want to magnify the image and make it upright, you must have a positive magnification of 2.

$$m = -\frac{s_i}{s_o}$$

$$2 = -\frac{s_i}{15.0 \text{ cm}}$$

$$s_i = -30.0 \text{ cm}$$

Now that we know the image distance we need, we can use the equation to tell us f:

$$\frac{1}{15.0 \text{ cm}} + \frac{1}{-30.0 \text{ cm}} = \frac{1}{f}$$

$$f = \underline{30.0 \text{ cm}}$$

SOLUTIONS TO THE PRACTICE PROBLEMS FOR MODULE #8

1. Kinetic energy depends on mass and speed squared. Since the mass will not change, we just have to see how the speed changes. We start by setting centripetal force equal to gravitational force:

$$\frac{\cancel{m}_{sat} \cdot v_{sat}^{2}}{R} = \frac{G \cdot \cancel{m}_{sat} \cdot m_e}{R^2}$$

$$v = \sqrt{\frac{G \cdot m_e}{R}}$$

If the radius increases by a factor of 3, then, the speed decreases by a factor of the square root of three. However, kinetic energy depends on v^2, so the new v^2 will be three times lower than the old v^2. That means the new kinetic energy is KE/3.

2. We start by setting centripetal force equal to gravitational force:

$$\frac{\cancel{m}_{sat} \cdot v_{sat}^{2}}{R} = \frac{G \cdot \cancel{m}_{sat} \cdot m_{Neptune}}{R^2}$$

$$m_{Neptune} = \frac{R \cdot v_{sat}^{2}}{G}$$

This isn't a good enough answer, however, because the mass must be only in terms of G, R, and T. However, if we know T, we know v, because in one orbit, the satellite travels a total distance of $2 \cdot \pi \cdot r$. Thus:

$$m_{Neptune} = \frac{R \cdot \left(\dfrac{2 \cdot \pi \cdot R}{T}\right)^2}{G}$$

$$\underline{m_{Neptune} = \frac{4 \cdot \pi^2 \cdot R^3}{G \cdot T^2}}$$

3. We can do this using energy arguments. When it starts, the rock has only potential energy. The height is so large that we cannot use m·g·h where g is the acceleration due to Mercury's gravity, however, because the acceleration due to gravity changes. Thus, we need to use the exact formula for potential energy:

$$U_{grav} = -\frac{G \cdot m_1 \cdot m_2}{r} = -\frac{(6.67 \times 10^{-11} \frac{N \cdot m^2}{kg^2}) \cdot (6.42 \times 10^{23} \ kg) \cdot (m)}{3.37 \times 10^6 \ m + 5.51 \times 10^6 \ m} = -(4.82 \times 10^6 \frac{J}{kg}) \cdot m$$

When it hits the surface, the potential energy is:

$$U_{grav} = -\frac{G \cdot m_1 \cdot m_2}{r} = -\frac{(6.67 \times 10^{-11} \frac{N \cdot m^2}{kg^2}) \cdot (6.42 \times 10^{23} \ kg) \cdot (m)}{3.37 \times 10^6 \ m} = -(1.27 \times 10^7 \frac{J}{kg}) \cdot m$$

This is a difference in potential energy of:

$$\Delta PE = (-1.27 \times 10^7 \frac{J}{kg}) \cdot m - (-4.82 \times 10^6 \frac{J}{kg}) \cdot m = -(7.9 \times 10^6 \frac{J}{kg}) \cdot m$$

This means PE decreased by $(7.9 \times 10^6 \ J/kg) \cdot m$. That all must have gone into kinetic energy, so $KE = (7.9 \times 10^6 \ J/kg) \cdot m$.

$$\frac{1}{2} \cdot m \cdot v^2 = (7.9 \times 10^6 \frac{J}{kg}) \cdot m$$

$$v = \sqrt{2 \cdot 7.9 \times 10^6 \frac{J}{kg}} = \underline{4.0 \times 10^3 \frac{m}{sec}}$$

Notice how the units work out. From $W = f \cdot d$, you know that a Joule is a $\frac{kg \cdot m^2}{sec^2}$. When you divide J by kg, then, you get m^2/sec^2, which becomes m/sec when you take the square root.

4. To get acceleration, use the gravitational force and set it equal to mass times acceleration. Thus, for mass 1:

$$F = m_1 \cdot a$$

$$\frac{G \cdot m_1 \cdot m_2}{\left(\frac{R}{2}\right)^2} = m_1 \cdot a$$

$$a = \underline{\frac{4 \cdot G \cdot m_2}{R^2}}$$

For mass 2, then,

$$a = \frac{4 \cdot G \cdot m_1}{R^2}$$

5. In black holes, the escape velocity is determined by energy arguments:

$$TE_{before} = TE_{after}$$

$$\frac{1}{2} \cdot \cancel{m} \cdot (2.998 \times 10^8 \ \frac{m}{sec})^2 - \frac{G \cdot \cancel{m} \cdot (5.67 \times 10^{35} \ kg)}{R} = 0$$

$$R = \frac{2 \cdot (6.67 \times 10^{-11} \ \frac{N \cdot m^2}{kg^2}) \cdot (5.67 \times 10^{35} \ kg)}{(2.998 \times 10^8 \ \frac{m}{sec})^2} = \underline{8.42 \times 10^8 \ m}$$

6. If we know how often the satellite orbits the earth, we know its speed. It travels a distance of $2 \cdot \pi \cdot r$ in one orbit, and it does so in 12.0 hours (43,200 sec).

$$\frac{\cancel{m}_{sat} \cdot v_{sat}^2}{R} = \frac{G \cdot \cancel{m}_{sat} \cdot m_e}{R^2}$$

$$\frac{\left(\frac{2 \cdot \pi \cdot R}{43,200 \ sec}\right)^2}{R} = \frac{G \cdot m_e}{R^2}$$

$$R^3 = \frac{G \cdot m_e \cdot (43,200 \ sec)^2}{4 \cdot \pi^2}$$

$$\underline{R = 2.66 \times 10^7 \ m}$$

7. You need to know the total energy before and after. Thus, we need potential and kinetic energy before:

$$U_{grav} = -\frac{G \cdot m_1 \cdot m_2}{r} = -\frac{(6.67 \times 10^{-11} \ \frac{N \cdot m^2}{kg^2}) \cdot (5.98 \times 10^{24} \ \cancel{kg}) \cdot (1123 \ \cancel{kg})}{2.66 \times 10^7 \ \cancel{m}} = -1.68 \times 10^{10} \ J$$

$$\frac{m_{sat} \cdot v_{sat}^2}{r} = \frac{G \cdot m_{sat} \cdot m_e}{r^2}$$

$$v_{sat} = \sqrt{\frac{G \cdot m_e}{r}} = \sqrt{\frac{(6.67 \times 10^{-11} \ \frac{N \cdot m^2}{kg^2}) \cdot (5.98 \times 10^{24} \ kg)}{2.66 \times 10^7 \ m}} = 3.87 \times 10^3 \ \frac{m}{sec}$$

$$KE = \frac{1}{2} \cdot m \cdot v^2 = \frac{1}{2} \cdot (1123 \ kg) \cdot (3,870 \ \frac{m}{sec})^2 = 8.41 \times 10^9 \ J$$

$$TE = PE + KE = -1.68 \times 10^{10} \ J + 8.41 \times 10^9 \ J = -8.4 \times 10^9 \ J$$

That's the total energy in the original orbit. Now we want to increase the radius by 25.0% to 3.33×10^7 m.

$$U_{grav} = -\frac{G \cdot m_1 \cdot m_2}{r} = -\frac{(6.67 \times 10^{-11} \ \frac{N \cdot m^2}{kg^2}) \cdot (5.98 \times 10^{24} \ kg) \cdot (1123 \ kg)}{3.33 \times 10^7 \ m} = -1.35 \times 10^{10} \ J$$

$$\frac{m_{sat} \cdot v_{sat}^2}{r} = \frac{G \cdot m_{sat} \cdot m_e}{r^2}$$

$$v_{sat} = \sqrt{\frac{G \cdot m_e}{r}} = \sqrt{\frac{(6.67 \times 10^{-11} \ \frac{N \cdot m^2}{kg^2}) \cdot (5.98 \times 10^{24} \ kg)}{3.33 \times 10^7 \ m}} = 3.46 \times 10^3 \ \frac{m}{sec}$$

$$KE = \frac{1}{2} \cdot m \cdot v^2 = \frac{1}{2} \cdot (1123 \ kg) \cdot (3,460 \ \frac{m}{sec})^2 = 6.72 \times 10^9 \ J$$

$$TE = PE + KE = -1.35 \times 10^{10} \ J + 6.72 \times 10^9 \ J = -6.8 \times 10^9 \ J$$

The difference in total energy:

$$-6.8 \times 10^9 \ J - (-8.4 \times 10^9 \ J) = \underline{1.6 \times 10^9 \ J}$$

represents the work done.

8. Reckoned from the earth, the ship will take:

$$x = v_o \cdot t$$

$$t = \frac{x}{v_o} = \frac{(677 \text{ yrs})c}{0.999 \cdot c} = 678 \text{ yrs}$$

That time, however, is less for the people in the ship, because they measure t', as given by the time dilation equation:

$$t' = (678 \text{ yrs}) \cdot \sqrt{1 - \left(\frac{0.999c}{c}\right)^2}$$

$$t' = 30.3 \text{ yrs}$$

Thus, even though it will take 678 yrs for the space ship to reach its destination to those on earth, for the people on the space ship, only 30.3 years will elapse.

To determine how far the people on the ship think they have traveled, we just take the speed times the time:

$$x = v_o \cdot t$$

$$x = (0.999c) \cdot (30.3 \text{ yrs}) = 30.3 \text{ c} \cdot \text{yrs} = \underline{30.3 \text{ light years}}$$

9. We need to know the total energy that the power plant produces in a year. We know that it produces 1.0000×10^9 Joules every second (Mega $= 10^6$, and a Watt is a J/s). Thus, if we multiply by the number of seconds in a year (31,557,600 seconds - there are 365.25 days in a year), we get the total energy produced in a year:

$$\frac{1.0000 \times 10^9 \text{ J}}{\text{sec}} \cdot \frac{31,557,600 \text{ sec}}{1 \text{ yr}} = 3.1558 \times 10^{16} \frac{\text{J}}{\text{yr}}$$

What amount of mass contains 3.1558×10^{16} Joules?

$$E = mc^2$$

$$m = \frac{E}{c^2} = \frac{3.1558 \times 10^{16} \text{ J}}{(2.998 \times 10^8 \frac{\text{m}}{\text{sec}})^2} = 0.3511 \text{ kg}$$

The nuclear power plant, then, would consume only 0.3511 kg of matter if it were 100% efficient. Of course, the power plants are not 100% efficient, and there are byproducts which must be disposed of. Also, only a small fraction of the fuel's mass is actually changed during the process of a nuclear reaction. Nevertheless, when all of those factors are taken into account, the nuclear power plant still consumes a *significantly* smaller amount of fuel.

10. Look at Figure 8.8. The people on the space station feel the floor of the space station pushing against them at F_c. To simulate earth conditions, then, the centripetal force must feel to them like their weight, because on earth, the floor pushes up against you with a force equal to your weight. Thus:

$$F_c = m \cdot g$$

Well, we have an equation for F_c, Equation (6.14). We can plug that into the equation above:

$$\frac{\cancel{m} \cdot v^2}{r} = \cancel{m} \cdot g$$

$$v = \sqrt{r \cdot g} = \sqrt{(3,500.0 \text{ m}) \cdot 9.81 \frac{m}{\sec^2}} = \underline{185 \frac{m}{\sec}}$$

SOLUTIONS TO THE PRACTICE PROBLEMS FOR MODULE #9

1. The problem here is that heat capacity has $^{\circ}C$, but the temperature given is $^{\circ}F$. Thus, we first have to convert:

$$^{\circ}C = \frac{5}{9}(75.0 - 32.0) = 23.9 \ ^{\circ}C$$

Now we can get the change in temperature:

$$q = m \cdot c \cdot \Delta T$$

$$\Delta T = \frac{q}{m \cdot c} = \frac{350.0 \ J}{(50.0 \, g) \cdot (0.250 \ \frac{J}{g \cdot ^{\circ}C})} = 28.0 \ ^{\circ}C$$

The final temperature, then, is 51.9 $^{\circ}C$. However, the mean guy who wrote this problem wants the temperature in $^{\circ}F$:

$$^{\circ}C = \frac{5}{9}(^{\circ}F - 32.0)$$

$$^{\circ}F = \frac{9}{5} \cdot ^{\circ}C + 32.0 = \frac{9}{5} \cdot (51.9) + 32.0 = \underline{125.4 \ ^{\circ}F}$$

2. We know what will happen. Energy will be lost by the hot water and be absorbed by the ice. First, the energy will be used to heat the ice up to 0.0 $^{\circ}C$. Next, the energy will be used to melt the ice. Then, any energy left will be used to heat up the resulting mixture of water.

How much energy will be lost?

$$q_{lost} = m \cdot c \cdot \Delta T = (300.0 \ g) \cdot (4.19 \ \frac{J}{g \cdot ^{\circ}C}) \cdot (T_{final} - 95.0 \ ^{\circ}C)$$

How much energy will be gained? The energy used to warm the ice plus the energy used to melt the ice plus the energy used to heat the resulting water:

$$q_{gained} = m_{ice} \cdot c_{ice} \cdot \Delta T_{ice} + m_{ice} \cdot L_{fus} + m_{ice} \cdot c_{water} \cdot (T_{final} - 0.0 \ C)$$

$$q_{gained} = (75.0 \ g) \cdot (2.02 \ \frac{J}{g \cdot ^{\circ}C}) \cdot (15.0 \ ^{\circ}C) + (75.0 \ g) \cdot (334 \ \frac{J}{g}) + (75.0 \ g) \cdot (4.19 \ \frac{J}{g \cdot ^{\circ}C}) \cdot (T_{final} - 0.0 \ C)$$

Since energy must be conserved, $q_{lost} = -q_{gained}$:

$$(300.0) \cdot (4.19 \; \frac{J}{^\circ C}) \cdot (T_{final} - 95.0 \; ^\circ C) = -(75.0) \cdot [(2.02 \; J) \cdot (15.0) + (334 \; J) + (4.19 \; \frac{J}{g \cdot ^\circ C}) \cdot (T_{final} - 0.0 \; ^\circ C)]$$

$$T_{final} - 95.0 \; ^\circ C = \frac{-(75.0)}{(300.0) \cdot (4.19 \; \frac{J}{^\circ C})} \cdot [30.3 \; J + 334 \; J + (4.19 \; \frac{J}{g \cdot ^\circ C}) \cdot (T_{final} - 0.0 \; ^\circ C)]$$

$$T_{final} - 95.0 \; ^\circ C = -0.0597 \; \frac{^\circ C}{\cancel{J}} \cdot [364 \; \cancel{J} + (4.19 \; \frac{\cancel{J}}{g \cdot ^\circ C}) \cdot (T_{final} - 0.0 \; ^\circ C)]$$

$$T_{final} - 95.0 \; ^\circ C = -21.7 \; ^\circ C - 0.250 \cdot T_{final}$$

$$\underline{T_{final} = 58.6 \; ^\circ C}$$

3. Just as it takes energy to vaporize liquid, energy is released when water vapor condenses. The amount of energy is given by Equation (9.5):

$$q = m \cdot L = (5.0 \; g) \cdot (2{,}260 \; \frac{J}{g}) = 11{,}000 \; J$$

If all of that energy went into the glass, it would heat up the glass according to Equation (9.3).

$$q = m \cdot c \cdot \Delta T$$

$$\Delta T = \frac{q}{m \cdot c} = \frac{11{,}000 \; \cancel{J}}{(200.0 \; g) \cdot (0.837 \; \frac{\cancel{J}}{g \, ^\circ C})} = \underline{66 \, ^\circ C}$$

This number seems large because only a small amount of the energy involved in condensation actually gets transferred to the surface on which the condensation takes place.

4. We do not know the original or final volume, but we know that the change in volume is 2.00% of the total. Thus, $\Delta V / V = 0.0200$.

$$\Delta V = \beta \cdot V_o \cdot \Delta T$$

$$\beta = \frac{\Delta V}{V_o \cdot \Delta T} = \frac{\Delta V}{V_o} \cdot \frac{1}{\Delta T} = (0.0200) \cdot \frac{1}{100.0 \; ^\circ C - 25.0 \; ^\circ C} = 0.000267 \; \frac{1}{^\circ C}$$

That's not the coefficient of linear expansion, however. It is the coefficient of volume expansion. However, the two are related:

$$\beta \approx 3 \cdot \alpha \text{ for most solids}$$

This, $\underline{\alpha \approx 0.0000890 \ 1/°C}$.

5. To get the volume of a gas given the number of moles, the temperature, and the pressure, we use the ideal gas law. At 25.0 °C:

$$PV = nRT$$

$$V = \frac{nRT}{P} = \frac{(1.00 \ \cancel{mole}) \cdot (8.31 \ \frac{J}{\cancel{mole} \cdot \cancel{K}}) \cdot (298.2 \ \cancel{K})}{1.013 \times 10^5 \ Pa} = \underline{0.0245 \ m^3}$$

At 50.0 °C:

$$PV = nRT$$

$$V = \frac{nRT}{P} = \frac{(1.00 \ \cancel{mole}) \cdot (8.31 \ \frac{J}{\cancel{mole} \cdot \cancel{K}}) \cdot (323.2 \ \cancel{K})}{1.013 \times 10^5 \ Pa} = \underline{0.0265 \ m^3}$$

6. We know the change in temperature and the resulting change in volume. Thus, we can get β:

$$\Delta V = \beta \cdot V_o \cdot \Delta T$$

$$\beta = \frac{\Delta V}{V_o \cdot \Delta T} = \frac{(0.0265 \ \cancel{m^3} - 0.0245 \ \cancel{m^3})}{(0.0245 \ \cancel{m^3}) \cdot (50.0 \ °C - 25.0 \ °C)} = \underline{0.0033 \ \frac{1}{°C}}$$

7. The gas occupied a volume of 0.0245 m³ at 25.0 °C. If pressure and volume are held constant, the gas must escape the container as the temperature increases. The ideal gas law will tell us how many *moles* of gas are left at 50.0 °C.

$$PV = nRT$$

$$n = \frac{PV}{RT} = \frac{(1.013 \times 10^5 \text{ Pa}) \cdot (0.0245 \text{ m}^3)}{(8.31 \frac{J}{\text{mole} \cdot \cancel{K}}) \cdot (323.2 \cancel{K})} = 0.924 \frac{\text{Pa} \cdot \text{m}^3 \cdot \text{mole}}{J} = 0.924 \frac{\frac{\cancel{N}}{\cancel{m^2}} \cdot \cancel{m}^3 \cdot \text{mole}}{\cancel{N} \cdot \cancel{m}} = 0.924 \text{ moles}$$

This is not the answer. The mean guy who wrote this problem wants the number of *molecules*. Since there are 6.02×10^{23} molecules in a mole:

$$\text{\# molecules} = (0.924 \cancel{\text{ moles}}) \cdot \left(\frac{6.02 \times 10^{23} \text{ molecules}}{1 \cancel{\text{ mole}}} \right) = \underline{5.56 \times 10^{23} \text{ molecules}}$$

8. In this problem, we are dealing with constant pressure, but we are given the C_v. Thus, we first have to convert:

$$C_p = C_v + R = 20.8 \frac{J}{\text{mole} \cdot K} + 8.31 \frac{J}{\text{mole} \cdot K} = 29.1 \frac{J}{\text{mole} \cdot K}$$

Now we can use the formula for constant pressure:

$$q = n \cdot C_p \cdot \Delta T$$

$$\Delta T = \frac{q}{n \cdot C_p} = \frac{(1,678 \cancel{J})}{(1.00 \cancel{\text{ mole}}) \cdot (29.1 \frac{\cancel{J}}{\cancel{\text{mole}} \cdot K})} = \underline{57.7 \text{ K}}$$

9. The average speed squared is given by:

$$\overline{v^2} = \frac{3kT}{m}$$

However, the "m" refers to the mass of a single molecule. All we know is that 4.50 moles has a mass of 319.5 grams. Thus, we need to divide that mass by the number of molecules to get the mass of a single molecule:

$$m = \frac{319.5 \text{ g}}{(4.50 \cancel{\text{ moles}}) \cdot (6.02 \times 10^{23} \frac{\text{molecules}}{\cancel{\text{mole}}})} = 1.18 \times 10^{-22} \text{ g} = 1.18 \times 10^{-25} \text{ kg}$$

Now we can get the average speed:

$$\overline{v} = \sqrt{\frac{3kT}{m}} = \sqrt{\frac{3 \cdot (1.38 \times 10^{-23} \frac{J}{K}) \cdot (323.2 \cancel{K})}{1.18 \times 10^{-25} \text{ kg}}} = \underline{337 \frac{m}{\text{sec}}}$$

10. To get β for this metal using the data given. Since the volume increased by a factor of 1.000006, we know that the ratio of ΔV to V_o is 0.000006:

$$\Delta V = \beta \cdot V_o \cdot \Delta T$$

$$\beta = \frac{\Delta V}{V_o} \cdot \frac{1}{\Delta T} = (0.000006) \cdot \frac{1}{10 \ ^\circ C} = 0.0000006 \ \frac{1}{^\circ C}$$

Of course, this is the coefficient of *volume* expansion. To get the coefficient of linear expansion, we use the relationship between the two:

$$\beta \approx 3 \cdot \alpha \text{ for most solids}$$

Thus, $\alpha = \underline{0.0000002 \ \frac{1}{^\circ C}}$.

SOLUTIONS TO THE PRACTICE PROBLEMS FOR MODULE #10

1. To get the change in internal energy, we need to get W and q. Getting q is easy, since we have C_p (everything is at the same pressure) and the two temperatures. However, we need to know the number of moles. The ideal gas law comes to our rescue there:

$$PV = nRT$$

$$n = \frac{PV}{RT} = \frac{(1.01 \times 10^5 \; Pa) \cdot (0.0050 \; m^3)}{(298 \; K) \cdot (8.31 \; \frac{Pa \cdot m^3}{mole \cdot K})} = 0.20 \; moles$$

Now that we have n, we have everything we need to calculate q:

$$q = n \cdot C_p \cdot \Delta T = (0.20 \; moles) \cdot (20.8 \; \frac{J}{mole \cdot K}) \cdot (268 \; K - 298 \; K) = -120 \; J$$

We are halfway home. Now we need W. To get W, we need ΔV. Once again, we need to use the ideal gas law to help us. We can use it to get the final V:

$$PV = nRT$$

$$V = \frac{nRT}{P} = \frac{(0.20 \; moles) \cdot (268 \; K) \cdot (8.31 \; \frac{Pa \cdot m^3}{mole \cdot K})}{(1.01 \times 10^5 \; Pa)} = 0.0044 \; m^3$$

Now we can determine W using Equation (10.4) since pressure stays constant:

$$W = P \cdot \Delta V = (1.01 \times 10^5 \; Pa) \cdot (0.0044 \; m^3 - 0.0050 \; m^3) = -60 \; J$$

Now we can finally determine ΔU:

$$\Delta U = q - W = -120 \; J - (-60 \; J) = \underline{-60 \; J}$$

2. Since the expansion is adiabatic, q = 0. This means that $\Delta U = -W$. Since the gas loses 1,560 J, $\Delta U = -1,560$ J. Thus, W = 1,560 J. Well, since the expansion is isobaric, we can use Equation (10.4) to relate W and ΔV:

$$W = P \cdot \Delta V$$

$$\Delta V = \frac{W}{P} = \frac{1,560 \; J}{1.0 \times 10^5 \; Pa} = 0.016 \; m^3$$

If the gas started out with a volume of 0.020 m³, and its volume changed by 0.016 m³, the final volume is <u>0.036 m³</u>.

3. Calculating the work done in the process illustrated by the dashed arrow is easy. P is constant the whole time. Thus, we just use Equation (10.4):

$$W = P \cdot \Delta V = (1.5 \times 10^5 \text{ Pa}) \cdot (0.040 \text{ m}^3 - 0.020 \text{ m}^3) = 3.0 \times 10^3 \text{ J}$$

The process illustrated by the solid arrows is harder, since P is not constant. Thus, we have to use the area under the curve method.

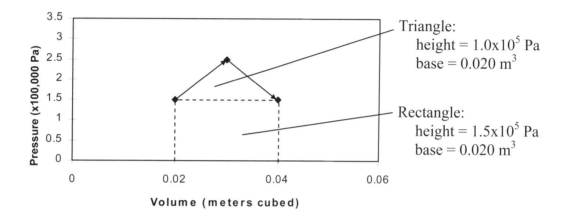

The work done is the total area of the triangle and the rectangle. Now remember, when doing the area method, we must determine whether W is positive or negative. In both the triangle and the rectangle, the gas has a higher final volume than initial volume. Thus, W is positive in both cases, because the gas expands.

$$W = \frac{1}{2} \cdot b \cdot h + b \cdot h = \frac{1}{2} \cdot (0.020 \text{ m}^3) \cdot (1.0 \times 10^5 \text{ Pa}) + (0.020 \text{ m}^3) \cdot (1.5 \times 10^5 \text{ Pa}) = 4.0 \times 10^3 \text{ J}$$

<u>The work done in the expansion of the first gas is 4.0x10³ J, while the work done in expansion of the second gas is 3.0x10³ J.</u>

4. We already have W (from question #3), so to determine ΔU, we must determine q. However, since pressure is constant, that's not too hard. We must start, however, with the ideal gas law to get temperatures. Initially:

$$PV = nRT$$

$$T = \frac{PV}{nR} = \frac{(1.5 \times 10^5 \ \cancel{Pa}) \cdot (0.020 \ \cancel{m^3})}{(1.5 \ \cancel{moles}) \cdot (8.31 \ \frac{\cancel{Pa} \cdot \cancel{m^3}}{\cancel{mole} \cdot K})} = 240 \ K$$

At the end:

$$PV = nRT$$

$$T = \frac{PV}{nR} = \frac{(1.5 \times 10^5 \ \cancel{Pa}) \cdot (0.040 \ \cancel{m^3})}{(1.5 \ \cancel{moles}) \cdot (8.31 \ \frac{\cancel{Pa} \cdot \cancel{m^3}}{\cancel{mole} \cdot K})} = 480 \ K$$

Now we can calculate q.

$$q = n \cdot C_p \cdot \Delta T = (1.5 \ \cancel{moles}) \cdot (20.8 \ \frac{J}{\cancel{mole} \cdot \cancel{K}}) \cdot (480 \ \cancel{K} - 240 \ \cancel{K}) = 7,500 \ J$$

Getting ΔU is now easy:

$$\Delta U = q - W = 7,500 \ J - 3.0 \times 10^3 \ J = \underline{4,500 \ J}$$

5. <u>There is no way to calculate q directly</u>. The only way you know how to calculate q directly is via Equation (9.13) or Equation (9.14). Well, Equation (9.13) works only if pressure is constant, and Equation (9.14) works only if volume is constant. Neither pressure nor volume is constant for the first gas, so the method used in question #4 will not work.

6. Remember, both gases started off at the same P and V and ended at the same P and V. Since they have the same n, that means the initial and final T's are the same, since PV = nRT. Thus, the two gases began at the same state and ended at the same state. This means that they must have exactly the same ΔU. You already calculated ΔU for the second gas (problem #4), so the ΔU for this gas must also be <u>4,500 J</u>.

7. Now that you know ΔU (from the previous problem) and W (from problem #3) for the first gas, calculating q is easy.

$$\Delta U = q - W$$

$$4,500 = q - 4.0 \times 10^3 \ J$$

$$q = \underline{8,500 \ J}$$

8. a. Since we are now considering this to be a cyclic process, $\Delta U = 0$. Thus, $q = W$. Well, W is easy to calculate. For cyclic processes, the area encompassed by the cycle in a P-V is the work done. Thus, we just need to know the area of the triangle. We actually had to determine that in problem #3. The height of the triangle is 1.0×10^5 Pa, and the base is 0.020 m^3. Thus, the area is:

$$W = \text{area of triangle} = \frac{1}{2} \cdot (0.020 \text{ m}^3) \cdot (1.0 \times 10^5 \text{ Pa}) = 1.0 \times 10^3 \text{ J}$$

We are not quite done yet, however! Remember, when using the area method, we must determine whether W is positive or negative. Well, the gas initially expands, but it then contracts. To do this, we can split the process into two parts. First, there is an expansion at constant pressure from 0.020 m^3 to 0.040 m^3. That involves positive work, because the gas expands. The total amount of positive work would be the area under that line. The second part is the compression. It goes in two steps, and the total work in those steps would be the area under the triangle formed by the lines that connect the dots in the two steps. This work would be negative, however, since the gas is being compressed. Well, the area under those two steps is much larger than that which is under the expansion. Thus, W is *negative*. Therefore, q and W are both -1.0×10^3 J.

b. This cycle best represents a refrigerator. After all, total work is negative, so work is done on the gas. Also, the gas is cooled, since q is negative. Thus, the gas is worked on (W is negative) and heat is removed. Thus, we are converting work into heat, which is what a refrigerator does. If the cycle went the other way - starting at $P = 1.5 \times 10^5$ Pa and $V = 0.040$ m^3, being isobarically compressed to $P = 1.5 \times 10^5$ Pa and $V = 0.020$ m^3 and then expanded back to the original point - that would be a heat engine.

9. a. Since the contraction is isothermal, $\Delta U = 0$. This means that $q = W$. We can calculate q from ΔS:

$$\Delta S_{rev} = \frac{q}{T}$$

$$q = \Delta S \cdot T = (-1.5 \frac{J}{K}) \cdot (315 \text{ K}) = -470 \text{ J}$$

This means $W = -470$ J. Thus, the gas was worked on (W is negative), and it lost heat (q is negative).

b. Since this process happened, the total ΔS must be greater than or equal to zero. Thus, the minimum change in entropy of the surroundings is 1.5 J/K. That's the entropy which would be gained by the surroundings absorbing the heat that the gas lost. If the work resulted in any disorder of the surroundings, that would make $\Delta S > 0$. If the work did not disorder the surroundings, $\Delta S = 0$. Either way, the process is consistent with the second law.

10. This is a simple application of Equation (10.9), but you must remember to convert from $^\circ$C to K:

$$e_{\text{Carnot}} = 1 - \frac{T_c}{T_h}$$

$$T_c = T_h - T_h \cdot e_{\text{Carnot}} = 838\,\text{K} - (838\ \text{K}) \cdot (0.800) = \underline{168\ \text{K}}$$

SOLUTIONS TO THE PRACTICE PROBLEMS FOR MODULE #11

1. In order for the particle to hang there, the electrostatic repulsion must counteract the gravitational force. Thus:

$$F_{elect} - m \cdot g = 0$$

$$q \cdot E = m \cdot g$$

$$q = \frac{m \cdot g}{E} = \frac{(0.0345 \ \cancel{kg}) \cdot (9.81 \ \frac{\cancel{m}}{\cancel{sec}^2})}{3.40 \times 10^5 \ \frac{N}{C}} = 9.95 \times 10^{-7} \ C$$

Note that since a Newton is a $\frac{kg \cdot m}{sec^2}$, the units work out. Thus, it takes a charge of only <u>9.95 x 10^{-7} C</u> for the system to overcome the gravitational force.

2. Remember, on a conductor, the electric field lines are perpendicular to the surface:

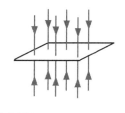

3. If the middle charge experiences no electrostatic force, then the forces that each of the other charges are exerting on it must cancel:

$$F_1 - F_2 = 0$$

$$\frac{k \cdot q \cdot (2 \cdot q)}{x^2} - \frac{k \cdot (3 \cdot q) \cdot (2 \cdot q)}{y^2} = 0$$

$$\frac{x^2}{y^2} = \frac{\cancel{k} \cdot \cancel{q} \cdot (\cancel{2 \cdot q})}{\cancel{k} \cdot (3 \cdot \cancel{q}) \cdot (\cancel{2 \cdot q})} = \frac{1}{3}$$

$$\frac{x}{y} = \sqrt{\frac{1}{3}} = \underline{\frac{\sqrt{3}}{3}}$$

4. We just have to sum up the forces from the other two charges. Since they both push the charge labeled "-q" away, the forces just add:

$$F_{tot} = F_1 + F_2$$

$$F_{tot} = \frac{(8.99 \times 10^9 \, \frac{N \cdot m^2}{C^2}) \cdot (3.0 \times 10^{-6} \, C) \cdot (6.0 \times 10^{-6} \, C)}{(0.500 \, m)^2} + \frac{(8.99 \times 10^9 \, \frac{N \cdot m^2}{C^2}) \cdot (3.0 \times 10^{-6} \, C) \cdot (9.0 \times 10^{-6} \, C)}{(1.000 \, m)^2}$$

$$F_{tot} = 0.89 \, N$$

Since the charge is repelled from the other two, the force is 0.89 N to the left.

5. Each of the two charges (-q and -3q) would attract a positive charge, pulling it in opposite directions. Thus, the two electric fields oppose one another. If I define motion to the right as positive:

$$E_{tot} = -E_1 + E_2$$

$$E_{tot} = -\frac{(8.99 \times 10^9 \, \frac{N \cdot m^2}{C^2}) \cdot (3.0 \times 10^{-6} \, C)}{(0.5000 \, m)^2} + \frac{(8.99 \times 10^9 \, \frac{N \cdot m^2}{C^2}) \cdot (9.0 \times 10^{-6} \, C)}{(0.5000 \, m)^2}$$

$$E_{tot} = 2.1 \times 10^5 \, \frac{N}{C}$$

The electric field, then, is 2.1 x 10⁵ N/C pointed to the right.

6. We need to do some geometry to get the distances and angles for electric field calculation and vector addition. Let's start with distances:

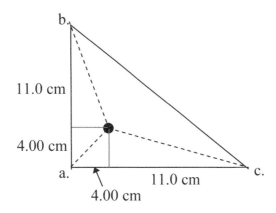

The two gray lines are the 4.00 cm distances from each leg to the point. Those two gray lines and the right angle of the triangle form a square. Thus, the gray lines split up each leg of the triangle into one 4.00 cm portion and one 11.0 cm portion.

The dashed line drawn from vertex "a" to the point of interest is the hypotenuse of a right triangle with two legs of 4.00 cm each. By the Pythagorean theorem, then, the length of that line is 5.66 cm. Thus, that's the distance to vertex "a." The dashed line from the point of interest to vertex "b" is the hypotenuse a right triangle with one leg that is 11.0 cm long and another leg that is 4.00 cm long. Thus, its length is 11.7 cm long, by the Pythagorean theorem. That's the distance to vertex "b." The line drawn from the point of interest to vertex "c" forms the same kind of triangle, so it is also 11.7 cm long. We now have the distances to each vertex.

Let's move on to the angles:

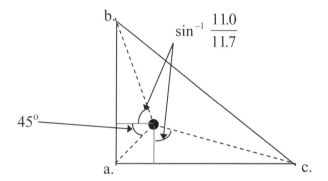

The angle of the dashed line to vertex "a" is easiest. It is the diagonal of a square. Thus, it forms a 45° angle with the sides of the square. Since the negative charge at vertex "a" will pull a positive charge to it, the electric field is pointed to vertex "a," along that dashed line. For proper vector addition, then, its angle is 225°. The angle between the horizontal and the dashed line to vertex "b" can be determined by the right triangle that the dashed line forms. The side opposite that angle is 11.0 cm, and the hypotenuse is 11.7 cm. Since the sine of an angle is the opposite over the hypotenuse:

$$\sin\theta = \frac{11.0 \text{ cm}}{11.7 \text{ cm}}$$

$$\theta = 70.1°$$

Once again, the negative charge at this vertex will pull positive charges towards it, so the electric field vector is pointed to vertex "b" along the dashed line. That makes its properly-defined angle 180.0 - 70.1 = 109.9°. The angle between the dashed line to vertex "c" and the vertical is also 70.1, so the properly-defined angle for the electric field vector from the charge at vertex "c" is 270.0 + 70.1 = 340.1°. Now we have all we need for the vector addition.

$$A_x = \frac{k \cdot Q}{r^2} \cdot \cos\theta = \frac{(8.99 \times 10^9 \; \frac{N \cdot m^2}{C^2}) \cdot (4.50 \times 10^{-6} C)}{(0.0566 \text{ m})^2} \cdot \cos(225) = -8.93 \times 10^6 \; \frac{N}{C}$$

$$A_y = \frac{k \cdot Q}{r^2} \cdot \sin\theta = \frac{(8.99 \times 10^9 \; \frac{N \cdot m^2}{C^2}) \cdot (4.50 \times 10^{-6} C)}{(0.0566 \text{ m})^2} \cdot \sin(225) = -8.93 \times 10^6 \; \frac{N}{C}$$

$$B_x = \frac{k \cdot Q}{r^2} \cdot \cos\theta = \frac{(8.99 \times 10^9 \; \frac{N \cdot m^2}{C^2}\} \cdot (4.50 \times 10^{-6} C)}{(0.117 \text{ m})^2} \cdot \cos(109.9) = -1.01 \times 10^6 \; \frac{N}{C}$$

$$B_y = \frac{k \cdot Q}{r^2} \cdot \sin\theta = \frac{(8.99 \times 10^9 \; \frac{N \cdot m^2}{C^2}) \cdot (4.50 \times 10^{-6} C)}{(0.117 \text{ m})^2} \cdot \sin(109.9) = 2.78 \times 10^6 \; \frac{N}{C}$$

$$C_x = \frac{k \cdot Q}{r^2} \cdot \cos\theta = \frac{(8.99 \times 10^9 \; \frac{N \cdot m^2}{C^2}) \cdot (4.50 \times 10^{-6} C)}{(0.117 \text{ m})^2} \cdot \cos(340.1) = 2.78 \times 10^6 \; \frac{N}{C}$$

$$C_y = \frac{k \cdot Q}{r^2} \cdot \sin\theta = \frac{(8.99 \times 10^9 \; \frac{N \cdot m^2}{C^2}) \cdot (4.50 \times 10^{-6} C)}{(0.117 \text{ m})^2} \cdot \sin(340.1) = -1.01 \times 10^6 \; \frac{N}{C}$$

Now we can just add the components and finish:

$$E_x = -8.93 \times 10^6 \; \frac{N}{C} - 1.01 \times 10^6 \; \frac{N}{C} + 2.78 \times 10^6 \; \frac{N}{C} = -7.16 \times 10^6 \; \frac{N}{C}$$

$$E_y = -8.93 \times 10^6 \; \frac{N}{C} + 2.78 \times 10^6 \; \frac{N}{C} - 1.01 \times 10^6 \; \frac{N}{C} = -7.16 \times 10^6 \; \frac{N}{C}$$

$$E = \sqrt{(-7.16 \times 10^6 \; \frac{N}{C})^2 + (-7.16 \times 10^6 \; \frac{N}{C})^2} = 1.01 \times 10^7 \; \frac{N}{C}$$

$$\theta = \tan^{-1}\left(\frac{-7.16 \times 10^6 \ \frac{N}{C}}{-7.16 \times 10^6 \ \frac{N}{C}}\right) = 45.0°$$

Since the vector has two negative components, it is in quadrant 3, so we add 180.0 degrees to the angle. Thus, the electric field is 1.01×10^7 N/C at 225.0°. Note that this means the electric field is pointed directly at vertex "a."

7. Since we know the electric field, this is easy:

$$\mathbf{F} = q \cdot \mathbf{E} = (-1.50 \times 10^{-6} \ C) \cdot (1.01 \times 10^7) \ \frac{N}{C} = -15.2 \ N$$

Remember, the negative tells us direction. The vector is pointing opposite the electric field. Thus, it is 15.2 N directly away from vertex "a." You could also say that a vector opposite the electric field vector at 225.0° is a vector at 225.0 - 180.0 = 45.0°. Thus, the force is 15.2 N directed at 45.0°.

8. a. Remember, the excess charge on a conductor rests only on the surface of the conductor. Thus, on the *interior* part of the sphere, there is no charge.

b. Since the excess resides on the outer surface, the exterior surface has a charge of +q.

9. a. This is the tricky one. Remember, the outer spherical shell is also a conductor. It "sees" a charge of +q inside of it. Thus, negative charges will try to get as close as possible to it, and positive charges will move away. Since this is a conductor, that can happen. This will continue until the charges are balanced. Thus, the charge on the interior surface is -q. Note that this *does not* contradict the statement that all excess charge lies at the outer surface of the conductor. On this conductor the *excess charge* is all on the outer surface. If the conductor were neutral, there would still be a charge of -q on the interior surface, because the spherical shell on the inside would attract negatives and repel positives. If any *excess* charge were then added to the shell, that excess charge would stay on the surface.

b. Remember, the spherical shell has a total excess charge of +2q. However, -q worth of charge is on the interior surface. Thus, on the exterior surface, there must be +3q. You could also think of it this way: When the excess charge of +2q is added, it stays on the outer surface. If the smaller shell was later added, it would pull -q worth of charge out to the outer surface, making the outer shell even more positive, for a total of +3q.

10. a. The electric field in a conductor is zero.
b. The electric field in a conductor is zero.
c. This might fool you. You might want to say 0 here, because it is inside the other conductor. However, the rule that the electric field in a conductor is zero applies to the electric field caused by the charge *in that conductor*. Thus, the charge of the outer shell produces no electric field.

However, we are now out of the inner shell, so it has an electric field. Since we can assume that the entire charge is concentrated at the center:

$$E = \frac{k \cdot q}{(3x)^2}$$

d. <u>O</u>nce again, we are actually in the conductive material. The -q sitting on the interior cancels the +q from the small shell. Thus, the electric field of the small shell is negated, and the answer is <u>zero</u>.

e. Now that we are outside both conductors, we see a +3q charge (that's what's on the surface of the big sphere, remember), and we can assume the charge is concentrated at the center. Thus:

$$E = \frac{k \cdot 3q}{(5x)^2}$$

SOLUTIONS TO THE PRACTICE PROBLEMS FOR MODULE #12

1. The first charge (let's start with the upper, left-hand corner) will take no work to put in place. However, the second charge (upper, right-hand corner) will be repelled by the first, so it will take work to get it in position. Before it comes near the first charge, its potential is zero. In the end, it will have a potential of:

$$V = \frac{k \cdot q}{r}$$

$$V = \frac{(8.99 \times 10^9 \; \frac{N \cdot m^2}{C^2}) \cdot (0.0110 \; C)}{0.500 \; \cancel{m}} = 1.98 \times 10^8 \; V$$

That will change its potential energy to:

$$\Delta U = q \cdot \Delta V$$

$$\Delta U = (0.0110 \; C) \cdot (1.98 \times 10^8 \; \frac{J}{C}) = 2.18 \times 10^6 \; J$$

That's the work required to bring the second charge in. The third charge (lower, left-hand corner) will now be repelled by *both* the first and second charges. It is 50.0 cm from the first charge and, by the Pythagorean theorem, it is 70.7 cm from the second charge. Its final potential will be:

$$V = \frac{k \cdot q_1}{r_1} + \frac{k \cdot q_2}{r_2}$$

$$V = \frac{(8.99 \times 10^9 \; \frac{N \cdot m^2}{C^2}) \cdot (0.0110 \; C)}{0.500 \; \cancel{m}} + \frac{(8.99 \times 10^9 \; \frac{N \cdot m^2}{C^2}) \cdot (0.0110 \; C)}{0.707 \; \cancel{m}} = 3.38 \times 10^8 \; V$$

That will change its potential energy to:

$$\Delta U = q \cdot \Delta V$$

$$\Delta U = (0.0110 \; C) \cdot (3.38 \times 10^8 \; \frac{J}{C}) = 3.72 \times 10^6 \; J$$

That's the work required to bring the third charge in. The fourth charge (lower, right-hand corner) will now be repelled by *all three* of the charges already in place. It will be 50.0 cm from two of the charges, and 70.7 cm from the other. Its final potential will be:

$$V = \frac{k \cdot q_1}{r_1} + \frac{k \cdot q_2}{r_2} + \frac{k \cdot q_3}{r_3}$$

$$V = 2 \cdot \frac{(8.99 \times 10^9 \, \frac{N \cdot m^2}{C^2}) \cdot (0.0110 C)}{0.500 \, m} + \frac{(8.99 \times 10^9 \, \frac{N \cdot m^2}{C^2}) \cdot (0.0110 C)}{0.707 \, m} = 5.35 \times 10^8 \, V$$

That will change its potential energy to:

$$\Delta U = q \cdot \Delta V$$

$$\Delta U = (0.0110 C) \cdot (5.35 \times 10^8 \, \frac{J}{C}) = 5.89 \times 10^6 \, J$$

That's the work required to bring the fourth charge in. Thus, the total work is:

$$W_{tot} = 2.18 \times 10^6 \, J + 3.72 \times 10^6 \, J + 5.89 \times 10^6 \, J = \underline{1.179 \times 10^7 \, J}$$

2. The electric potential will just be the sum of the electric potentials from all four charges. However, to calculate that, we need to worry about distance. The center of the square lies on the diagonal, which we know is 70.7 cm long. It will be at the midpoint of the diagonal, so each charge is 35.4 cm from the center of the square. Since all charges are the same and at the same distance from the center, the electric potential is just 4 times the electric potential from one charge:

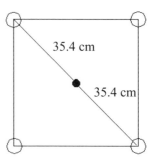

$$V = \frac{k \cdot q_1}{r_1} + \frac{k \cdot q_2}{r_2} + \frac{k \cdot q_3}{r_3} + \frac{k \cdot q_4}{r_4} = 4 \cdot \frac{k \cdot q}{r}$$

$$V = 4 \cdot \frac{(8.99 \times 10^9 \, \frac{N \cdot m^2}{C^2}) \cdot (0.0110 C)}{0.354 \, m} = \underline{1.12 \times 10^9 \, V}$$

3. This question really is from the previous module, but I wanted to make a point from it. The electrical field at the center is <u>zero</u>, since all four charges' electric fields cancel out. The point I wanted to make is that even though the potential is HUGE, the electric field is zero!

4. Since the electrostatic force is conservative, the path is not important. Look at the end result. Since the particle moves in a semicircle, it is directly to the right of where it started, and it is at a distance of 2·r away. Thus, the particle essentially moved a distance of 2·r parallel to the electric field. Thus, the work done is simply:

$$W = q \cdot E \cdot x \cdot \cos\theta = (-0.0345 \ C) \cdot (45.6 \ \frac{N}{C}) \cdot (0.300 \ m) \cdot \cos(0) = \underline{-0.472 \ J}$$

The negative simply means the work was done against the electric field. That makes sense, because a negative charge is accelerated opposite the electric field.

5. To solve this problem, we need to find out where the kinetic energy of the particle equals zero. That's the point at which the particle stops and turns around. So, first we have to figure out how much kinetic energy the particle must lose:

$$KE = \frac{1}{2} \cdot m \cdot v^2$$

$$KE_{initial} = \frac{1}{2} \cdot (5.0 \, kg) \cdot (245 \, \frac{m}{sec})^2$$

$$KE_{initial} = 1.5 \times 10^5 \ J$$

All of that energy must be converted to potential energy. Thus, $\Delta U = 1.5 \times 10^5$ J. Thus, the particle must travel through the following potential difference:

$$\Delta U = q \cdot \Delta V$$

$$\Delta V = \frac{\Delta U}{q} = \frac{1.5 \times 10^5 \ J}{0.0038 \ C} = 3.9 \times 10^7 \ V$$

That's what the change in potential must be. Well, we know the original potential:

$$V = \frac{k \cdot q}{r}$$

$$V_{initial} = \frac{(8.99 \times 10^9 \, \frac{N \cdot m^2}{C^2}) \cdot (1.5 \times 10^{-3} \, C)}{1.2 \, m} = 1.1 \times 10^7 \, \frac{N \cdot m}{C} = 1.1 \times 10^7 \, \text{Volts}$$

Now we can get the final potential:

$$\Delta V = V_{final} - V_{initial}$$

$$V_{final} = \Delta V + V_{initial} = 3.9 \times 10^7 \, V + 1.1 \times 10^7 \, V = 5.0 \times 10^7 \, V$$

At what distance will the particle have that potential?

$$V = \frac{k \cdot q}{r}$$

$$5.0 \times 10^7 \, \text{Volts} = \frac{(8.99 \times 10^9 \, \frac{N \cdot m^2}{C^2}) \cdot (1.5 \times 10^{-3} \, C)}{r}$$

$$r = \frac{(8.99 \times 10^9 \, \frac{N \cdot m^2}{C^2}) \cdot (1.5 \times 10^{-3} \, C)}{5.0 \times 10^7 \, \frac{N \cdot m}{C}} = 0.27 \, m$$

So, we finally see that the particle can travel until it is 0.27 m away from the charge. At that point, the particle stops, turns around, and heads away from the stationary charge.

6. As the proton moves from one plate of the capacitor to the other, it experiences a change in electric potential. We can use Equation (12.9) to determine the amount of change:

$$\Delta V = \frac{Q}{C}$$

$$\Delta V = \frac{2.2 \times 10^{-3} \, C}{1.4 \times 10^{-6} \, \frac{C}{V}} = 1.6 \times 10^3 \, V$$

Now we have to worry about sign here. The fact that the proton moves from the positive plate to the negative one means that it experiences a decrease in potential. Remember, negative charges are accelerated to areas of higher potential, so positive charges are accelerated to areas of lower potential. So the change in potential is really -1.6×10^3 Volts.

This change in potential, then, will lead to a change in potential energy:

$$\Delta U = q \cdot \Delta V = (1.6 \times 10^{-19} \text{ C}) \cdot (-1.6 \times 10^3 \text{ V}) = -2.6 \times 10^{-16} \text{ J}$$

Since the result of the equation is negative, this tells us that the proton's potential energy decreased. Well, if the potential energy of the proton decreased by 2.6×10^{-16} J, then its kinetic energy must have increased by the same amount. Since the kinetic energy started at zero and increased by 2.6×10^{-16} J, we know that the final kinetic energy of the proton is 2.6×10^{-16} J. We can now determine the final speed:

$$KE = \frac{1}{2} \cdot m \cdot v^2$$

$$2.6 \times 10^{-16} \text{ J} = \frac{1}{2} \cdot (1.7 \times 10^{-27} \text{ kg}) \cdot v^2$$

$$v^2 = 3.1 \times 10^{11} \, \frac{\text{m}^2}{\text{sec}^2}$$

$$v = 5.5 \times 10^5 \, \frac{\text{m}}{\text{sec}}$$

The proton, therefore, moves at the speed of <u>5.5×10^5 m/sec</u>.

7. What we need to figure out here is the potential. That way, we can determine the charge on the capacitor. Thus, we need to work this problem backwards. Since we know that the electron ends up with a speed of 3.2×10^5 m/sec, we can determine its final kinetic energy:

$$KE = \frac{1}{2} \cdot m \cdot v^2 = \frac{1}{2} \cdot (9.1 \times 10^{-31} \text{ kg}) \cdot (3.2 \times 10^5 \, \frac{\text{m}}{\text{sec}})^2 = 4.7 \times 10^{-20} \text{ J}$$

This kinetic energy came from a decrease in the potential energy. Thus, we know that the potential energy decreased by 4.7×10^{-20} J. Using Equation (12.7), then, we can determine the change in electric potential:

$$\Delta U = q \cdot \Delta V$$

$$-4.7 \times 10^{-20} \text{ J} = (-1.6 \times 10^{-19} \text{ C}) \cdot \Delta V$$

$$\Delta V = \frac{4.7 \times 10^{-20} \text{ J}}{1.6 \times 10^{-19} \text{ C}} = 0.29 \text{ Volts}$$

Now that we know the electric potential, we can solve for the charge needed to produce such a potential.

$$\Delta V = \frac{Q}{C}$$

$$0.29 \text{ V} = \frac{Q}{5.1 \times 10^{-6} \text{ F}}$$

$$Q = (0.29 \text{ V}) \cdot (5.1 \times 10^{-6} \frac{C}{V}) = 1.5 \times 10^{-6} \text{ C}$$

In order to achieve the proper speed, then, the physicist must store 1.5×10^{-6} C of charge on the positive plate of the capacitor.

8. The first part of the problem gives us enough to determine the capacitance:

$$C = \frac{\varepsilon_o \cdot A}{d}$$

$$C = \frac{8.85 \times 10^{-12} \frac{C^2}{N \cdot m^2} \cdot (0.00327 \text{ m}) \cdot (0.00327 \text{ m})}{0.000200 \text{ m}} = 4.73 \times 10^{-13} \frac{C}{V}$$

If it is has to hold 35.0 mC of charge, it will have to have the following potential difference:

$$\Delta V = \frac{Q}{C}$$

$$\Delta V = \frac{3.50 \times 10^{-6} \text{ C}}{4.73 \times 10^{-13} \frac{C}{V}} = \underline{7.40 \times 10^{6} \text{ V}}$$

9. This is pretty easy:

$$\Delta V = E \cdot d$$

$$E = \frac{\Delta V}{d} = \frac{7.40 \times 10^6 \text{ V}}{0.000200 \text{ m}} = 3.70 \times 10^{10} \frac{V}{m}$$

You learned in the module that a V/m is equivalent to a N/C, so the electric field has a strength of <u>3.70 x 10^{10} N/C</u>.

10. We could use a couple of equations here, but we know ΔV and Q, so let's use this one:

$$U_{cap} = \frac{1}{2} \cdot Q \cdot \Delta V = \frac{1}{2} \cdot (3.50 \times 10^{-6} \text{ C}) \cdot (7.40 \times 10^6 \frac{J}{C}) = \underline{13.0 \text{ J}}$$

SOLUTIONS TO THE PRACTICE PROBLEMS FOR MODULE #13

1. Since the motor is a 5.00 Watt motor, the power drawn by the circuit is 5.00 Watts. Using Equation (13.4), we can get the current:

$$P = I \cdot V$$

$$I = \frac{P}{V} = \frac{5.00 \frac{J}{sec}}{9.00 \frac{J}{C}} = 0.556 \frac{C}{sec} = 0.556 \text{ A}$$

Now we can get resistance from either Ohm's Law or Equation (13.5). I choose Ohm's Law:

$$V = I \cdot R$$

$$R = \frac{V}{I} = \frac{9.00 \text{ V}}{0.556 \text{ A}} = 16.2 \frac{V}{A} = \underline{16.2 \ \Omega}$$

2. To solve this problem, we just need to reduce all of these resistors to one effective resistor. We start by taking care of the parallel resistors. The 35.0 Ω and 30.0 Ω resistors are in parallel.

$$\frac{1}{R_{eff}} = \frac{1}{R_1} + \frac{1}{R_2} = \frac{1}{35.0 \ \Omega} + \frac{1}{30.0 \ \Omega} = 0.0619 \frac{1}{\Omega}$$

$$R_{eff} = \frac{1}{0.0619 \frac{1}{\Omega}} = 16.2 \ \Omega$$

That reduces the circuit to:

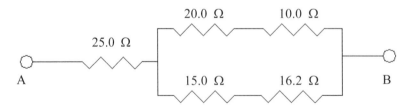

Adding up the 20.0 Ω and 10.0 Ω resistors (they are in series) and the 15.0 Ω and 16.2 Ω resistors (they are in series) gives us:

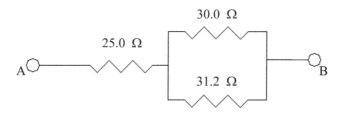

The 30.0 Ω and 31.2 Ω resistors are now in parallel:

$$\frac{1}{R_{eff}} = \frac{1}{R_1} + \frac{1}{R_2} = \frac{1}{30.0 \ \Omega} + \frac{1}{31.2 \ \Omega} = 0.0654 \ \frac{1}{\Omega}$$

$$R_{eff} = \frac{1}{0.0654 \ \dfrac{1}{\Omega}} = 15.3 \ \Omega$$

Thus, the circuit can be reduced to two series resistors, one that is 25.0 Ω and another that is 15.3 Ω. Resistors in series just add, so the total resistance is 40.3 Ω. That's what will be read if an ohmmeter reads the resistance from point A to point B.

3. You have to start off with the hint here. You already know that the total resistance from point A to point B is 40.3 Ω. If 5.00 A crosses that resistance, you get a voltage drop of:

$$V = I \cdot R = (5.00 \ A) \cdot (40.3 \ \Omega) = 202 \ V$$

Thus, this is like having point A and point B hooked up to a 202 V battery :

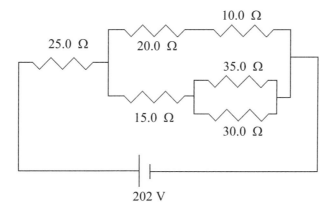

We also know the total current, $I_{tot} = 5.00$ A. That will help in the calculation. We need to determine the current going through the 35.0 Ω resistor, so we will have to use Kirchhoff's Rules. Let's start by choosing a loop:

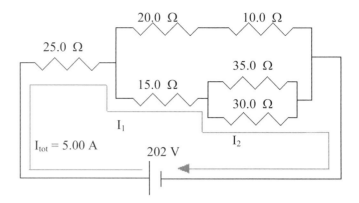

In this loop, the current (5.00 A) leaves the "battery" and travels through the 25.0 Ω resistor. Then, the current must split. Thus, only part of it (I_1) goes through the 15.0 Ω resistor. Then, the current splits again, so only a part of I_1 goes through the 30.0 Ω resistor. The currents then recombine and meet the negative side of the "battery." This leads to the following equation:

$$202 \text{ V} - (5.00 \text{ A}) \cdot (25.0 \text{ Ω}) - I_1 \cdot (15.0 \text{ Ω}) - I_2 \cdot (30.0 \text{ Ω})$$

We have two unknowns, so we need to choose another loop. In this loop, the current (5.00 A) leaves the "battery" and once again passes through the 25.0 Ω resistor. Once again, it splits, and I_1 goes through the 15.0 Ω resistor. Then, it splits again. Only some of I_1, which we will call I_3, goes through the 35.0 Ω resistor. Then, the currents recombine, and we reach the negative side of the "battery." This produces the following equation:

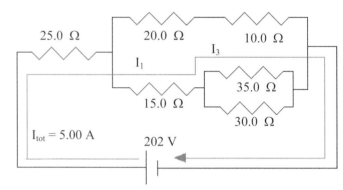

$$202 \text{ V} - (5.00 \text{ A}) \cdot (25.0 \text{ Ω}) - I_1 \cdot (15.0 \text{ Ω}) - I_3 \cdot (35.0 \text{ Ω})$$

We now have 2 equations and 3 unknowns. Should we do another loop? We certainly could, but we don't need to. After all, we can relate the 3 unknowns. How? Well, I_1 splits up into I_2 and I_3. Then, I_2 and I_3 recombine, and they must be equal to I_1 by the junction rule. Thus:

$$I_1 = I_2 + I_3$$

We can use our first equation to get I_2 in terms of I_1:

$$202 \text{ V} - (5.00 \text{ A}) \cdot (25.0 \text{ Ω}) - I_1 \cdot (15.0 \text{ Ω}) - I_2 \cdot (30.0 \text{ Ω}) = 0$$

$$I_2 = \frac{77 \text{ V} - I_1 \cdot (15.0 \text{ Ω})}{30.0 \text{ Ω}}$$

We can do the same thing with the second equation to get I_3 in terms of I_1:

$$202 \text{ V} - (5.00 \text{ A}) \cdot (25.0 \text{ Ω}) - I_1 \cdot (15.0 \text{ Ω}) - I_3 \cdot (35.0 \text{ Ω}) = 0$$

$$I_3 = \frac{77 \text{ V} - I_1 \cdot (15.0 \text{ Ω})}{35.0 \text{ Ω}}$$

Now we can put those expressions into the last equation:

$$I_1 = I_2 + I_3$$

$$I_1 = \frac{77 \text{ V} - I_1 \cdot (15.0 \text{ } \Omega)}{30.0 \text{ } \Omega} + \frac{77 \text{ V} - I_1 \cdot (15.0 \text{ } \Omega)}{35.0 \text{ } \Omega}$$

$$(35.0 \text{ } \Omega) \cdot I_1 = 9.0 \times 10^1 \text{ V} - I_1 \cdot (17.5 \text{ } \Omega) + 77 \text{ V} - I_1 \cdot (15.0 \text{ } \Omega)$$

$$I_1 = \frac{167 \text{ V}}{67.5 \text{ } \Omega} = 2.47 \text{ A}$$

Of course, this really isn't the answer we need. The question asks for the current which travels through the 35.0 Ω resistor. That's I_3:

$$I_3 = \frac{77 \text{ V} - I_1 \cdot (15.0 \text{ } \Omega)}{35.0 \text{ } \Omega} = \frac{77 \text{ V} - (2.47) \cdot (15.0 \text{ } \Omega)}{35.0 \text{ } \Omega} = \underline{1.1 \text{ A}}$$

4. This problem obviously will require Kirchhoff's Rules, so let's start with a loop. In the loop drawn to the right, the current leaves the battery and goes through the 15.0 Ω resistor. It then has to split, so only part of it (I_2) goes through the 20.0 Ω resistor. It then recombines with the rest of the current and goes to the 5.00 V battery, negative side first. This leads to:

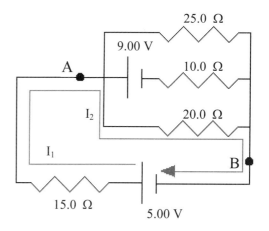

$$5.00 \text{ V} - I_1 \cdot (15.0 \text{ } \Omega) - I_2 \cdot (20.0 \text{ } \Omega) = 0$$

This equation has two variables in it, so we will need to choose another loop. That's no problem, however, since there are several.

In the loop drawn to the right, the current leaves the battery and goes through the 15.0 Ω resistor. It then has to split, so only part of it (I_3) goes through the 9.00 V battery and the 10.0 Ω resistor. It passes through the battery positive side first, however, so the voltage must be subtracted! It then recombines with the rest of the current and goes to the 5.00 V battery, negative side first. This leads to:

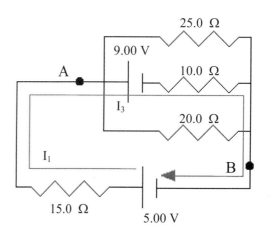

$$5.00 \text{ V} - 9.00 \text{ V} - I_1 \cdot (15.0 \text{ } \Omega) - I_3 \cdot (10.0 \text{ } \Omega) = 0$$

We still have too many variables, so we need to try another loop. In the loop drawn to the right, the current leaves the battery and goes through the 15.0 Ω resistor. It then has to split, so only part of it (I_4) goes through the 25.0 Ω resistor. It then recombines with the rest of the current and goes to the 5.00 V battery, negative side first. This leads to:

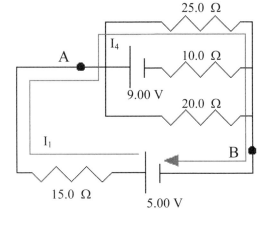

$$5.00 \text{ V} - I_1 \cdot (15.0 \ \Omega) - I_4 \cdot (25.0 \ \Omega) = 0$$

We still have one too many variables, but there is one equation we have yet to write down. Since I_1 splits into I_2, I_3, and I_4, then we know from the junction rule that:

$$I_1 = I_2 + I_3 + I_4$$

Now we have our 4 equations and 4 unknowns. Let's take the first three equations and get I_2, I_3, and I_4 in terms of I_1. First, we get I_2 in terms of I_1.

$$5.00 \text{ V} - I_1 \cdot (15.0 \ \Omega) - I_2 \cdot (20.0 \ \Omega) = 0$$

$$I_2 = \frac{5.00 \text{ V} - I_1 \cdot (15.0 \ \Omega)}{20.0 \ \Omega}$$

Next, we get I_3 in terms of I_1.

$$5.00 \text{ V} - 9.00 \text{ V} - I_1 \cdot (15.0 \ \Omega) - I_3 \cdot (10.0 \ \Omega) = 0$$

$$I_3 = \frac{-4.00 \text{ V} - I_1 \cdot (15.0 \ \Omega)}{10.0 \ \Omega}$$

Then, we get I_4 in terms of I_1.

$$5.00 \text{ V} - I_1 \cdot (15.0 \ \Omega) - I_4 \cdot (25.0 \ \Omega) = 0$$

$$I_4 = \frac{5.00 \text{ V} - I_1 \cdot (15.0 \ \Omega)}{25.0 \ \Omega}$$

Now we take those expressions and put them in the last equation:

$$I_1 = I_2 + I_3 + I_4$$

$$I_1 = \frac{5.00\ \text{V} - I_1 \cdot (15.0\ \Omega)}{20.0\ \Omega} + \frac{-4.00\ \text{V} - I_1 \cdot (15.0\ \Omega)}{10.0\ \Omega} + \frac{5.00\ \text{V} - I_1 \cdot (15.0\ \Omega)}{25.0\ \Omega}$$

$$(25.0\ \Omega) \cdot I_1 = 6.25\ \text{V} - I_1 \cdot (18.8\ \Omega) - 10.0\ \text{V} - I_1 \cdot (37.5\ \Omega) + 5.00\ \text{V} - I_1 \cdot (15.0\ \Omega)$$

$$I_1 = \frac{1.3\ \text{V}}{96.3\ \Omega} = 0.013\,\text{A}$$

The problem, of course, doesn't ask for this. It wants I_4, the current that travels through the 25.0 Ω resistor:

$$I_4 = \frac{5.00\ \text{V} - (0.013\ \text{A}) \cdot (15.0\ \Omega)}{25.0\ \Omega} = \underline{0.192\ \text{A}}$$

5. To draw the actual currents, we have to see what I_2 and I_3 are.

$$I_2 = \frac{5.00\ \text{V} - (0.013\,\text{A}) \cdot (15.0\ \Omega)}{20.0\ \Omega} = 0.240\,\text{A}$$

$$I_3 = \frac{-4.00\ \text{V} - (0.013\,\text{A}) \cdot (15.0\ \Omega)}{10.0\ \Omega} = -0.420\ \text{A}$$

What does this tell us? Since I_1, I_2, and I_4 are all positive, we had those drawn correctly. However, I_3 is drawn backwards in our drawings, because the result is negative. Thus, we have to draw I_3 opposite the way we originally drew it.

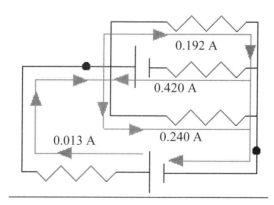

6. To calculate the potential difference, you just have to follow one of the current branches from point A to point B. For example, when I_4 travels from point A to point B, it passes through a

25.0 Ω resistor. That is the only thing which affects the potential, and it will drop the potential by:

$$V = I \cdot R = (0.192 \text{ A}) \cdot (25.0 \text{ Ω}) = 4.80 \text{ V}$$

Thus, <u>point A is at a potential which is 4.80 V greater than point B</u>. You would get the same result using any branch. If you followed I_3, for example, you would be crossing a battery positive side first, which means you would subtract 9.0 V, and you would be passing through a resistor *opposite* the current, which means you would add (0.420 A)·(10.0 Ω). The result would be -4.80, which means that point A is 4.80 V higher than point B, which is the same result we got above.

7. The 20.0 Ω resistor has 0.240 A running through it. That means its power is:

$$P = I^2 \cdot R = (0.240 \, \frac{\text{C}}{\text{sec}})^2 \cdot (20.0 \, \frac{\text{V}}{\text{A}}) = (0.240)^2 \cdot (20.0) \frac{\cancel{\text{C}}^2 \cdot \frac{\text{J}}{\cancel{\text{C}}}}{\text{sec}^2 \cdot \frac{\cancel{\text{C}}}{\cancel{\text{sec}}}} = 1.15 \, \frac{\text{J}}{\text{sec}}$$

In 1.00 minute, 60.0 seconds pass. Thus:

$$P = \frac{W}{\Delta t}$$

$$W = P \cdot \Delta t = (1.15 \, \frac{\text{J}}{\cancel{\text{sec}}}) \cdot (60.0 \, \cancel{\text{sec}}) = 69.0 \text{ J}$$

8. Once again, we need to use Kirchhoff's Rules here, so we should start by choosing a loop. In this loop, the current leaves the battery, passing through the 11.0 Ω resistor. Then, it must split. A portion of it (I_2) passes through the 13.0 Ω resistor, and then it recombines to become I_1 again, passing through the 12.0 Ω resistor and encountering the battery, negative side first.

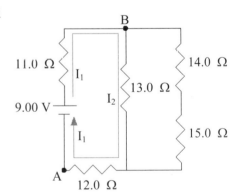

$$9.00 \text{ V} - I_1 \cdot (11.0 \text{ Ω}) - I_2 \cdot (13.0 \text{ Ω}) - I_1 \cdot (12.0 \text{ Ω}) = 0$$

We have two unknowns here, so we need another equation and therefore another loop.

In this loop, the current leaves the battery, passing through the 11.0 Ω resistor. Then, it must split. A portion of it (I_3) passes through the 14.0 Ω and 15.0 Ω resistors, and then it recombines to become I_1 again, passing through the 12.0 Ω resistor and encountering the battery, negative side first.

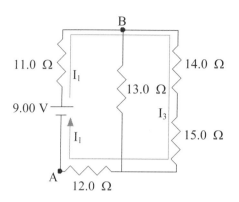

$$9.00 \text{ V} - I_1 \cdot (11.0 \text{ Ω}) - I_3 \cdot (14.0 \text{ Ω}) - I_3 \cdot (15.0 \text{ Ω}) - I_1 \cdot (12.0 \text{ Ω}) = 0$$

By the junction rule, we also know that:

$$I_1 = I_2 + I_3$$

Getting I_2 in terms of I_1:

$$9.00 \text{ V} - I_1 \cdot (11.0 \text{ Ω}) - I_2 \cdot (13.0 \text{ Ω}) - I_1 \cdot (12.0 \text{ Ω}) = 0$$

$$I_2 = \frac{9.00 \text{ V} - I_1 \cdot (23.0 \text{ Ω})}{13.0 \text{ Ω}}$$

Getting I_3 in terms of I_1:

$$9.00 \text{ V} - I_1 \cdot (11.0 \text{ Ω}) - I_3 \cdot (14.0 \text{ Ω}) - I_3 \cdot (15.0 \text{ Ω}) - I_1 \cdot (12.0 \text{ Ω}) = 0$$

$$I_3 = \frac{9.00 \text{ V} - I_1 \cdot (23.0 \text{ Ω})}{29.0 \text{ Ω}}$$

Substituting these expressions in the last equation:

$$I_1 = I_2 + I_3$$

$$I_1 = \frac{9.00 \text{ V} - I_1 \cdot (23.0 \text{ Ω})}{13.0 \text{ Ω}} + \frac{9.00 \text{ V} - I_1 \cdot (23.0 \text{ Ω})}{29.0 \text{ Ω}}$$

$$(29.0 \text{ Ω}) \cdot I_1 = 20.1 \text{ V} - I_1 \cdot (51.3 \text{ Ω}) + 9.00 \text{ V} - I_1 \cdot (23.0 \text{ Ω})$$

$$I_1 = \frac{29.1 \text{ V}}{103.3 \text{ Ω}} = 0.282 \text{ A}$$

To calculate the potential difference I will need to follow the current from A to B. From point A, I_1 travels through the battery (negative side first) and then through the 11.0 Ω resistor. That means it experiences an increase (+9.00 V) in potential from the battery and then a decrease (I·R) in potential from the resistor. The total change in potential, then, is:

$$9.00 \text{ V} - (0.282 \text{ A}) \cdot (11.0 \text{ } \Omega) = 5.90 \text{ V}$$

Since the total change in potential is positive, this means that point B is at a higher potential than point A. Thus, point A is 5.90 V lower in potential than point B.

9. I do not have to go through this whole problem again! All I have to do is realize that the 3.0 Ω internal resistance is in *series* with the 11.0 Ω resistor. Thus, the 11.0 Ω resistor becomes a 14.0 Ω resistor. What does that do to our equations? Well, look at the equation we had for I_2:

$$9.00 \text{ V} - I_1 \cdot (11.0 \text{ } \Omega) - I_2 \cdot (13.0 \text{ } \Omega) - I_1 \cdot (12.0 \text{ } \Omega) = 0$$

$$I_2 = \frac{9.00 \text{ V} - I_1 \cdot (23.0 \text{ } \Omega)}{13.0 \text{ } \Omega}$$

Since the 11.0 Ω resistor is now a 14.0 Ω resistor, that changes the equation to:

$$9.00 \text{ V} - I_1 \cdot (14.0 \text{ } \Omega) - I_2 \cdot (13.0 \text{ } \Omega) - I_1 \cdot (12.0 \text{ } \Omega) = 0$$

$$I_2 = \frac{9.00 \text{ V} - I_1 \cdot (26.0 \text{ } \Omega)}{13.0 \text{ } \Omega}$$

In the same way, the equation for I_3 changes to:

$$9.00 \text{ V} - I_1 \cdot (14.0 \text{ } \Omega) - I_3 \cdot (14.0 \text{ } \Omega) - I_3 \cdot (15.0 \text{ } \Omega) - I_1 \cdot (12.0 \text{ } \Omega) = 0$$

$$I_3 = \frac{9.00 \text{ V} - I_1 \cdot (26.0 \text{ } \Omega)}{29.0 \text{ } \Omega}$$

That means our final equation changes to:

$$I_1 = I_2 + I_3$$

$$I_1 = \frac{9.00 \text{ V} - I_1 \cdot (26.0 \text{ } \Omega)}{13.0 \text{ } \Omega} + \frac{9.00 \text{ V} - I_1 \cdot (26.0 \text{ } \Omega)}{29.0 \text{ } \Omega}$$

$$(29.0 \ \Omega) \cdot I_1 = 20.1 \ V - I_1 \cdot (58.0 \ \Omega) + 9.00 \ V - I_1 \cdot (26.0 \ \Omega)$$

$$I_1 = \frac{29.1 \ V}{113.0 \ \Omega} = 0.258 \ A$$

That changes the final potential calculation to:

$$9.00 \ V - (0.258 \ A) \cdot (14.0 \ \Omega) = 5.39 \ V$$

Thus, with the internal resistance taken into consideration, <u>point A is 5.39 V lower in potential than point B</u>.

10. First, we need to replace the many capacitors with one effective capacitor. The 25.0 μF and 15.0 μF capacitors are in series, so they can be replaced with this equivalent capacitor:

$$\frac{1}{C_{eff}} = \frac{1}{C_1} + \frac{1}{C_2} = \frac{1}{25.0 \ \mu F} + \frac{1}{15.0 \ \mu F}$$

$$C_{eff} = 9.372 \ \mu F$$

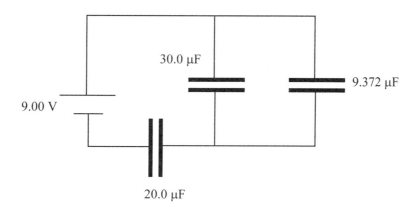

The 30.0 μF and 9.372 μF capacitors are in parallel, so they can be replaced by a 39.4 μF capacitor:

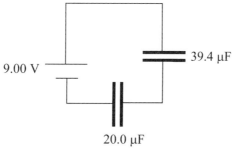

These two capacitors are in series, so their effective capacitance is:

$$\frac{1}{C_{eff}} = \frac{1}{C_1} + \frac{1}{C_2} = \frac{1}{39.4 \ \mu F} + \frac{1}{20.0 \ \mu F}$$

$$C_{eff} = 13.3 \ \mu F$$

Thus, we have a 13.3 µF capacitor hooked up to a 9.00 V battery. The charge stored on this effective capacitor is:

$$\Delta V = \frac{Q}{C}$$

$$Q = \Delta V \cdot C = (9.00 \ \cancel{V}) \cdot (1.33 \times 10^{-5} \ \frac{C}{\cancel{V}}) = 1.20 \times 10^{-4} \ C$$

What does this tell us? Well, the 20.0 µF capacitor is in series with the effective capacitor of 39.4 µF (see diagram above). They must each store the same charge. Thus, the 20.0 µF capacitor stores 1.20 x 10^{-4} C of charge.

What about the other capacitors? Well, we first have to figure out the voltage. The 20.0 µF capacitor has the following potential difference between the plates:

$$\Delta V = \frac{Q}{C}$$

$$\Delta V = \frac{1.20 \times 10^{-4} \ \cancel{C}}{2.00 \times 10^{-5} \ \frac{\cancel{C}}{V}} = 6.00 \ V$$

Use Kirchhoff's Rules at this point. After all, capacitors are like batteries when they are fully charged.

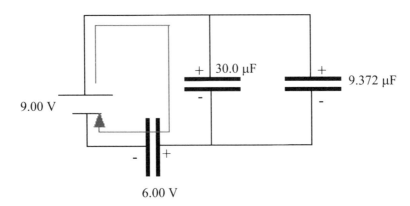

In a loop that contains the 30.0 μF capacitor, the current leaves the battery, hits the 30.0 μF capacitor positive side first, hits the 20.0 μF capacitor (which has a potential difference of 6.00 V) positive side first, and then hits the battery negative side first. Thus, Kirchhoff's Rules say:

$$9.00 \text{ V} - V_{30.0 \text{ μF}} - 6.00 \text{ V} = 0$$

This tells us that the potential across the 30.0 μF resistor must be 3.00 V!

$$\Delta V = \frac{Q}{C}$$

$$Q = \Delta V \cdot C = (3.00 \text{ V}) \cdot (3.00 \times 10^{-5} \frac{C}{V}) = 9.00 \times 10^{-5} \text{ C}$$

Thus, the 30.0 μF capacitor stores 9.00 x 10⁻⁵ C of charge. Since capacitors in parallel experience the same potential, the effective 9.372 μF capacitor also has 3.00 V across its place:

$$\Delta V = \frac{Q}{C}$$

$$Q = \Delta V \cdot C = (3.00 \text{ V}) \cdot (9.37 \times 10^{-6} \frac{C}{V}) = 2.81 \times 10^{-5} \text{ C}$$

That tells us that the two capacitors which make up that effective capacitor both carry 2.81 x 10⁻⁵ C. Thus, the 25.0 μF capacitor and the 15.0 μF capacitor both store 2.81 x 10⁻⁵ C of charge.

SOLUTIONS TO THE PRACTICE PROBLEMS FOR MODULE #14

1. This is a pretty direct application of Equation (14.1).

$$\mathbf{F} = q \cdot (\mathbf{v} \times \mathbf{B})$$

$$F = q \cdot v \cdot B \cdot \sin\theta$$

Since the velocity and magnetic fields are perpendicular:

$$F = q \cdot v \cdot B \cdot \sin\theta = (-2.50 \; C) \cdot (3{,}014 \; \frac{m}{sec}) \cdot (0.0456 \; \frac{N}{A \cdot m}) \cdot \sin(90) = -344 \; N$$

The negative tells us that the force is directed opposite the result of the right hand rule. The right hand rule says that the cross product is pointed down (fingers point to the right and curl out of the paper), so the force is pointed up. Thus, <u>the particle experiences 344 N of force directed</u> <u>upwards</u>.

2. The particle exits on the same side that it enters the field because it travels in a circle while in the field. Thus, the path looks something like that drawn to the right. The distance between the point of exit and the point of entry, then, is the *diameter* of the circle, which is twice the radius. Well, Equation (14.5) allows us to calculate the radius:

$$r = \frac{(4.60 \times 10^{-6} \; kg) \cdot (3014 \; \frac{m}{sec})}{(2.50 \; C) \cdot (0.0456 \; \frac{N}{A \cdot m})} = 0.122 \; \frac{kg \cdot m^2 \cdot A}{C \cdot sec \cdot N} = 0.122 \; \frac{kg \cdot m^2 \cdot C}{C \cdot sec^2 \cdot N} = 0.122 \; \frac{N \cdot m}{N} = 0.122 \; m$$

If that's the radius, then the distance between the point of entry and the point of exit is simply twice that, or <u>0.244 m</u>. <u>The point of exit is above the point of entry.</u>

3. This looks tricky at first, but it is not bad once you realize that the speed cannot change, because the magnetic field cannot work on the particle. Thus, the speed stays 3,104 m/sec the whole way. Well, the particle travels in a perfect semicircle, so the distance traveled is half the circumference, or π·r. We know r, so we can calculate the time:

$$x = v_o t + \frac{1}{2} a t^2$$

$$\pi \cdot r = (3014 \; \frac{m}{sec}) \cdot t + \frac{1}{2} \cdot (0) \cdot t^2$$

$$t = \frac{\pi \cdot (0.122 \text{ m})}{3014 \dfrac{\text{m}}{\text{sec}}} = \underline{1.27 \times 10^{-4} \text{ sec}}$$

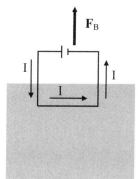

4. The battery tells us the direction of the conventional current, which is shown in the drawing to the right. In order to counteract gravity, the magnetic force ($\mathbf{F_B}$) must point straight up. Thus, the net force on the circuit must be pointed straight up. Now, the magnetic field will exert a force on the bottom part of the square as well as the 3.50 cm sections of the sides that are in the magnetic field. If I tried to use the magnetic force exerted on the sides, however, there would be a problem, because the force on one side will be opposite the force on the other, due to the direction of the current in each section. Thus, let's concentrate on the bottom wire.

If I want the net force to be up, I point my right hand fingers to the right (in the direction of the current) and figure out how I must curl them to get my thumb to point up. Thus, the magnetic field must go *into* the paper, because if I point my right hand fingers to the right and curl them into the paper, my thumb points up.

Now, what about the other sides of the circuit? If the magnetic field lines go into the paper, the 3.50 cm section of the left-hand side of the circuit experiences a magnetic pull to the right, according to the right hand rule. According to that same rule, the right-hand side experiences a pull to the left. Thus, the forces on those two sides cancel out as long as the magnetic field points into the paper.

Thus, the only net force is the one working on the bottom of the circuit. Since that force must negate the gravitational force:

$$F_b = m \cdot g$$

$$I \cdot \ell \cdot B \cdot \sin \theta = m \cdot g$$

$$B = \frac{m \cdot g}{I \cdot \ell \cdot \sin \theta} = \frac{(0.0500 \text{ kg}) \cdot (9.81 \dfrac{\text{m}}{\text{sec}^2})}{(3.40 \text{ A}) \cdot (0.100 \text{ m})} = 1.44 \frac{\text{N}}{\text{A} \cdot \text{m}} = 1.44 \text{ T}$$

The magnetic field, then, must be <u>1.44 T directed into the page</u>.

5. If the magnetic field were pointed directly to the right, there would be no force on the bottom segment of the circuit, because the current and magnetic field would be parallel, making the cross product zero. Applying the cross product to the left-hand portion of the circuit, the resulting force points out of the plane of the paper. On the right-hand side, the cross product indicates that the resulting force points into the paper. Thus, we have two forces that will act as torques, and <u>the circuit will spin about the dashed line drawn in the figure to the right</u>.

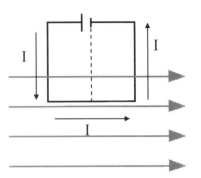

The torque on one side is easily found. The force is given by Equation (14.7), but you must realize that only 3.50 cm of the wire is in the magnetic field, so you can only use 3.50 cm as the magnitude of ℓ. The torque is given by the cross product of the lever arm and **F**. Since the two are perpendicular, the magnitude of the cross product is given simply by multiplying the two. The lever arm will be half the width of the circuit, since the lever arm is defined by the axis of rotation.

$$\tau = r \cdot I \cdot \ell \cdot B = (0.0500 \text{ m}) \cdot (3.40 \text{ A}) \cdot (0.0350 \text{ m}) \cdot (1.44 \ \frac{N}{A \cdot m}) = 0.00857 \text{ N} \cdot \text{m}$$

There is a torque on the other side, and it results in rotational motion in the same direction. Thus, the total torque is twice the torque of one side, or <u>0.0171 N·m</u>.

6. We know that the potential difference will be given by Equation (14.10):

$$\Delta V = v \cdot B \cdot \ell$$

$$v = \frac{\Delta V}{B \cdot \ell} = \frac{1.86 \text{ V}}{0.861 \ \frac{N}{A \cdot m} \cdot (0.250 \text{ m})} = 8.64 \ \frac{\frac{J}{C} \cdot \frac{C}{sec}}{N} = 8.64 \ \frac{\frac{N \cdot m}{sec}}{N} = 8.64 \ \frac{m}{sec}$$

The electrons in the conductor will experience a force opposite the cross product of the velocity and magnetic field. If you point your right hand fingers to the right (the direction of **v**), and curl them out of the paper (the direction of **B**), your thumb points down. Thus, the electrons will move up. That makes the top of the conductor negative and the bottom positive. So, <u>the bottom will be at a higher potential</u>.

7. When the conductor is at rest, there is no potential difference. As soon as the conductor starts moving, the electrons feel a force and begin to move in response to it. Once they start moving, however, a potential difference gets established, and the electrons are moving *against* that potential difference. Thus, the current reduces. Eventually, the force experienced by the electrons due to the potential difference will reach the magnitude of the force exerted by the magnetic field, and the electrons will no longer move. At that point, the full emf is established,

and no more current flows, because there is not a circuit to connect the positive end of the conductor to the negative end. As a result, the current looks something like this:

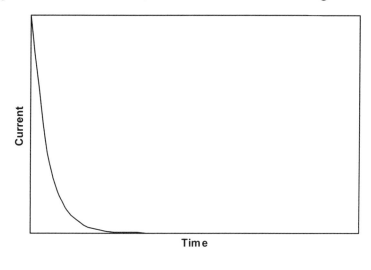

8. When both wires carry equal current, the total magnetic field at a point in between them is zero, because they produce equal but opposite magnetic fields. Thus, at the beginning, the flux through the wire is zero. However, once the bottom wire is reduced to carrying no current, the top wire's magnetic field is the only one present, and it has a strength of:

$$B = \frac{\mu_0 \cdot I}{2\pi \cdot r} = \frac{4\pi \times 10^{-7} \frac{T \cdot m}{A} \cdot (1.00 \ A)}{2\pi \cdot (0.0500 \ m)} = 4.00 \times 10^{-6} \ T$$

The area of the loop of wire is given by $\pi \cdot r^2$, where this "r" is the radius of the loop, 0.500 cm. The magnetic field is parallel to the vector **A**, so the flux is given by:

$$\Phi = B \bullet A = B \cdot A \cdot \cos(0) = (4.00 \times 10^{-6} \ T) \cdot \pi \cdot (0.00500 \ m)^2 = 3.14 \times 10^{-10} \ T \cdot m^2 = 3.14 \times 10^{-10} \ Wb$$

The change in flux per unit time, then, is:

$$\frac{\Delta \Phi}{\Delta t} = \frac{3.14 \times 10^{-10} \ T \cdot m^2 - 0}{0.500 \ sec} = 6.28 \times 10^{-10} \ \frac{\frac{N}{A \cdot m} \cdot m^2}{sec} = 6.28 \times 10^{-10} \ \frac{\frac{J \cdot sec}{C}}{sec} = 6.28 \times 10^{-10} \ V$$

According to Ohm's Law, the current is:

$$V = I \cdot R$$

$$I = \frac{V}{R} = \frac{6.28 \times 10^{-10} \ V}{0.0340 \ \Omega} = 1.85 \times 10^{-8} \ A$$

The magnetic field from the top wire is pointed into the paper where the loop of wire is. As the bottom wire's current is reduced, that magnetic field begins to make a net flux. So the flux is increasing into the paper. To oppose that, the current in the loop must produce a magnetic field that comes out of the paper. Thus, the current will flow <u>counterclockwise with an average magnitude of 1.85 x 10^{-8} A</u>.

9. <u>The current will be zero</u>. The flux must be changing to generate emf. Once the bottom wire's current is at zero, the total magnetic field through the loop will be simply that of the top wire. If that current doesn't change, the flux will not change, so there will be no emf and no current.

10. To determine the current, we need the emf, and to get that, we need to determine the rate of change of the flux. The flux starts out at:

$$\Phi_o = B \bullet (500 \cdot A) = B \cdot 500 \cdot A \cdot \cos(0) = (0.987 \text{ T}) \cdot (500) \cdot (0.500 \text{ m}) \cdot (0.500 \text{ m}) = 123 \text{ Wb}$$

The flux ends up at zero, since the vector **A**, which is perpendicular to the surface, will be perpendicular to the field, making the dot product zero. Thus, the change in flux over the change in time is:

$$\frac{\Delta\Phi}{\Delta t} = \frac{0 \text{ T} \cdot \text{m}^2 - 123 \text{ T} \cdot \text{m}^2}{0.300 \text{ sec}} = -4.10 \times 10^2 \frac{\frac{\text{N}}{\text{A} \cdot \cancel{\text{m}}} \cdot \text{m}^2}{\text{sec}} = -4.10 \times 10^2 \frac{\frac{\text{J} \cdot \cancel{\text{sec}}}{\text{C}}}{\cancel{\text{sec}}} = -4.10 \times 10^2 \text{ V}$$

That's the emf. It is negative because the flux decreased. We will deal with that when we determine direction. For now, let's just determine the current:

$$V = I \cdot R$$

$$I = \frac{V}{R} = \frac{4.10 \times 10^2 \text{ V}}{1.20 \text{ }\Omega} = 342 \text{ A}$$

Now, the magnetic field lines point to the right (from north to south). The flux *decreases*. To oppose that decrease, the current's magnetic field must also point to the right. Thus, <u>the current flows counterclockwise with a magnitude of 342 A</u>.

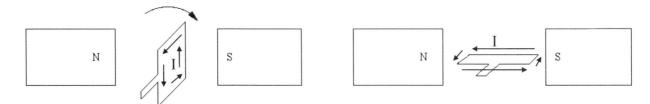

SOLUTIONS TO THE PRACTICE PROBLEMS FOR MODULE #15

1. First, we need to know how much energy the light is supplying to the electrons. Thus, we must first get the frequency:

$$f = \frac{v}{\lambda} = \frac{2.998 \times 10^8 \; \frac{\cancel{m}}{sec}}{1.54 \times 10^{-7} \; \cancel{m}} = 1.95 \times 10^{15} \; \frac{1}{sec}$$

Now we can get the energy:

$$E = h \cdot f = (4.14 \times 10^{-15} \; eV \cdot \cancel{sec}) \cdot (1.95 \times 10^{15} \; \frac{1}{\cancel{sec}}) = 8.07 \; eV$$

That's the maximum energy which can be transferred to an electron. However, the electron will lose the energy which is needed to escape (the work function). Thus, the maximum KE is:

$$max \; KE = 8.07 \; eV - 6.35 \; eV = \underline{1.72 \; eV}$$

2. If electrons are being emitted, then they had more energy than the work function. How much more? The maximum kinetic energy. Thus, the maximum energy the electrons got from the light is:

$$maximum \; energy \; given \; by \; light = 4.08 \; eV + 1.02 \; eV = 5.10 \; eV$$

This maximum energy given to the electrons by the light would be the energy of one photon. The corresponds to a frequency of:

$$E = h \cdot f$$

$$f = \frac{E}{h} = \frac{5.10 \; \cancel{eV}}{4.14 \times 10^{-15} \; \cancel{eV} \cdot sec} = 1.23 \times 10^{15} \; \frac{1}{sec}$$

This corresponds to a wavelength of:

$$f = \frac{v}{\lambda}$$

$$\lambda = \frac{v}{f} = \frac{2.998 \times 10^8 \; \frac{m}{\cancel{sec}}}{1.23 \times 10^{15} \; \frac{1}{\cancel{sec}}} = \underline{2.44 \times 10^{-7} \; m}$$

3. The wavelength of a particle is given by Equation (15.3). Since the wavelengths are the same, we can set the expression for the wavelength of the proton equal to that of the electron.

$$\lambda_p = \lambda_e$$

$$\frac{\hbar}{p_p} = \frac{\hbar}{p_e}$$

$$\frac{1}{m_p \cdot v_p} = \frac{1}{m_e \cdot v_e}$$

$$v_p = \frac{m_e \cdot v_e}{m_p} = \frac{9.11 \times 10^{-31} \text{ kg}}{1.67 \times 10^{-27} \text{ kg}} \cdot v_e = 0.000546 \cdot v_e$$

The proton's speed, then, must be <u>0.000546·v_e</u>.

4. Equation (15.13) gives us the energy for an electron in a given Bohr orbit. For this problem, n = 2 and Z = 2.

$$E = -R_h \cdot Z^2 \cdot \left(\frac{1}{n}\right)^2$$

$$E = -(13.6 \text{ eV}) \cdot 2^2 \cdot \left(\frac{1}{2}\right)^2$$

$$\underline{E = -13.6 \text{ eV}}$$

5. To jump from low energy orbits to high energy orbits, electrons must absorb energy. The amount of energy is determined by the difference in energy between the two orbits, which is calculated using Equation (15.15). Since we are dealing with hydrogen, Z = 1.

$$\Delta E = (13.6 \text{ eV}) \cdot Z^2 \cdot \left[\left(\frac{1}{n_{final}}\right)^2 - \left(\frac{1}{n_{initial}}\right)^2\right]$$

$$\Delta E = (13.6 \text{ eV}) \cdot 1^2 \cdot \left[\left(\frac{1}{4}\right)^2 - \left(\frac{1}{1}\right)^2\right] = -12.8 \text{ eV}$$

The negative sign simply means that the electron absorbs energy rather than emits it. Thus, the electron must absorb <u>12.8 eV</u> of energy.

6. In this problem, Z = 3 because we are dealing with a lithium ion. The electron starts out in the third Bohr orbit, so $n_{initial}$ = 3. It ends up in the first Bohr orbit, so n_{final} = 1.

$$\Delta E = (13.6 \text{ eV}) \cdot Z^2 \cdot \left[\left(\frac{1}{n_{final}} \right)^2 - \left(\frac{1}{n_{initial}} \right)^2 \right]$$

$$\Delta E = (13.6 \text{ eV}) \cdot 3^2 \cdot \left[\left(\frac{1}{1} \right)^2 - \left(\frac{1}{3} \right)^2 \right] = 109 \text{ eV}$$

This tells us, then, that the electron must emit light with energy of 109 eV to make the transition. From the energy, we can get the frequency:

$$E = h \cdot f$$

$$109 \text{ eV} = (4.14 \times 10^{-15} \text{ eV} \cdot \text{s}) \cdot f$$

$$f = 2.63 \times 10^{16} \, \frac{1}{s}$$

Then, we use the speed of light to go from frequency to wavelength.

$$f = \frac{v}{\lambda}$$

$$2.63 \times 10^{16} \, \frac{1}{s} = \frac{2.998 \times 10^8 \, \frac{m}{s}}{\lambda}$$

$$\lambda = 1.14 \times 10^{-8} \text{ m}$$

The electron must emit light with a wavelength of 1.14 x 10^{-8} m.

7. In this problem, $Z = 1$ because we are dealing with hydrogen. The first thing to realize is that we have the frequency of the light emitted. In order to find the final orbit (n_{final}), we are going to need to know the energy. Thus, we first need to calculate the energy:

$$E = h \cdot f$$

$$E = (4.14 \times 10^{-15} \text{ eV} \cdot \text{s}) \cdot (3.16 \times 10^{15} \text{ Hz}) = 13.1 \text{ eV}$$

Now that we know the energy of the light emitted, we can use Equation (15.15) to determine n_{final}:

$$\Delta E = (13.6 \text{ eV}) \cdot Z^2 \cdot \left[\left(\frac{1}{n_{final}} \right)^2 - \left(\frac{1}{n_{initial}} \right)^2 \right]$$

$$13.1 \text{ eV} = (13.6 \text{ eV}) \cdot 1^2 \cdot \left[\left(\frac{1}{n_{final}} \right)^2 - \left(\frac{1}{5} \right)^2 \right]$$

$$\frac{13.1 \text{ eV}}{13.6 \text{ eV} \cdot 1^2} = \left(\frac{1}{n_{final}} \right)^2 - \frac{1}{25}$$

$$0.963 + \frac{1}{25} = \left(\frac{1}{n_{final}} \right)^2$$

$$\frac{1}{n_{final}} = 1.00$$

$$n_{final} = 1$$

The electron lands in the <u>first Bohr orbit</u>.

8. In its ground state, an electron in a He^+ ion is in the $n = 1$ orbit. Since we are dealing with the helium atom, $Z = 2$.

$$r = (0.529 \text{ Å}) \cdot \frac{n^2}{Z}$$

$$r = (0.529 \text{ Å}) \cdot \frac{1^2}{2}$$

$$r = \underline{0.265 \text{ Å}}$$

9. To determine the radius of an electron's orbit, we need to know the value for "n." Equation (15.13) allows us to calculate that from the energy:

$$E = -R_h \cdot Z^2 \cdot \left(\frac{1}{n}\right)^2$$

$$-0.379 \text{ eV} = -(13.6 \text{ eV}) \cdot 1^2 \cdot \left(\frac{1}{n}\right)^2$$

$$\left(\frac{1}{n}\right)^2 = \frac{0.379 \text{ eV}}{13.6 \text{ eV}} = 0.0279$$

$$\frac{1}{n} = 0.167$$

$$n = 5.99$$

Since "n" must be an integer, we round 5.99 to n = 6. Now we can calculate the radius:

$$r = (0.529 \text{ Å}) \cdot \frac{n^2}{Z}$$

$$r = (0.529 \text{ Å}) \cdot \frac{6^2}{1}$$

$$r = \underline{19.0 \text{ Å}}$$

10. To determine an electron's energy, we need to know the value for "n." We can calculate that value from the radius:

$$0.265 \text{ Å} = (0.529 \text{ Å}) \cdot \frac{n^2}{Z}$$

$$0.265 \text{ Å} = (0.529 \text{ Å}) \cdot \frac{n^2}{2}$$

$$n = 1$$

Now we can calculate the electron's energy.

$$E = -R_h \cdot Z^2 \cdot \left(\frac{1}{n}\right)^2$$

$$E = -(13.6 \text{ eV}) \cdot 2^2 \cdot \left(\frac{1}{1}\right)^2$$

$$E = -54.4 \text{ eV}$$

SOLUTIONS TO THE PRACTICE PROBLEMS FOR MODULE #16

1. Since fluorine's atomic number is 9, all fluorine atoms have 9 protons. The mass number, which is the sum of the protons and neutrons in a nucleus, therefore indicates that a ^{19}F nucleus has 10 neutrons. The sum of the masses of 9 protons and 10 neutrons is:

$$9 \times (1.0073 \text{ amu}) + 10 \times (1.0087 \text{ amu}) = 19.1527 \text{ amu}$$

Since the mass of a ^{19}F nucleus is only 18.9984 amu, there is a mass deficit of 0.1543 amu. This mass deficit is converted to energy according to Equation (8.7). To use this equation, however, we must have consistent units. Since we have the speed of light in m/sec, then the energy will come out in Joules as long as the mass is in kilograms (remember, a Joule is a $(\text{kg} \cdot \text{m}^2)/\text{sec}^2$). Thus, we must first convert the mass deficit to kg:

$$\frac{0.1543 \text{ amu}}{1} \times \frac{1.6605 \times 10^{-27} \text{ kg}}{1 \text{ amu}} = 2.562 \times 10^{-28} \text{ kg}$$

Now we can use Equation (8.7):

$$E = m \cdot c^2 = (2.562 \times 10^{-28} \text{ kg}) \cdot (2.998 \times 10^8 \frac{\text{m}}{\text{sec}})^2 = 2.303 \times 10^{-11} \text{ J}$$

To get the binding energy per nucleon, we must divide by the number of nucleons (19):

$$\frac{2.303 \times 10^{-11} \text{ J}}{19 \text{ nucleons}} = \underline{1.212 \times 10^{-12} \frac{\text{J}}{\text{nucleon}}}$$

2. Since we know that there are 27 protons and 32 neutrons in a ^{59}Co nucleus, we can figure out the mass of the nucleons:

$$27 \times (1.0073 \text{ amu}) + 32 \times (1.0087 \text{ amu}) = 59.4755 \text{ amu}$$

This isn't the mass of the nucleus, however, because the nucleons always lose some mass when they form a nucleus. How much mass do these nucleons lose? We can calculate it from the binding energy:

$$E = m \cdot c^2$$

$$8.326 \times 10^{-11} \text{ J} = m \cdot (2.998 \times 10^8 \frac{\text{m}}{\text{sec}})^2$$

$$m = 9.263 \times 10^{-28} \text{ kg}$$

We can convert that to amu:

$$\frac{9.263 \times 10^{-28} \text{ kg}}{1} \times \frac{1 \text{ amu}}{1.6605 \times 10^{-27} \text{ kg}} = 0.5578 \text{ amu}$$

Now remember, this is the mass that the nucleons *lose* when they make a nucleus. Thus, the mass of the nucleus is:

$$59.4755 \text{ amu} - 0.5578 \text{ amu} = \underline{58.9177 \text{ amu}}$$

3. In beta decay, the nucleus emits a beta particle $_{-1}^{0}e$ so that a neutron can turn into a proton. ^{131}I has 53 protons and 78 neutrons. When a neutron turns into a proton, the result will be a nucleus with 54 protons and 77 neutrons. That is ^{131}Xe. The reaction, then, is:

$$_{53}^{131}\text{I} \rightarrow \ _{54}^{131}\text{Xe} \ + \ _{-1}^{0}e$$

4. In the decay, ^{222}Rn (86 protons and 136 neutrons) decays into ^{218}Po (84 protons and 134 neutrons). The only way this can happen is for the ^{222}Rn to lose 2 protons and 2 neutrons. That's an alpha particle. Thus, this is alpha decay.

5. Since ^{14}N is stable, it will not need to change. It just needs to lose energy. This can happen with gamma decay.

6. In 30 seconds (half a minute), the nucleus will go through 15 half-lives. This means its mass will be cut in half 15 times. Thus, the number of grams left will be:

$$1.00 \times 10^{3} \text{g} \div 2 \div 2 \div 2 \div 2 \div 2 \div 2 \div 2 \div 2 \div 2 \div 2 \div 2 \div 2 \div 2 \div 2 \div 2 = \underline{0.0305 \text{ g}}$$

7. This problem is not as easy as #6, because the elapsed time is not an integral multiple of the half-life. Thus, we will have to do this the hard way:

$$4.20 \text{ min} = \frac{0.693}{k}$$

$$k = \frac{0.693}{4.20 \text{ min}} = 0.165 \ \frac{1}{\text{min}}$$

Now we can use Equation (16.5). Remember, "N" can refer to number of grams or number of nuclei.

$$N = N_o \cdot e^{-kt}$$

$$N = (1.2 \text{ x } 10^{23} \text{ nuclei}) \cdot e^{-(0.165\frac{1}{\text{min}}) \cdot (10.0 \text{ min})} = 2.3 \times 10^{22} \text{ nuclei}$$

8. This is how half-lives are measured today. We know the initial amount, the final amount, and the time. We can use Equation (16.5) to get k:

$$N = N_o \cdot e^{-kt}$$

$$13.6 \text{ g} = (14.0 \text{ g}) \cdot e^{-k(22.2 \text{ min})}$$

$$\frac{13.6 \text{ g}}{14.0 \text{ g}} = e^{-k(22.2 \text{ min})}$$

$$-0.0290 = -k \cdot (22.2 \text{ min})$$

$$k = 0.00131 \frac{1}{\text{min}}$$

Now we can get the half-life:

$$t_{1/2} = \frac{0.693}{k}$$

$$t_{1/2} = \frac{0.693}{0.00131 \frac{1}{\text{min}}} = 529 \text{ min}$$

9. The reaction starts out as:

$$_0^1 n \ + \ _{94}^{239}\text{Pu} \ \rightarrow$$

This means that on the left side, the subscripts add to 94 and the superscripts add to 240. If 4 neutrons are produced, then the equation becomes:

$$_0^1 n \ + \ _{94}^{239}\text{Pu} \ \rightarrow 4_0^1 n + 2 \text{ ?}$$

We know that there are 2 of the same nucleus produced because the problem told us that the rest of the nucleus was cut in half. The only way I can get the equation to balance is for $^{118}_{47}\text{Ag}$. The reaction, then, is

$$^{1}_{0}\text{n} \ + \ ^{239}_{94}\text{Pu} \ \rightarrow \ 4\,^{1}_{0}\text{n} + 2\,^{118}_{47}\text{Ag}$$

10. The problem says:

$$^{27}_{13}\text{Al} \ + \ ^{3}_{1}\text{H} \ \rightarrow \ ^{27}_{12}\text{Mg} \ + \ ?$$

The only way that the superscripts and subscripts will balance is if the missing nucleus is $^{3}_{2}\text{He}$.

Tests

TEST FOR MODULE #1

1. The volume of a sphere is given as $V = \frac{4}{3} \cdot \pi \cdot r^3$. A sphere has a radius of 3.2 m. What is the volume in cm^3?

2. Consider the following diagram:

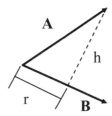

Give a formula for **B•A** using only A (the magnitude of **A**), B (the magnitude of **B**), r, and h.

3. Using the diagram above, give a formula for the magnitude of **B** x **A** using only A (the magnitude of **A**), B (the magnitude of **B**), r, and h.

4. Given the diagram in #2, what is the direction of **B** x **A**? Give your answer in terms of whether or not the vector is pointing behind the plane of the paper or above the plane of the paper.

5. Given the following vectors:

A = 6.1·**i** + 2.8·**j**
B = 4.6·**i** + 5.5·**j**

Determine **A** + **B** in unit vector notation.

6. Using the vectors in problem #5, give the magnitude and direction of **A** - **B**.

7. Using the vectors in problem #5, compute **A•B**.

8. Using the vectors in problem #5, compute **A** x **B** and give your answer in unit vector notation.

9. The standard unit for power is the Watt, which is a $\frac{kg \cdot m^2}{sec^3}$.

Convert 1.00 Watt into $\frac{g \cdot cm^2}{minute^3}$.

10. A construction worker is pushing a box across the floor. He applies 56 N of constant force, and the box moves 15.1 m. If the work accomplished was 711 J, what was the angle between the force applied and the displacement of the box?

11. If the construction worker in problem #10 wanted to maximize the work he was doing, in what direction should he apply the force? Give your answer in terms of the angle between the force and the displacement of the box.

12. An assembly line worker is tightening bolts with a wrench. He applies the force 0.035 m from the center of the bolt at an angle of 42 degrees. The resulting torque is 1.3 N·m. What is the magnitude of the force that he is using?

13. If the assembly line worker in the problem wanted to generate the most torque possible without altering the force he used, what *two* things could he do?

14. Is work a scalar or a vector?

15. Is torque a scalar or a vector?

TEST FOR MODULE #2

1. An object travels in one dimension from point A to point B. As it travels, it slows down. Draw the velocity and acceleration vectors (don't worry about the magnitudes) for the object when it is halfway in between the two points.

A   ●   **B**

2. John and Joe race each other in a 100-meter sprint. John beats Joe by 5 meters. To try and give Joe a "fair shot," John agrees to start 5 meters behind Joe in the next race. If all factors between the two races are identical, will the race end in a tie? Why or why not?

3. A student observes an object traveling to the right. He looks away for a few moments and, when he looks back, he notices that the object is now moving to the left. The student says, "The acceleration of this object was not constant while I was looking away, because it changed direction." Is the student right or wrong. Why?

4. An object's speed is increasing. Can its acceleration be decreasing at the same time? Why or why not?

5. Cold air is more dense than warm air. A plane travels at the same altitude for the same distance on two separate trips. The only important difference is that on the second trip, the outside temperature is significantly warmer than it was on the first trip. On which trip will the airplane burn more fuel?

6. A rock slides across a sidewalk that is covered with ice. It starts with an initial velocity of 2.5 m/sec to the west. It takes 50.0 meters to stop.

     a. What is the acceleration (include direction) of the rock?
     b. How long does it take for the rock to stop?
     c. What was its velocity after it had traveled halfway (25.0 m)?

7. A stone is thrown upwards from the edge of a cliff with a speed of 10.0 ft/sec. It just misses the edge of the cliff and eventually lands on the ground below the cliff. The cliff is 50.0 ft higher than the ground upon which the rock lands.

     a. How long is the rock in the air?
     b. What is the rock's maximum height from the ground below the cliff?

8. A baseball player throws a ball straight up in the air. When it is halfway to its maximum height, a radar gun measures its velocity to be 15.1 m/sec.

     a. What is its maximum height?
     b. What was its acceleration at its maximum height?
     c. What was its velocity 4.0 seconds after it was thrown?

9. Consider the following situation, in which a football player kicks a football off of a hill:

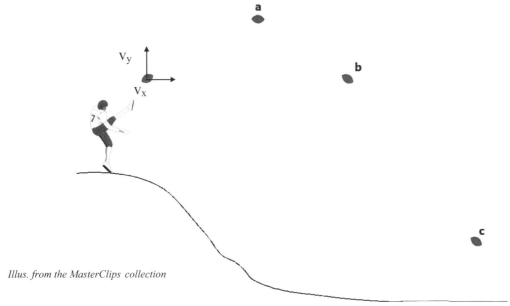

Illus. from the MasterClips collection

The drawing depicts the ball at four points along its trajectory. The horizontal and vertical components of the ball's velocity are shown for the first point. Draw the horizontal and vertical components of the velocity at the other points in the figure. Ignore air resistance.

a. This is the highest point on the trajectory.

b. This is at exactly the same height as the first point shown on the trajectory.

c. This is significantly lower than the first point on the trajectory.

d. Now think about air resistance. At which point in the figure is the ball experiencing the most air resistance? At which point is it experiencing the least?

10. Suppose that in the situation pictured above, the football is kicked with an initial speed of 35.0 m/sec at an angle of 35.0 degrees. If the ball lands 175.0 meters away from the kicker, how high (relative to the point at which the ball lands) is the point at which the ball was kicked?

11. During World War II, the Germans had a gun called "Big Bertha." This gun had a maximum range of 183 miles (295,000 m). If the Germans used the gun to shell Paris, they had to shoot it with an angle of 55.0 degrees. Assuming that Paris and the gun are at the same elevation (and ignoring air resistance), how far was Paris from the gun?

12. A marksman aims at a target that is 100.0 meters away and exactly the same height as his rifle, which can fire bullets with an initial speed of 75.0 m/sec. Ignore air resistance.

a. The marksman knows that his gun cannot be fired horizontally and still hit the target dead center. Why not?

b. The sight (the aiming device) on a gun usually accounts for the fact in (a). Assume that the marksman uses the rifle's sight to hit the target at dead center. If the target is moved to a distance of 50.0 meters and the marksman uses the sight to aim *exactly* the same as before, will he hit the target dead center? If not, will he hit above or below the center?

c. Going back to the situation where the target was 100.0 m from the rifle, at what angle was the gun elevated so that the marksman did hit the target dead center?

TEST FOR MODULE #3

1. An elevator operator (in elegant establishments, they pay a person to stand in the elevator and hit the buttons for you) is working on an elevator whose lights are all broken. Thus, he has no idea whether the elevator is going up or down. However, this elevator operator took physics and thus makes his own acceleration detector. He takes a 50-pound weight and puts it on bathroom scales and puts it on the elevator floor. He knows that reading variations in the weight will tell him something about how the elevator is moving.

a. When the scale reads a weight of more than 50 pounds, what is happening to the elevator?
b. When the scale reads a weight of less than 50 pounds, what is happening to the elevator?
c. Under what conditions will this "elevator motion detector" *not* allow the elevator man to know which way the elevator is moving?
d. What will the scale read when the elevator is an inertial reference frame?

2. Suppose the elevator man could not find bathroom scales and instead found a balance like the one pictured to the right. He puts the 50-pound weight on one side and enough mass to balance the weight on the other. Will this system work as a elevator motion detector? Why or why not?

3. Consider an astronaut who is floating freely in a spaceship. The astronaut has a wrench in his hands, and he throws it towards the front of the ship.

a. What will happen to the astronaut as a result?
b. What exerted the force which causes this to happen?
c. If the astronaut's ship is near a planet, is the ship an inertial reference frame?

4. A baseball player swings a baseball bat and hits a ball. At the moment that the ball is hit, the bat is exerting two forces. What are those two forces acting on, and what are the sources of the equal and opposite forces demanded by Newton's Third Law? Ignore air resistance and wind.

5. Two blocks (m_1 = 10.0 kg, m_2 = 30.0 kg) are fastened to the ceiling of an elevator as shown to the right.

a. When the elevator is at rest, what is the tension in each of the two ropes?
b. What is the tension in each rope when the elevator accelerates downward at 2.0 m/sec^2?

6. Three blocks are pushed on either side with different forces, as shown to the right. Ignoring friction, what is the acceleration of the system? List the magnitude and direction of each force exerted on the 15.0 kg block.

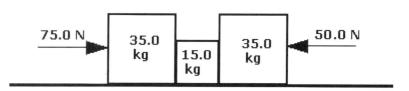

7. In the following situation:

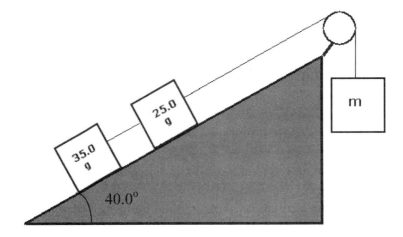

The coefficient of static friction is 0.500, and the coefficient of kinetic friction is 0.250.

a. What must the value of m be to just get the two masses moving up the incline?
b. Once it is moving, what will the acceleration be?
c. Once it is moving, what is the tension in each string?

TEST FOR MODULE #4

1. A block whose weight is 50.0 Newtons is lifted at a constant speed straight up from the floor to a table whose height is 1.20 m.

a. How much work is done in this process?
b. If the person exerts 45.0 Watts, what is the speed of the block as it is being lifted?

2. A toy car (m = 5.0 kg) is moving at a constant speed of 1.5 m/sec. It then accelerates to a speed of 3.5 m/sec. How much work was done on the car?

3. Two toy cars crash head on. The first is traveling east and is three times heavier than the second.

a. If the cars are initially traveling at equal speeds and the collision is perfectly inelastic, will the final velocity of the system be pointed east or west?

b. If the collision results in both cars coming to a halt, what can you say about the relative speeds of the two cars?

4. An object is moving along a floor at constant velocity. Thinking about this situation as realistically as possible, is work being done on the object? Why or why not?

5. Three balls of equal mass are thrown off of a cliff, each with identical speeds. One is thrown straight up, one is thrown straight down, and one is thrown at an angle of 45 degrees. Ignoring air resistance, compare the speed of the balls right before they impact the ground at the bottom of the cliff. Assume that the ground is perfectly level at the bottom of the cliff.

6. The total energy of a particle is zero. Is its velocity necessarily zero? Why or why not?

7. Two objects collide, one of which is initially at rest. No external forces work on the system. Is it possible for both to be at rest after the collision? Why or why not?

8. In the question above, is it possible for both objects to be moving after the collision? Why or why not?

9. A marksman wants to practice hitting a moving target. He drills a 50.0 cm hole in the ground and puts a mass/spring system into the hole (illustrated as part A in the figure). The spring has a force constant of 123 N/m, and when relaxed, the mass/spring system has a length of 50.0 cm. In other words, when it is relaxed, the top of the mass on the mass/spring system is level with the ground. The marksman then has a friend place a round, 100.0 g target on the mass, compress the mass by 15.0 cm (illustrated as part B in the figure), and release. The marksman's goal is to hit the round target just as it reaches its maximum height. What is the ball's maximum height relative to the ground?

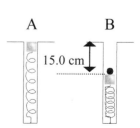

10. Assume that the marksman in problem 9 does, indeed, hit the round target just as it reaches its maximum height, and the bullet (m = 15.0 g, **v** = 155 m/sec at 0.00° relative the ground) imbeds itself into the target. What will be the velocity of the bullet/target system right after the collision?

11. Ignoring air resistance and assuming that the ground is perfectly level in #10, what will be the speed of the bullet/mass system when it hits the ground?

12. A box sits at the top of a ramp (h = 1.50 m, θ = 35.0°). It slides down the ramp and, when it reaches the bottom, slides across a level floor. During the trip down the ramp, the coefficient of kinetic friction between the box and the ramp is 0.250. Then, once it leaves the ramp, there is essentially no friction. Once the box has traveled across the floor, it hits

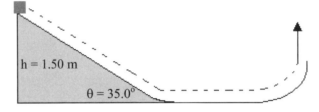

another ramp (also frictionless) which causes the box to travel straight up in the air. What is the maximum height that the box will reach?

13. Two billiard balls of equal mass collide elastically. One is initially at rest. If the ball that was initially moving ends up with a velocity that is oriented 41.2° relative to its initial velocity, what is the angle of the other ball's velocity vector? Make sure the angle you report is defined properly.

14. A 5.00 kg ball is hung from a string. As the ball hangs motionless from the string, a 20.0 kg block is placed next to the ball so that it is just barely touching the ball. The ball is then raised so that it is at a height of 0.350 m relative to its original position. It is then released so that it collides with the block elastically. The coefficient of kinetic friction between the block and the floor is 0.250 .

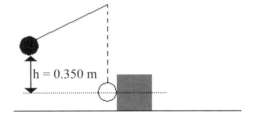

a. How far will the block travel after the collision?

b. To what height will the ball rise after the collision ?

15. Two billiard balls of equal mass collide. One is initially at rest, and the other moves towards it with a speed of 3.55 m/sec. After the collision, the ball that was originally moving has a velocity that is pointed 41.2° relative to its initial velocity. The other ball has a velocity vector pointed -45.5° relative to the moving ball's original velocity. Give the speed of each ball and the percentage of energy lost in the collision.

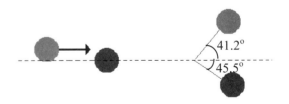

TEST FOR MODULE #5

Moments of Inertia:

A solid sphere rotating about its diameter: $I = \frac{2}{5} \cdot M \cdot R^2$

A mass rotating about a fixed point in space: $I = M \cdot R^2$

A hoop rotating about its central axis: $I = M \cdot R^2$

A solid cylinder or disk rotating about its central axis: $I = \frac{1}{2} \cdot M \cdot R^2$

1. In the diagram below, a uniform rod of length L is attached to a wall at an angle of θ. It is held on the other end by a string. What is the tension in the string in terms of m, g, L, and θ (you may not end up using all four). (HINT: When two parallel lines are cut by a transversal, alternating interior angles are congruent as are corresponding angles.)

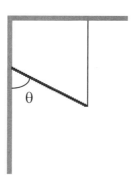

2. A spherical object is acted on by only one force. Where must that force be applied if the object is rotating at a constant angular velocity?

3. It is very difficult to keep your balance on a bicycle that is stationary. Once the bicycle starts moving, however, it is much easier to keep your balance. Why?

4. A child is playing tether ball, as shown in the figure to the right. He hits the ball and watches it as the string winds around the pole. What will he observe about the speed of the ball as the string winds itself around the pole?

5. The net force acting on a system is zero. Does that mean the net torque is also zero?

Illus. from the MasterClips collection

6. A ball is placed at the top of a hemispherical bowl as shown in the diagram. It is then released and rolls without slipping. Ignore any energy losses due to friction.

a. If the bowl is 10.0 cm deep, what is the speed of the ball when it reaches the bottom of the bowl?

b. What is the speed of the ball when it is only halfway to the bottom?

7. A truck needs to lift a very heavy (2507 kg) construction vehicle out of a hole. A pulley is constructed of a wheel with a smaller, inner rim. The radius of the wheel is 2.00 meters while the inner rim has a radius of 0.750 m. With what force must the truck pull to raise the construction vehicle at a constant velocity?

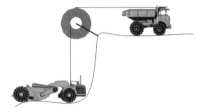

Illus. from the MasterClips collection

8. a. What is the angular velocity of the second hand on a clock?
   b. What is its angular acceleration?

9. The system shown to the right is made up of 6 bars. The four outside bars are all uniform rods of mass 45.0 kg and length 5.00 m. The two inner bars are uniform rods of mass 12.0 kg. They cross at a point that is in the middle of the square and 1.00 m from the top bar. What is the center of mass of the system? Give the position relative to the bottom, left-hand corner of the apparatus.

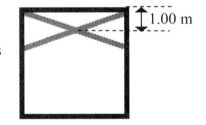

10. A disk (m = 1.00 kg, r = 3.00 cm) is spinning about its central axis at 3.00 revolutions per second. As it spins, a student pours glue on the disk which hardens instantly. It forms a thin shell on the outside of the disk.

Illus. from the MasterClips collection

a. What happens to the speed of the disk as the student pours the glue?

b. Suppose the student pours 250.0 g of glue. How many revolutions per second will the system make? Ignore losses due to friction.

11. Two masses (m_1 = 15.0 kg, m_2 = 10.0 kg) are on a frictionless, triangular ramp as shown to the right. The wheel is a disk (M = 2.00 kg, R = 10.0 cm).

a. What is the acceleration of the system?

b. What is the tension in the string that is attached to the heavier mass?

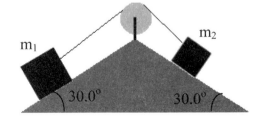

TEST FOR MODULE #6

1. Think about a mass/spring system in simple harmonic motion. When the acceleration is at its maximum, is the speed at its maximum or minimum value? Is the acceleration in the same direction or the opposite direction as the displacement?

2. A mass/spring system is undergoing simple harmonic motion with an amplitude of A. At what displacement (in terms of A) will the system's energy be evenly split between kinetic and potential energy?

3. A simple pendulum is undergoing simple harmonic motion with a maximum angle of θ, which corresponds to a height of h from its equilibrium position. At what height (in terms of h) will the system's energy be evenly split between kinetic and potential energy?

4. A mass/spring system is set in vertical simple harmonic motion near the surface of the earth. Its period is measured as T. The system is then taken to the moon, where the acceleration due to gravity is one-sixth of its value on earth. Once again, it is set in vertical simple harmonic motion, and its period is measured. What is the period of the system on the moon in terms of T?

5. The period of a simple pendulum is measured on earth as T. The simple pendulum is then taken to the moon, where the acceleration due to gravity is one-sixth of its value on earth. What is the period of the simple pendulum in terms of T?

6. A block (m = 5.00 kg) is attached to a spring (k = 315 N/m) and placed on a frictionless surface. The block is displaced 15.0 cm to the left of its equilibrium position and released at time = 0. Where is the block at t = 0.555 sec? Make sure you give your answer as a distance to the *left* or *right* of equilibrium.

7. A student sets up a simple pendulum that has a period of T. Another student wants to set up a physical pendulum made from a uniform rod pivoting about its end ($I = \frac{1}{3} \cdot M \cdot L^2$). How much longer must the student's physical pendulum be in order to have the same period as the other student's simple pendulum?

8. Two waves approach each other on water. The first wave has an amplitude of 13.0 cm. As it encounters the other wave, the maximum height of the water is reduced to 9.0 cm. Did the waves interfere constructively or destructively? What was the amplitude of the other wave?

9. A wave ($\lambda = 5.50$ cm) travels on a string ($\mu = 0.350$ kg/m). If the frequency of the wave is 60.0 Hz, what is the tension in the string?

10. A wave ($\lambda = 10.0$ m) travels on a rope at 5.00 m/sec. A person is looking at the rope at a particular position, and notes when the crest of the wave passes by. At that instant, the person starts a watch. At what time on the watch will the person see the *trough* of the wave?

11. What is the frequency of a wave that is given by the following equation?

$$y = (0.250 \text{ m}) \cdot \sin\left[\frac{2\pi}{(0.150 \text{ m})} \cdot ([35.0 \frac{\text{m}}{\text{sec}}] \cdot t + x)\right]$$

12. What is the difference between a longitudinal wave and a transverse wave?

13. A wave is generated on a string that is fixed on one end. A student observes how that wave reflects off of the fixed end of the string. Is the reflected wave identical to the original wave, or is it inverted?

14. A string supports a standing wave whose wavelength is 65.0 cm. The wave has 5 antinodes. What is the length of the string?

15. A 15.0 m rope ($\mu = 0.550$ kg/m) is stretched between two fixed points with a tension of 50.0 N. The rope supports a standing wave with a frequency of 1.27 Hz. How many nodes are on the wave?

TEST FOR MODULE #7

1. A sound wave with a frequency of 295 Hz travels through air at a temperature of 28.0 °C. What is the wavelength?

2. A person is listening to the sound wave in question #1, and suddenly, the loudness of the sound wave begins to increase and decrease at a steady frequency of 2 Hz. The person reasons that another sound wave with a similar frequency must be being produced somewhere near. What are the two possible frequencies of that other sound wave?

3. Suppose you are standing 20 cm away from a very loud (95 dB) gasoline powered mower. You decide to move so that you are now 200 meters from the mower. What is the loudness of the mower at your new location?

4. Air is vibrating at a frequency of 736 Hz in a tube that is closed on one end. If the tube is 35.0 cm long and contains air at 20.0 °C, at what harmonic is the air vibrating?

5. A person is listening to a siren on a police car that is traveling towards him at a speed of "v." He hears a the siren at a certain pitch. Now suppose that the police car is stationary and the man is driving towards the police car with a speed of "v." Would he hear exactly the same pitch as he did before? Why or why not?

6. Doppler weather radar is able to determine the speed of weather fronts. Given the fact that a weather front represents a change in density between one mass of air and another, explain how Doppler weather radar works.

7. A police has a siren that squeals at 500.0 Hz when the car and observer are both stationary. Suppose a stationary criminal hears the siren from the police car approaching him at a speed of 25.0 m/sec. At what frequency does the siren sound to the criminal? Assume that the speed of sound is 345 m/sec.

8. Suppose the criminal in problem #7 starts running away from the police car at 6 m/sec. At what frequency does he hear the siren? Assume the car is still approaching at 25.0 m/sec.

9. Light is incident on a pane of glass with an angle of 55° relative to the perpendicular. If the reflected beam of light is perpendicular to the refracted beam of light, what is the index of refraction of the glass?

10. Blue light has an index of refraction of 1.428 in a given type of glass. What is the speed of blue light in this glass? The speed of light in a vacuum is 2.998×10^8 m/sec.

11. Is the speed of orange light higher, lower, or the same as the speed of blue light in problem #10?

12. An object is placed 15.0 cm from a concave mirror whose radius of curvature is 20.0 cm. Draw a ray tracing diagram to illustrate the position and relative size of the image. Is the image real or virtual? Is it upright or inverted?

13. Use the mirror equation to determine numbers for both the position and the relative size of the image in problem #12.

14. An object is placed 20.0 cm from a converging lens whose focal length is 10.0 cm. Draw a ray tracing diagram to illustrate the position and relative size of the image. Is the image real or virtual? Is it upright or inverted?

15. Use the equation to determine numbers for both the position and the relative size of the image in problem #14.

16. The diagram below shows where the image appears for a nearby object in an eye that is farsighted. In order for the image to be seen clearly, it should be focused right on the retina. If you were to use glasses to correct this problem, would the glasses be made of converging or diverging lenses?

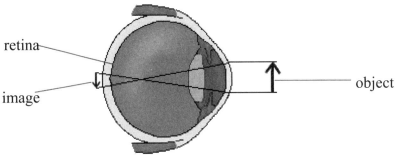

Illus. by Megan Whitaker

TEST FOR MODULE #8

$$(G = 6.67\text{x}10^{-11} \ \frac{N \cdot m^2}{kg^2} \ , \ c = 2.998\text{x}10^8 \ m/sec)$$

1. Two satellites orbit the earth. The orbit of the first is R, and its speed in that orbit is v. If the orbit of the second is 2·R, what is the speed of the second satellite in terms of v?

2. An object has a mass of m and a weight of w on earth. It is then taken to a planet whose mass is ½ that of earth and whose radius is also ½ that of earth. What is the mass and weight of the object on the surface of this planet, in terms of m and w?

3. An object of mass m exerts a gravitational force of size F on another object of mass 2m. What is the force that the object of mass 2m exerts on the object of mass m, in terms of F?

4. For the problem above, if the acceleration of the object of mass m is a, what is the acceleration of the object of mass 2m, in terms of a?

5. An object is dropped on the moon (m = 7.36x10²² kg, R = 1.74x10⁶ m) from an altitude of 1120 km above the moon's surface. Ignoring all resistive forces, at what speed will the object strike the surface of the moon?

6. An object is at several different locations inside of a sphere whose center is hollowed out. For the locations illustrated below, indicate which location is the one in which the object feels the greatest gravitational force from the sphere. Indicate all locations below in which the object feels the same gravitational force.

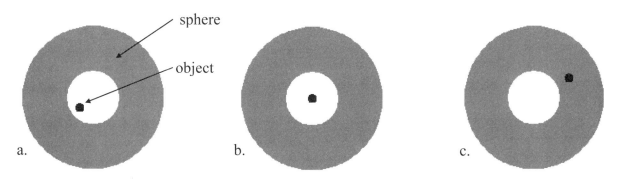

a.   b.   c.

7. Saturn is 9.53 times farther from the sun than is the earth. How many years does it take Saturn to make one trip around the sun?

8. A space ship lands on a planet. In order to escape the planet's gravitational field when it leaves, the space ship must reach a speed of 1.568x10⁴ m/sec. What is the ratio of the planet's mass to its radius?

9. Venus orbits the sun at a distance of 1.08x10¹¹ m. This is 0.722 times the distance from the sun to the earth. What is the mass of the sun?

10. The total energy of a satellite (m = 1456 kg) orbiting earth (m = 5.98×10^{24} kg) in a circular orbit is -1.23×10^{10} J. What is the radius of the satellite's orbit?

11. Two space ships approach each other head-on. Relative to the earth, each has a speed of 0.750c. The first ship fires its lasers (weapons using high-energy light) at the second ship.

a. At what speed do the defensive tracking systems of the second ship say that the laser light is approaching them?

b. At what speed do the offensive tracking systems of the first ship say that the laser light is traveling away from them?

12. A person on earth is watching the battle between the two space ships. He measures the time that it takes for the laser light from the first ship to travel to the second ship as 3.45×10^{-4} seconds.

a. How far did the laser light travel, according to the person on earth?

b. What travel time does the first space ship measure from the time it fires the lasers to the time the laser light hits the second ship?

c. How far did the laser light travel, according to the first space ship?

d. How far did the laser light travel, according to the second space ship?

TEST FOR MODULE #9

Avogadro's number = 6.02×10^{23}, k = 1.38×10^{-23} J/K

1. When you walk outside on a cold day with no coat on, you start to shiver. Most people say you are shivering due to the cold. However, it is really more physically accurate to say that you are shivering due to *heat*. Why?

2. The graph below plots the temperature of a substance versus the time it spends over a flame. The substance starts out as a solid. At what temperature does this substance boil?

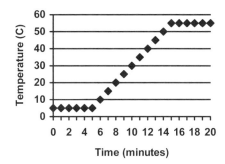

3. A 150.0 gram sample of metal is initially at 25.0 °C. How much energy must it release to reach 10.0 °C? [c = 0.236 J/(g °C)]

4. A 50.0 gram sample of liquid freezes. If it releases 7,850 J of energy when it freezes, what is the latent heat of fusion for the liquid?

5. An ice cube initially at -9.1 °C is dropped into 300.0 g of water that is at 95.0 °C. If the final temperature of the system is 2.1 °C, what is the mass of the ice cube? Assume that this system is perfectly insulated from the surroundings. (c_{ice} = 2.02 J/(g·°C), L_{fusion} = 334 J/g for water)

6. The coefficient of volume expansion for glass is 2.7×10^{-5} 1/°C. A thin tube of glass is 1.000 meters long at 25.0 °C. Approximately how long is it at 150.0 °C?

7. For the glass tube mentioned above, what is the ratio of its volume at the higher temperature to its volume at the lower temperature?

8. A hydraulic lift (illustrated to the right) uses the concept of pressure to make things easier to lift. In a hydraulic lift, you push down on one end, and the lift pushes up on the other end. The *pressure* with which you push down is equal to the *pressure* with which the hydraulic lift pushes up. However, the *area* of the side that you push down on (A_1) is significantly smaller than the *area* of the side that pushes up (A_2). Suppose A_2 = 100·A_1. If you push down with a force of 1 N, at what force will the hydraulic lift push up on the other side? Remember, the pressure is the same on both sides.

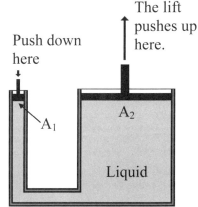

9. A sample of gas contains 1.8×10^{24} molecules. How many moles are in the sample?

10. The distribution of speeds in a sample of gas is given below:

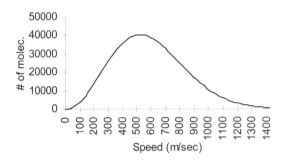

What is the approximate average speed of the molecules?

11. Suppose the average speed of molecules in a gas is 417 m/sec. If a mole of the gas has a mass of 32.0 grams, what is the temperature of the gas?

12. A 3.45-mole sample of gas occupies 0.234 m³ at 25.0 °C. What is the pressure of the gas?

13. A 2.50-mole sample of gas is held at constant pressure. If it absorbs 345.0 J of energy and its temperature increases by 5.7 °C, what is its molar heat capacity at constant pressure?

14. What is the molar heat capacity of the gas discussed above at constant volume?

15. What would be the change in temperature of the gas in problem #13 if it were held at constant volume rather than constant pressure?

TEST FOR MODULE #10

1. Two bricks are put into contact with one another. Before they contact one another, the first brick has a temperature of 50 °C and the second has a temperature of 30 °C.

    a. Which brick will have a positive q? Which will have a negative q?
    b. Which law of thermodynamics did you use to answer part (a)?
    c. Which brick will have a positive ΔS and which will have a negative ΔS?
    d. How can this process be consistent with the Second Law of Thermodynamics if one of the bricks has a negative ΔS?

2. A gas undergoes an isothermal expansion.

    a. Does the internal energy of the gas increase, decrease, or stay the same?
    b. Is q greater than, less than, or equal to zero in this process?

3. A gas undergoes an adiabatic compression.

    a. Does the internal energy of the gas increase, decrease, or stay the same?
    b. Does the temperature of the gas increase, decrease, or stay the same?
    c. Does the entropy of the gas increase, decrease, or stay the same?

4. A gas experiences an increase in entropy during an isothermal process.

    a. Is W positive, negative, or zero?
    b. Did the gas expand or contract?

5. A 5.0-mole sample of gas undergoes an isobaric expansion at 4.5×10^5 Pa. The volume increases from 0.0205 m^3 to 0.0359 m^3. (C_p = 20.8 J/[mole·K])

    a. What is W for this process?
    b. What is ΔU?

6. What is the maximum efficiency of a heat engine whose heat source has a temperature of 789 K and whose heat sink has a temperature of 298 K?

7. A gas is isothermally compressed at a temperature of 516 K. If 5,160 J of work must be done on the gas, what is the ΔS of the gas? What is the minimum ΔS of the surroundings?

8. In a Carnot engine, which of the four steps involves the gas absorbing energy and doing work?

9. In a Carnot engine, which of the four steps involves the gas increasing in temperature but not exchanging heat with the surroundings?

Questions 10 - 13 refer to a 5.0-mole sample of gas [$C_p = 20.8$ J/(mole·K), $C_v = 12.5$ J/(mole·K)] which undergoes the cyclic process illustrated below:

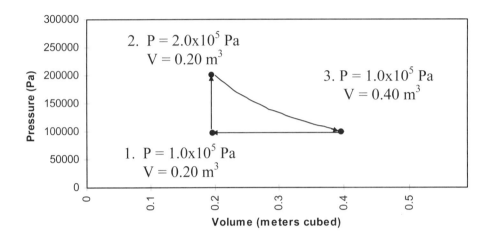

10. If the work done by the gas from step 2 to step 3 is equal to 27,000 J, what is the total work done through one cycle?

11. What is the total heat absorbed in one cycle?

12. What is the total heat absorbed during the process which leads from 2 to 3?

13. What is the name for the kind of expansion which occurs from 2 to 3?

TEST FOR MODULE #11

$$(k = 8.99 \times 10^9 \ \frac{N \cdot m^2}{C^2})$$

1. A negative charge is fixed so that it cannot move. Another negative charge is brought in close to the fixed charge and then released. Which of the curves (A-D) on the following graph best represents the acceleration of the freely-moving particle as a function of the distance from the fixed charge?

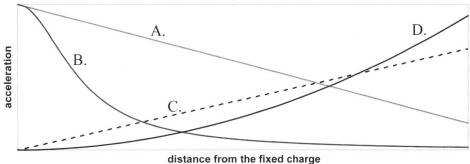

2. A dipole is formed from two 5.00 μC charges which are placed 75.0 cm away from each other. What is the electric field at the midpoint of the dipole?

3. Three particles, all charged to +5.00 μC, sit at the vertices of an equilateral triangle whose legs are 50.0 cm long.

a. Draw the resulting electric field.
b. Where is the electric field zero?
c. What is the magnitude and direction of the electric field at the midpoint of the left leg (the point on the figure to the right)?

4. A particle of charge -q is fixed so that it cannot move. The electric field generated by this charge is measured at a distance of 5.0 cm from the charge and called $\mathbf{E}_1$. The electric field is also measured at 9.0 cm from the charge and is called $\mathbf{E}_2$.

a. What is $\dfrac{E_1}{E_2}$?

b. If the particle were then given a charge of +3q rather than -q, what would be the electric field at a point 5.0 cm away from the charge? Give your answer in terms of $\mathbf{E}_1$.

5. Three charges are arranged as follows:

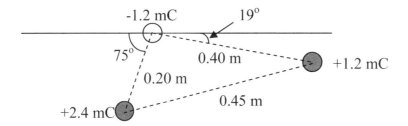

a. What is the electrostatic force on the -1.2 mC object?
b. What is the electric field to which the -1.2 mC charge is exposed?

6. Given the electric field diagram to the right:

a. What is the sign of the charge on particle 1?
b. What is the sign of the charge on particle 2?
c. If the magnitude of the charge on particle 1
is Q, what is the magnitude of the charge on
particle 2?

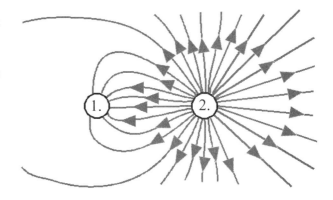

Questions 7-10 refer to the following situation:

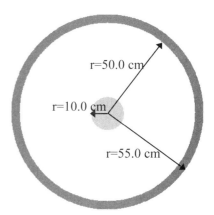

A plastic (insulating) ball (r = 10.0 cm) carries an excess
charge of -5.00 mC. It is distributed uniformly throughout the
entire ball. That ball is then placed at the center of a spherical
shell made of a conducting material such as copper (as shown
on the right). The inner radius of the shell is 50.0 cm , and the
outer radius is 55.0 cm. The shell has no net charge.

7. What is the charge on the inner surface of the conductive
spherical shell?

8. What is the charge on the outer surface of the conductive spherical shell?

9. What is the magnitude of the electric field at 20.0 cm from the center of the spherical shell?

10. What is the magnitude of the electric field at 53.0 cm from the center of the spherical shell?

11. What is the magnitude of the electric field at 60.0 cm from the center of the spherical shell?

TEST FOR MODULE #12

$$(k = 8.99 \times 10^{9} \; \frac{N \cdot m^{2}}{C^{2}}, \; \varepsilon_{o} = 8.85 \times 10^{-12} \; \frac{C^{2}}{N \cdot m^{2}})$$

1. A physicist is working with a parallel plate capacitor. As the physicist increases the potential difference between the plates, what happens to the capacitance?

2. The 45.6 µC charge in the drawing on the right starts at point A, which is 3.0 cm due north of a stationary, 12.2 mC charge. It then travels to point B, which is 5.0 cm due east of the same stationary charge. How much work is done by the electric field generated by the 12.2 mC stationary charge?

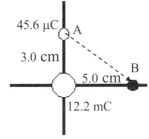

3. A particle is moving parallel to and in the same direction as an electric field. The work being done on the particle is positive. Is this particle positively charged or negatively charged?

4. A charged particle (q = -2.36 µC) is moved from the positive plate of a parallel-plate capacitor to the negative plate according to the diagram on the right. If the electric field between the plates is 78.2 N/C, how much work is done moving the particle in this way? The plates of the capacitor are 3.46 cm apart.

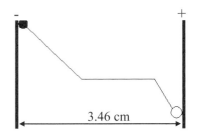

5. Four charged particles are in an electric field as shown to the right. The charges all have the same sign, but they do not necessarily have the same magnitude.

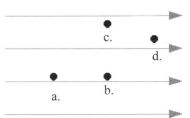

    a. Which particle has the highest potential?

    b. If particle (c) has twice the potential energy of particle
        (b), what is the ratio of the charge on particle (c) to the charge on particle (b)?

6. A charged particle (q = -6.34 mC, m = 1.45 kg) is shot straight down, towards the midpoint between two stationary charges ($q_1 = q_2 = $ -9.12 mC) which are placed 1.00 m apart. It starts out far from the midpoint and has an initial speed of 607 m/sec.

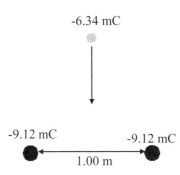

    a. As it travels towards the midpoint, is it moving towards a
       higher potential or a lower potential?

    b. What will be the vertical distance between the midpoint and
       the moving charge when the moving charge stops?

    c. What will its speed be when it gets back to the point at which it was originally shot?

7. A physicist makes a parallel plate capacitor and charges it up so that it holds a charge of Q at a potential difference between the plates of ΔV_1. The energy stored in the capacitor is measured as E_1. The physicist then puts a dielectric in between the plates of the capacitor. The dielectric constant is 2, which means that this dielectric doubles the capacitance. The physicist then charges the capacitor so that it holds the same amount of charge, Q.

    a. What is the new potential difference, in terms of ΔV_1?

    b. What is the new energy stored in the capacitor, in terms of E_1?

8. Suppose the physicist in problem #7 wanted to double the capacitance of the original capacitor but does not have a dielectric to put in between the plates.

    a. If he wanted to change the plate size to double the capacitance, how and by what factor would he have to change the length of each side of the plates?

    b. If he wanted to change the distance between the plates to double the capacitance, how and by what factor would he have to change the distance between the plates?

9. A parallel plate capacitor stores a charge of 45.6 μC and 1,090 J of energy. If the plates are squares with sides that are 34.1 mm long, what is the distance between the plates?

10. A parallel plate capacitor has a capacitance of 1.34×10^{-6} F. It holds 96.6 μC of charge. An electron ($q = -1.6 \times 10^{-19}$ C, m $= 9.31 \times 10^{-31}$ kg) starts from rest at the negative plate and moves under the influence of the electric field to the positive plate of the capacitor.

    a. What is the speed of the electron when it reaches the positive plate?

    b. If the distance between the plates is 3.5 mm, what is the strength of the electric field?

TEST FOR MODULE #13

1. A 15.0 Watt motor draws 1.43 A of current. What is the resistance of the motor?

Questions 2 - 5 refer to the following circuit diagram:

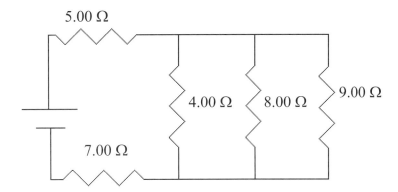

2. Suppose a resistor broke and could no longer conduct electricity. Which resistor(s) in the diagram above could break without halting current flow through the rest of the circuit?

3. All of the resistors are made of the same material and are the same length. If the cross-sectional area of the 5.00 Ω resistor is A, what is the cross-sectional area of the 9.00 Ω resistor in terms of A?

4. The circuit must draw a total of 1.00 A from the battery. What must the battery's voltage be?

5. Given the voltage you just determined, how much energy is dissipated by the entire circuit in 1.00 hour?

6. A battery has an emf of 9.00 V and an internal resistance of 2.0 Ω.

    a. What is the potential difference between the positive and negative sides of the battery when no current is flowing?

    b. What is the potential difference between the positive and negative sides of the battery when the battery is hooked to a circuit whose total resistance is 25.0 Ω?

7. In the circuit drawn to the right, the switch starts out open and then is closed.

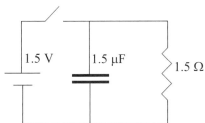

a. After a long time, what will be the potential difference across the plates of the capacitor?

b. If, after the switch has been closed for a long time, the switch is suddenly opened again, will current immediately stop flowing? Why or why not?

Questions 8 - 10 refer to the following circuit diagram:

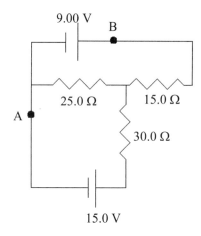

8. What is the current flowing through the 30.0 Ω resistor?

9. Draw the flow of current throughout the circuit, labeling both the direction and the value of the current.

10. What is the potential difference between points A and B?

11. In the diagram below, what is the total resistance between point A and point B?

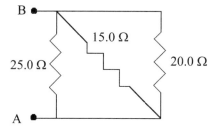

Questions 12 and 13 refer to the circuit diagram below:

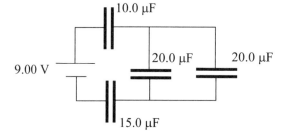

12. What is the equivalent capacitance of the circuit?

13. How much charge is stored on the 10.0 μF capacitor?

TEST FOR MODULE #14

$$(\mu_0 = 4\pi \times 10^{-7} \frac{T \cdot m}{A})$$

Questions 1-3 refer to the following situation:

A current-carrying wire is composed of two "legs" that rise up from the surface of a table. Those "legs" are connected by a 50.0 cm wire that is free to slide on the legs. A magnetic field exists between the legs (see figure below). Initially, there is no current running through the wire assembly. As the current is increased, the connecting wire rises up the legs.

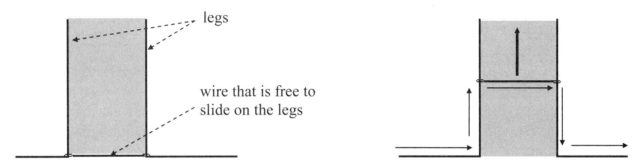

1. What is the direction of the magnetic field?

2. The physicist running this experiment notices that when the magnetic field is turned off (and the connecting wire does not move), he needs to apply a certain voltage, V, to get a certain current, I. When the magnetic field is turned on and the connecting wire rises, however, he must supply slightly more than V in order to get the same current, I. Why?

3. If the strength of the magnetic field is 0.367 T, what current would be required to suspend the connecting wire so that it floats in the position given on the right-hand side of the figure? The mass of the wire is 15.0 g.

4. A loop of wire has a current-carrying wire passing through its center, as shown to the right. If the loop has a radius of 25.0 cm, and the wire carries a constant current of 1.00 A, what is the emf generated in the loop?

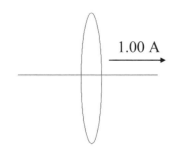

5. A charged particle (mass m, charge q) is given an initial speed of v and placed in a perpendicular magnetic field of strength B. Assuming that the magnetic field covers a large enough area, how long will it take for the particle to return to its starting point? Give your answer in terms of m, B, and q.

6. A square of wire (R = 0.00341 Ω) is placed in a perpendicular magnetic field as shown to the right. Each side of the square is 25.0 cm long, and the strength of the magnetic field is 0.654 T. The magnetic field strength is uniformly decreased to zero over a period of 1.00 sec.

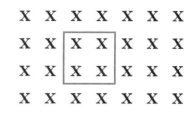

     a. What is the current produced over this time period?
     b. What is the direction of the current?

7. Two wires run parallel to one another but carry current in opposite directions, as shown in the diagram to the right.

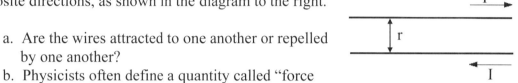

     a. Are the wires attracted to one another or repelled by one another?
     b. Physicists often define a quantity called "force per unit length," which is simply the force experienced by the wire divided by the length of the wire. In terms of I, μ_o, π, and r, what is the force per unit length experienced by each wire?

8. A conductive bar sits on a set of conductive rails as shown to the right. The magnetic field has a constant strength of 0.500 T. Ignore friction.

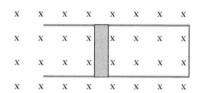

     a. There are no outside forces acting on the bar. Will the bar move in response to the constant magnetic field?
     b. If the bar is given an initial shove to the left but then not acted on by any other outside force, what will happen to the bar's motion over time?
     c. If the magnetic field strength is suddenly doubled, in which direction will current flow?
     d. In what direction will the bar move while the magnetic field is being changed?
     e. What will happen to the motion of the bar once the magnetic field is held constant again?

9. A charged particle is traveling to the right and encounters a parallel plate capacitor that has a perpendicular magnetic field in between the plates, as shown to the right. Is it possible to adjust the electric field and the magnetic field so as to keep the particle traveling in a straight line but keep each field nonzero? If so, what must the charge of the particle be?

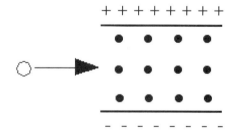

TEST FOR MODULE #15

$h = 6.63 \times 10^{-34}$ J·s $= 4.14 \times 10^{-15}$ eV·s   1 nm $= 10^{-9}$ m
$R_h = -2.18 \times 10^{-18}$ J $= 13.6$ eV   atomic number of hydrogen $= 1$
1 eV $= 1.602 \times 10^{-19}$ J   atomic number of He $= 2$
$c = 2.998 \times 10^{8}$ m/sec   atomic number of Li $= 3$

(You may use the Periodic Table of Elements for this test.)

1. A single electron in an atom is orbiting the nucleus with an energy of -35 eV. The next orbit it could jump to has an energy of -25 eV, and the next one has an energy of -10 eV. If a beam of photons whose energy is 15 eV strikes the atom, what will happen?

2. Copper's work function is 4.70 eV. If you wanted to shine light on copper so that it would emit electrons, what is the minimum frequency of light that you could use?

3. Which of the following equations did Bohr use to assert his quantum assumption?

$$\text{a.} \quad \frac{m_e \cdot v^2}{r} = \frac{k \cdot e \cdot Z \cdot e}{r^2} \qquad\qquad \text{b.} \quad m_e \cdot v \cdot r = n \cdot \hbar$$

4. Suppose an electron in the Bohr atom absorbs energy and jumps to the $n = 4$ orbit. How many different possible wavelengths of light might the electron emit in getting back to the $n = 1$ orbit?

5. A scientist is determining the makeup of a molecule by shining light on a sample and looking at what wavelengths do not pass through it. Is this atomic emission or atomic absorption spectroscopy?

6. A hydrogen atom is compared to a Li^{2+} ion. If the distance from the center of the nucleus to the electron in a Li^{2+} ion is "a," what is the corresponding distance in the hydrogen atom?

7. An electron in a hydrogen atom starts out in the second Bohr orbit and jumps to the fourth Bohr orbit. How much energy must it absorb?

8. An electron jumps from the $n = 4$ orbit of a He^+ ion to the $n = 2$ orbit. What is the wavelength of the light emitted?

9. An electron jumps from the fourth Bohr orbit to a lower orbit in a hydrogen atom. If the light emitted has a energy of 4.09×10^{-19} J, what orbit did the electron end up in?

10. An electron in a Li^{2+} has an energy of -30.6 eV. How far from the nucleus is it orbiting?

11. Consider three orbits for an electron. They have the following energies:

$$-34.5 \text{ eV} \qquad -22.6 \text{ eV} \qquad -10.1 \text{ eV}$$

    a. Which is the ground state of the electron?
    b. If the electron were in the ground state, how much energy would it have to absorb to be free of the atom?
    c. Suppose it went from the lowest-energy orbit listed here to the highest-energy orbit listed here. What energy would it have to absorb?

12. What is the speed of an electron ($m = 9.11 \times 10^{-31}$ kg) whose de Broglie wavelength is 812 nm?

13. The maximum kinetic energy of electrons coming from a sheet of illuminated silver is 3.22 eV. If the light used to illuminate the silver has a frequency of 1.92×10^{15} Hz, what is the work function of the silver?

TEST FOR MODULE #16
(You may use the Periodic Table of Elements and Figure 16.2 for this test.)

(The mass of a proton is 1.0073 amu, and the mass of a neutron is 1.0087 amu. The speed of light is 2.998 x 10^8 m/sec, and 1 amu=1.6605 x 10^{-27} kg.)

1. Which nucleus has more binding energy per nucleon than any other nucleus in Creation?

2. What are pions, and why are they important in nuclear chemistry?

3. A chemist studies two nuclei. The second has 40% more binding energy than the first, and it also has twice as many nucleons as the first. Which atom is more stable?

4. An electron collides with another particle and disappears. The only thing left in its place is a gamma ray. With what did the electron collide?

5. Which of the following are stable nuclei?

$$^{12}C, \ ^{145}Nd, \ ^{75}Mg, \ ^{65}Zn, \ ^{80}Zr, \ ^{170}Pt$$

6. A scientist claims that he has designed a nuclear power plant that runs on the fission of ^{40}Ar. Why is this not possible?

7. The mass of ^{12}C is 11.9967 amu. What is its binding energy per nucleon?

8. The binding energy of ^6Li is 5.16 x 10^{-12} J. What is its mass in amu?

9. ^{248}Np decays by beta emission. Write an equation for this process.

10. Write an equation for the alpha decay of ^{218}Po.

11. ^{32}P is a radioactive isotope with a half-life of 14.3 days. If a chemist makes 44.0 grams of ^{32}P, how much will be left in 28.6 days?

12. The radioactive isotope ^{85}Kr has a half-life of 10.76 years. If a nuclear power plant leaks 15.0 grams of ^{85}Kr into the atmosphere, how much of it will be left in 20.0 years?

Solutions To The

Tests

SOLUTIONS TO THE TEST FOR MODULE #1

1. Using the formula is easy:

$$V = \frac{4}{3} \cdot \pi \cdot r^3 = \frac{4}{3} \cdot (3.1416) \cdot (3.2 \text{ m})^3 = 140 \text{ m}^3$$

The mean guy who wrote this problem, however, wants the answer in cm^3. To convert from cm^3 to m^3, we must cube the relationship between m and cm:

$$1 \text{ cm} = 0.01 \text{ m}$$

$$1 \text{ cm}^3 = 0.000001 \text{ m}^3$$

Now we can convert:

$$\frac{140 \text{ m}^3}{1} \times \frac{1 \text{ cm}^3}{0.000001 \text{ m}^3} = \underline{1.4 \times 10^8 \text{ cm}^3}$$

2. Remember, the dot product takes the magnitude of the first vector (B) and multiplies it by the magnitude of the component of the second vector which is parallel to the first vector. In the diagram, r is the length of the component of **A** that is parallel to **B**. Thus, the dot product is simply $\underline{B \cdot r}$.

3. The cross product is like the dot product, but it uses the component that is *perpendicular* to the first vector. That's h in the figure. Thus, the magnitude of the cross product is $\underline{B \cdot h}$.

4. To determine direction, we use the right hand rule. If you point the fingers of your right hand in the direction of **B** and then curl your fingers along the arc of the angle between the vectors, your thumb points up out of the page. Thus, <u>it is pointing above the plane of the paper</u>.

5. $\mathbf{A} + \mathbf{B} = (A_x + B_x) \cdot \mathbf{i} + (A_y + B_y) \cdot \mathbf{j} = (6.1 + 4.6) \cdot \mathbf{i} + (2.8 + 5.5) \cdot \mathbf{j}$

$$\underline{\mathbf{A} + \mathbf{B} = 10.7 \cdot \mathbf{i} + 8.3 \cdot \mathbf{j}}$$

Notice that the x-component has 3 significant figures. That's because we are adding, and in adding, you do not count significant figures. You go by precision. Both numbers go out to the tenths place, so the answer is reported to the tenths place.

6. $\mathbf{A} - \mathbf{B} = (A_x - B_x) \cdot \mathbf{i} + (A_y - B_y) \cdot \mathbf{j} = (6.1 - 4.6) \cdot \mathbf{i} + (2.8 - 5.5) \cdot \mathbf{j}$

$$\underline{\mathbf{A} - \mathbf{B} = 1.5 \cdot \mathbf{i} - 2.7 \cdot \mathbf{j}}$$

Those are the components. Now we have to find magnitude and direction:

$$\text{magnitude} = \sqrt{(1.5)^2 + (2.7)^2} = 3.1$$

$$\theta = \tan^{-1}\left(\frac{-2.7}{1.5}\right) = -61°$$

Since the vector has a positive x-component and a negative y-component, it is in quadrant IV, which means we add 360.0° to get the angle properly defined. Thus, the vector is <u>3.1 at 299°</u>.

7. Using Equation (1.5):

$$\mathbf{A} \bullet \mathbf{B} = A_x \cdot B_x + A_y \cdot B_y$$

$$\mathbf{A} \bullet \mathbf{B} = (6.1) \cdot (4.6) + (2.8) \cdot (5.5) = \underline{43}$$

8. The vectors are two-dimensional and have only **i** and **j** unit vectors. Thus, we can use the simpler version of the cross product formula, Equation (1.10):

$$\mathbf{A} \times \mathbf{B} = (A_x \cdot B_y - A_y \cdot B_x) \cdot \mathbf{k}$$

$$\mathbf{A} \times \mathbf{B} = (6.1 \cdot 5.5 - 2.8 \cdot 4.6) \cdot \mathbf{k} = \underline{21 \cdot \mathbf{k}}$$

9. We know the relationship between kg and g. However, to get the relationship between cm^2 and m^2, we will have to square the relationship between cm and m.

$$1 \text{ cm} = 0.01 \text{ m}$$

$$1 \text{ cm}^2 = 0.0001 \text{ m}^2$$

In the same way, we need to cube the relationship between seconds and minutes to get the relationship between sec^3 and $minute^3$.

$$1 \text{ minute} = 60 \text{ sec}$$

$$1 \text{ minute}^3 = 216,000 \text{ sec}^3$$

Now we can convert:

$$\frac{1.00 \text{ kg} \cdot m^2}{sec^3} \times \frac{1,000 \text{ g}}{1 \text{ kg}} \times \frac{1 \text{ cm}^2}{0.0001 \text{ m}^2} \times \frac{216,000 \text{ sec}^3}{1 \text{ minute}^3} = \underline{2.16 \times 10^{12} \frac{g \cdot cm^2}{minute^3}}$$

10. Work is **F•x**. We can use Equation (1.6) for the dot product:

$$W = F \cdot x \cdot \cos\theta$$

$$711 \ J = (56 \ N) \cdot (15.1 \ m) \cdot \cos\theta$$

$$\theta = \cos^{-1}\left(\frac{711 \ \cancel{N} \cdot \cancel{m}}{(56 \ \cancel{N}) \cdot (15.1 \ \cancel{m})}\right) = \underline{33^{\circ}}$$

11. Since the work depends on the cosine of θ, and since the maximum value for the cosine occurs at 0 degrees, the angle between the force and the displacement of the box should be 0 degrees.

12. This problem uses Equation (1.9):

$$|\mathbf{r}\mathbf{x}\mathbf{F}| = r \cdot F \cdot \sin\theta$$

$$1.3 \ N \cdot m = (0.035 \ m) \cdot (F) \cdot \sin(42)$$

$$F = \frac{1.3 \ N \cdot \cancel{m}}{(0.035 \ \cancel{m}) \cdot [\sin(42)]} = \underline{56 \ N}$$

13. The torque depends on the magnitude of the force, the magnitude of the lever arm, and the angle. Since the problem says he can't change the force, there are two things he could do:

a. Increase the magnitude of the lever arm. He could do that by getting a larger wrench or, if he is not applying the force at the end of the wrench, move his hand to the end of the wrench.

b. Increase the angle between the wrench and the force. The closer the angle gets to 90 degrees, the better, because that's where the sine is at its maximum.

14. Work is a scalar. It has no direction.

15. Torque is a vector. That's why we have to write it in vector notation or use the right hand rule to determine direction.

SOLUTIONS TO THE TEST FOR MODULE #2

1. If the object is moving from A to B, its velocity points to the right. If it is slowing down, the acceleration points in the opposite direction.

2. The race will NOT end in a tie. John was able to run 100 meters in the same time it took Joe to run 95 meters. Thus, when Joe reaches 95 meters in the second race, John will be caught up to him, because he can run 100 meters in that same time frame. The race will be tied when there are still 5 meters to go. Since everything is the same, John runs faster than Joe, so he will still win, because he will cover those last 5 meters faster than Joe.

3. The student is wrong. Had the object been slowing down at a constant acceleration, it could have come to rest while he was looking away. If so, the constant acceleration would then start causing it to move in the opposite direction.

4. Yes, the acceleration can be decreasing as the velocity increases. Acceleration is the *change in velocity*. If acceleration is 10 m/sec^2 and then slows to 5 m/sec^2, the velocity will *still increase* (assuming acceleration and velocity are pointing in the same direction), it just won't increase *as much* as it could have if the acceleration had stayed at 10 m/sec^2.

5. The second trip had warmer, less dense air. That means the air resistance was lower on the second trip. Thus, the plane burned more fuel on the first trip.

6.   a. We know that it comes to rest when the velocity is 0.

$$\mathbf{v}^2 = \mathbf{v}_o{}^2 + 2\mathbf{a}\mathbf{x}$$

$$0^2 = (2.5\ \frac{\text{m}}{\text{sec}})^2 + 2 \cdot (\mathbf{a}) \cdot (50.0\ \text{m})$$

$$a = -0.063\frac{\text{m}}{\text{sec}^2}$$

The negative sign tells us that the acceleration is 0.063 m/sec^2 to the east.

b. Now that we know the acceleration, Equation (2.3) is the easiest one to use:

$$\mathbf{v} = \mathbf{v}_o + \mathbf{a}t$$

$$0 = 2.5 \frac{m}{sec} + (-0.063 \frac{m}{sec^2}) \cdot t$$

$$\underline{t = 4.0 \times 10^1 \text{ sec}}$$

c. Even though 25.0 m is halfway in distance, it will not be halfway in time. Thus, we really need to use Equation (2.4) here.

$$v^2 = v_o^2 + 2ax$$

$$v^2 = (2.5 \frac{m}{sec})^2 + 2 \cdot (-0.063 \frac{m}{sec^2}) \cdot (25.0 \text{ m})$$

$$v^2 = 3.1 \frac{m^2}{sec^2}$$

$$v = \pm 1.8 \frac{m}{sec}$$

Since we know that the rock is moving to the west, the positive answer is the right one. The rock is moving at 1.8 m/sec to the west.

7. a. The total displacement of the rock is -50.0 ft (it lands 50.0 ft below where it was thrown). To solve for time, we use Equation (2.5):

$$x = v_o t + \frac{1}{2} \cdot a \cdot t^2$$

$$-50.0 \text{ ft} = (10.0 \frac{ft}{sec}) \cdot t + \frac{1}{2} \cdot (-32.2 \frac{ft}{sec^2}) \cdot t^2$$

$$(16.1 \frac{ft}{sec^2}) \cdot t^2 - (10.0 \frac{ft}{sec}) \cdot t - 50.0 \text{ ft} = 0$$

This is a quadratic equation. We can solve it with the quadratic formula.

$$t = \frac{10.0 \frac{ft}{sec} \pm \sqrt{(10.0 \frac{ft}{sec})^2 - 4 \cdot (16.1 \frac{ft}{sec^2}) \cdot (-50.0 \text{ ft})}}{2 \cdot (16.1 \frac{ft}{sec^2})} = \frac{10.0 \frac{ft}{sec} \pm 57.6 \frac{ft}{sec}}{32.2 \frac{ft}{sec^2}} = 2.10 \text{ sec}$$

There are actually two answers, but the second one is negative, which makes no sense for time. Thus, the time is <u>2.10 sec</u>.

b. The maximum height occurs when v = 0.

$$v^2 = v_o^2 + 2ax$$

$$0 = (10.0 \frac{ft}{sec})^2 + 2 \cdot (-32.2 \frac{ft}{sec^2}) \cdot (x)$$

$$x = \frac{(10.0 \frac{ft}{sec})^2}{2 \cdot (32.2 \frac{ft}{sec^2})} = 1.55 \ ft$$

That, however, is the maximum height *from which it was thrown*. The ground is another 50.0 ft below that, so the maximum height relative to the ground is <u>51.6 ft</u>.

8. In this problem, you have to be comfortable working with variables. Let's call the maximum height h_m. We know that at $\frac{1}{2} \cdot h_m$, v = 15.1 m/sec. We also know that at h_m, v = 0. We can use these two facts to determine h_m.

a. Let's start with the situation at h_m and solve for v_o in terms of h_m.

$$\mathbf{v}^2 = \mathbf{v}_o^2 + 2\mathbf{ax}$$

$$0 = \mathbf{v}_o^2 + 2 \cdot (-9.81 \frac{m}{sec^2}) \cdot h_m$$

$$\mathbf{v}_o = \sqrt{(19.6 \frac{m}{sec^2}) \cdot h_m}$$

In reality, there are two answers here: a positive one and a negative one. However, we know that the initial velocity is positive, because it is being thrown upwards. Thus, I will ignore the negative answer. Now I can use *this* expression for v_o in the situation at $\frac{1}{2} \cdot h_m$:

$$\mathbf{v}^2 = \mathbf{v}_o^2 + 2\mathbf{ax}$$

$$(15.1 \frac{m}{sec})^2 = \left(\sqrt{(19.6 \frac{m}{sec^2}) \cdot h_m} \right)^2 + 2 \cdot (-9.81 \frac{m}{sec^2}) \cdot \frac{1}{2} \cdot h_m$$

$$(15.1 \frac{m}{sec})^2 = (19.6 \frac{m}{sec^2}) \cdot h_m - 9.81 \frac{m}{sec^2} \cdot h_m$$

$$h_m = 23 \ m$$

The maximum height, then, is <u>23 meters</u>.

b. The acceleration during the *entire* trip is a constant <u>9.81 m/sec^2 downwards</u>.

c. To determine this, we need to know a number for the initial velocity. That's easy, though, because in (a) we determined an equation that related h_m and v_o.

$$v_o = \sqrt{(19.6 \frac{m}{sec^2}) \cdot h_m} = \sqrt{(19.6 \frac{m}{sec^2}) \cdot (23 \ m)} = 21 \frac{m}{sec}$$

Now that we know the initial velocity, the velocity at 4.0 seconds is a snap:

$$v = v_o + at$$

$$v = 21 \frac{m}{sec} + (-9.81 \frac{m}{sec^2}) \cdot (4.0 \ \text{sec}) = -18 \frac{m}{sec}$$

The negative means the velocity is <u>-18 m/sec downwards</u>.

9. In the drawing, (a) should have no vertical component, because at the highest point, the vertical component of the velocity is zero. The vertical component at point (b) should be the same size as the original vertical component but pointing down. The vertical component at point (c) should be pointing down and significantly longer than the original. At all points, the horizontal component should be identical to the original.

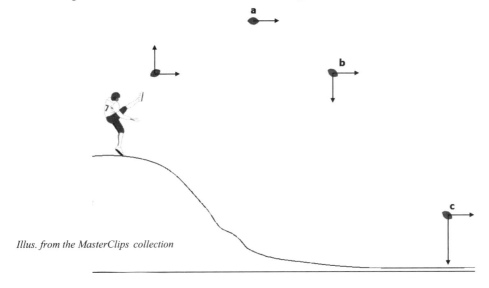

Illus. from the MasterClips collection

d. Air resistance depends on many factors that are based on the shape and size of the projectile. In this case, however, those are the same at all four points because the object is the same. In addition, it depends on the density of air, but that is essentially the same everywhere. The only thing that changes to any great degree is velocity. Of the points drawn on the figure, the largest velocity is a point (c), so <u>the greatest air resistance is at point (c)</u>. The lowest velocity occurs where there is no vertical component at all, so <u>at point (a) the ball experiences the least air resistance</u>.

10. To determine the height, we need to know how long the ball was in the air. That can be solved in the horizontal dimension, where the initial velocity is (35.0 m/sec)·cos(35.0) = 28.7 m/sec.

$$\mathbf{x} = \mathbf{v}_o t + \frac{1}{2} \cdot \mathbf{a} t^2$$

$$175.0 \text{ m} = (28.7 \, \frac{m}{sec}) \cdot t + \frac{1}{2} \cdot (0) \cdot t^2$$

$$t = 6.10 \text{ sec}$$

Now we can determine the height by going to the vertical dimension, where the initial velocity is (35.0 m/sec)·sin(35.0) = 20.1 m/sec:

$$x = v_o t + \frac{1}{2} \cdot a t^2$$

$$x = (20.1 \, \frac{m}{sec}) \cdot (6.10 \, \cancel{sec}) + \frac{1}{2} \cdot (-9.81 \, \frac{m}{sec^2}) \cdot (6.10 \, \cancel{sec})^2$$

$$x = 123 \text{ m} - 183 \text{ m} = -6.0 \times 10^1 \text{ m}$$

Notice how the significant figures worked out. Since we are subtracting, we can only report our answer to the ones place, and that turns out to be a zero. Thus, the answer must be reported in scientific notation to keep the zero significant. This means that the ball landed 6.0×10^1 m below where it started. Thus, <u>the ball was kicked 6.0×10^1 m above where it landed</u>.

11. The maximum range is a way of giving the initial velocity. We can use the range equation with θ = 45.0 degrees to determine that.

$$R = \frac{(v_o^2) \cdot \sin(2\theta)}{g}$$

$$295,000 \text{ m} = \frac{(v_o^2) \cdot \sin(90.0)}{(9.81 \frac{m}{\sec^2})}$$

$$v_o = \sqrt{(295,000 \text{ m}) \cdot (9.81 \frac{m}{\sec^2})} = 1.70 \times 10^3 \frac{m}{\sec}$$

Now that we know the initial velocity, we can use the range equation to determine the distance.

$$R = \frac{(v_o^2) \cdot \sin(2\theta)}{g}$$

$$R = \frac{(1.70 \times 10^3 \frac{m}{\sec})^2 \cdot \sin(2 \cdot 55.0)}{(9.81 \frac{m}{\sec^2})} = \underline{277,000 \text{ m}}$$

Please note that you did not need to use the range equation. You could have split the problem up into two dimensions and done it the long way. All you needed to realize is that the maximum range occurs when $\theta = 45.0$ degrees.

12. a. <u>Gravity will pull the bullet down.</u> Thus, if the gun is fired horizontally, the bullet will hit the target *below* center.

b. <u>The marksman will not hit the target dead center; instead, it will be *above* center.</u> If the sight gave the marksman the proper angle of elevation to hit the target 100.0 m away, then that same angle will be *too high* for the target if it is only 50.0 m away. Think about the trajectory. If the marksman hit the target dead center at 100.0 m away, consider where the bullet was when it was 50.0 m away from the rifle. In order to hit the target 100.0 m away, it would need to be *higher* than the center of the target when it was only 50.0 m away from the rifle. Thus, if the target were there, it would hit high of the mark.

c. When the horizontal distance is 100.0 m, the vertical displacement must be zero. Let's look at the horizontal dimension first, where we know the displacement must be 100.0 m. The initial velocity in the horizontal dimension is $(75.0 \text{ m/sec}) \cdot \cos\theta$.

$$100.0 \text{ m} = (75.0 \frac{m}{\sec}) \cdot \cos\theta \cdot t + \frac{1}{2} \cdot (0) \cdot t^2$$

$$t = \frac{1.33 \text{ sec}}{\cos\theta}$$

When the bullet has traveled for that amount of time, it is 100.0 m from the rifle. At that same time, it must have a vertical displacement of 0. Thus:

$$0 = (75.0 \frac{m}{sec}) \cdot \sin\theta \cdot (\frac{1.33 \ sec}{\cos\theta}) + \frac{1}{2} \cdot (-9.81 \frac{m}{sec^2}) \cdot (\frac{1.33 \ sec}{\cos\theta})^2$$

$$0 = (99.8 \ m) \cdot (\frac{\sin\theta}{\cos\theta}) - (8.68 \ m) \cdot (\frac{1}{\cos^2\theta})$$

Now we can use the three identities discussed in the text:

$$0 = (99.8 \ m) \cdot \tan\theta - (8.68 \ m) \cdot (1 + \tan^2\theta)$$

$$0 = (99.8 \ m) \cdot \tan\theta - 8.68 \ m - (8.68 \ m) \cdot \tan^2\theta$$

$$(8.68 \ m) \cdot \tan^2\theta - (99.8 \ m) \cdot \tan\theta + 8.68 \ m = 0$$

Now we can use the quadratic formula to solve for $\tan\theta$:

$$\tan\theta = \frac{99.8 \ m \pm \sqrt{(99.8 \ m)^2 - 4 \cdot (8.68 \ m) \cdot (8.68 \ m)}}{2 \cdot (8.68 \ m)} = \frac{99.8 \ m \pm 98.3 \ m}{17.4 \ m}$$

This gives us two possible answers.

$$\tan\theta = \frac{198.1}{17.4} \quad \tan\theta = \frac{1.5}{17.4}$$
$$\text{or}$$
$$\theta = 85.0° \quad \theta = 4.9°$$

Either one of those angles will work, however, the sight will use the smaller one. Thus, the proper answer is 4.9 degrees. You could use the other one, however.

SOLUTIONS TO THE TEST FOR MODULE #3

1. a. When the scale reads a weight of more than 50 pounds, <u>the elevator is accelerating upwards</u>. It is not enough to say *moving* upwards. If the word accelerating is not there, count ½ off. After all, if it is moving upwards at a constant velocity, the scale will read 50 pounds. Also, if the elevator is moving downwards but *slowing down*, the acceleration is upwards and the scale will read more than 50 pounds.

b. When the scale reads a weight of less than 50 pounds, <u>the elevator is accelerating downwards</u>. The same note applies here. Acceleration must be in the answer to receive full credit.

c. You only need to list one, but there are three possibilities. <u>First, this is insensitive to motion at constant velocity. Second, if the elevator is moving upwards but *slowing down*, the scale will read less than 50 pounds, making the elevator operator think that the elevator is moving downwards. Third, if the elevator is moving downwards but *slowing down*, the scale will read more than 50 pounds, making the elevator operator think that the elevator is moving upwards.</u>

d. <u>It will read 50 pounds</u>. If the elevator is an inertial reference frame, it is moving with constant velocity relative to the earth. That means acceleration is zero.

2. <u>A balance will not work. The acceleration of the elevator will affect each side of the balance in exactly the same way, and the balance will stay balanced regardless of the acceleration of the elevator.</u>

3. a. <u>The astronaut will begin to float towards the back of the ship</u>. You could also just say it is in the opposite direction as compared to that in which the wrench is thrown.

b. <u>The wrench exerted the force</u>. Newton's Third Law says that for every force, there is an equal but opposite reaction force. The astronaut exerted a force on the wrench to throw it, and the wrench exerted a force back on the astronaut.

c. <u>This is not an inertial reference frame</u>. If a planet is near, then there is gravity present. However, the astronaut is floating in the ship. Thus, the ship must be in free fall (probably because it is in orbit). Thus, it is accelerating and is not an inertial reference frame.

4. <u>The bat is exerting a force on the baseball. The equal and opposite force is exerted by the ball on the bat. The bat also exerts a force on the player, which is done in response to the force that the player exerts on the bat in order to swing it.</u> (This problem is worth 4 points: one for each force.)

5. a. When the elevator is at rest, the blocks just hang, so the acceleration is zero. Thus, the forces must sum to zero. The second block has two forces acting on it: The tension in the second string and the weight of the block.

$$T_2 - m_2 \cdot g = 0$$

$$T_2 \;=\; m_2{\cdot}g$$

$$T_2 \;=\; \underline{294\ N}$$

There are three forces which act on m_1: The tension in the first string pulls it up, and the tension in the second string pulls it down. In addition, its weight pulls it down:

$$T_1 \;\text{-}\; T_2 \;\text{-}\; m_1{\cdot}g \;=\; 0$$

$$T_1 \;=\; T_2 \;+\; m_1{\cdot}g$$

$$\underline{T_1 \;=\; 392\ N}$$

b. When the elevator is accelerating, the forces sum to the mass of the block times the acceleration. Thus, from m_2:

$$T_2 \;-\; m_2 \cdot g \;=\; m_2 \cdot a$$

$$T_2 = (30.0\,\mathrm{kg}) \cdot (-2.0\ \frac{m}{\sec^2}) + (30.0\,\mathrm{kg}) \cdot (9.81\ \frac{m}{\sec^2}) = \underline{234\ N}$$

Notice that the acceleration is negative. That's because the acceleration is downwards. Now don't get confused here. When you see "g," it is always positive. That's the *magnitude* of the acceleration due to gravity. The direction of that acceleration is taken care of by the direction definition. We subtracted $m_2{\cdot}g$ because gravitational acceleration is downwards.

From m_1:

$$T_1 \;-\; T_2 \;-\; m_1 \cdot g \;=\; m_1 \cdot a$$

$$T_1 = 234\ N + (10.0\,\mathrm{kg}) \cdot (-2.0\ \frac{m}{\sec^2}) + (10.0\,\mathrm{kg}) \cdot (9.81\ \frac{m}{\sec^2}) = \underline{312\ N}$$

6. Since we are ignoring friction, we do not need to worry about calculating the normal force. Thus, to determine the acceleration, we just have to concentrate on the horizontal dimension. On the first 35.0 kg block, there are two forces acting in the horizontal dimension. The 75.0 N force pushing it to the left, and the reaction force caused by the fact that the 35.0 kg block pushes against the 15.0 kg block. We will call that push "P_1." These forces sum up to give the mass times the acceleration .

$$75.0\ N \;\text{-}\; P_1 \;=\; (35.0\,\mathrm{kg}){\cdot}a$$

$$P_1 = 75.0 \text{ N} - (35.0 \text{ kg}) \cdot a$$

For the 15.0 kg mass, there are two forces acting in the horizontal dimension. The 35.0 kg mass to the left pushes to the right with a force we already called "P_1." The 15.0 kg block pushes on the 35.0 kg block to the right, which causes a reaction force pushing the 15.0 kg block to the left. We will call that force "P_2."

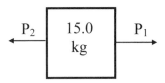

$$P_1 - P_2 = (15.0 \text{ kg}) \cdot a$$

$$P_2 = -(15.0 \text{ kg}) \cdot a + 75.0 \text{ N} - (35.0 \text{ kg}) \cdot a$$

Finally, the other 35.0 kg block also has two forces acting on it: the P_2 force from the 15.0 kg block that pushes it, and the 50.0 N force.

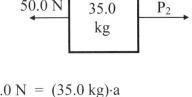

$$P_2 - 50.0 \text{ N} = (35.0 \text{ kg}) \cdot a$$

$$-(15.0 \text{ kg}) \cdot a + 75.0 \text{ N} - (35.0 \text{ kg}) \cdot a - 50.0 \text{ N} = (35.0 \text{ kg}) \cdot a$$

$$\underline{a = 0.294 \text{ m/sec}^2}$$

We could have gotten that answer by just adding the masses and treating them as one mass. However, we would not have been able to answer the second part of the question, and that is to list the magnitude and directions of all the forces on the 15.0 kg block. The question asks for *all* of the forces, so we need to include the vertical ones as well, even though they did not come into play in the solution to the problem. Since there is no motion in the vertical dimension, the normal force equals the weight.

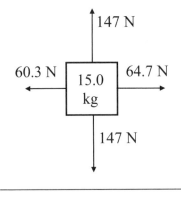

7. a. To get the system moving, the sum of the forces must be just barely greater than zero. Thus, let's set them equal to zero to get the lower limit of the mass.

Let's analyze the easiest mass first: m. There are only two forces acting on it, and they sum to give the mass times the acceleration.

$$T_1 - m \cdot g = 0$$

$$T_1 = m \cdot g$$

This gives us an equation for the tension in the *first* string. However, there are two strings, so that complicates matters. Now let's look at the 25.0 g mass:

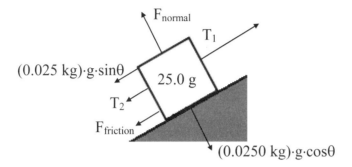

The tension in the second string, the component of the gravitational force parallel to the incline, and friction all pull downward on the mass. Only the tension of the first string pulls upward on the mass. Since we are dealing with friction, we have to determine the normal force. That's easy, however. The sum of the forces perpendicular to the incline tells us that $F_{normal} = (0.0250 \text{ kg}) \cdot g \cdot \cos\theta$. Since we know g and θ we can evaluate this. The normal force is 0.188 N. This means the static frictional force is 0.0939 N.

Now we can sum up the forces parallel to the incline that work on this block:

$$T_2 + F_{friction} + (0.0250 \text{ kg}) \cdot g \cdot \sin\theta - T_1 = 0$$

Plugging in what we know ($F_{friction}$, g, θ, and the equation for T_1):

$$T_2 + 0.0939 \text{ N} + 0.158 \text{ N} - m \cdot g = 0$$

We can't solve this equation because it has two unknowns. However, we can solve for T_2 in terms of a and hope that the last mass gives us what we need.

$$T_2 = m \cdot g - 0.252 \text{ N}$$

The last mass is a bit easier. It has T_2 pulling it up the incline, and friction plus the gravitational force component parallel to the incline pulling it down. Since we are dealing with friction, we must also use the dimension perpendicular to the incline to determine the normal force.

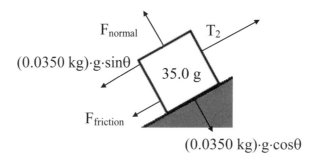

The vertical dimension tells us that $F_{normal} = (0.0350\ kg) \cdot g \cdot cos\theta$. This tells us that the frictional force is 0.132 N. Summing up the forces parallel to the incline gives us:

$$(0.0350\ kg) \cdot g \cdot sin\theta + F_{friction} - T_2 = 0$$

Now we can plug in what we know and solve for a:

$$0.221\ N + 0.132\ N - m \cdot g + 0.252\ N = 0$$

$$m = \frac{.605\ N}{9.81\ \frac{m}{sec^2}} = \underline{0.0617\ kg}$$

b. The sum of forces on each block stays the same; however, when it gets moving, the sum of the forces equals the mass times the acceleration. From the hanging mass, then:

$$T_1 - m \cdot g = m \cdot a$$

$$T_1 = (0.0617\ kg) \cdot a + 0.605\ N$$

From m_2:

$$T_2 + F_{friction} + (0.0250\ kg) \cdot g \cdot sin\theta - T_1 = (0.0250\ kg) \cdot a$$

$$T_2 + F_{friction} + (0.0250\ kg) \cdot g \cdot sin\theta - (0.0617\ kg) \cdot a - 0.605\ N = (0.0250\ kg) \cdot a$$

$$T_2 = -0.0470\ N - 0.158\ N + (0.0617\ kg) \cdot a + 0.605\ N + (0.0250\ kg) \cdot a$$

$$T_2 = 0.400\ N + (0.0867) \cdot a$$

From m_3:

$$(0.0350\ kg) \cdot g \cdot sin\theta + F_{friction} - T_2 = (0.0350\ kg) \cdot a$$

$$0.221 \text{ N} + 0.0658 \text{ N} - 0.400 \text{ N} - (0.0867 \text{ kg}) \cdot a = (0.0350 \text{ kg}) \cdot a$$

$$a = \frac{-0.113 \text{ N}}{0.1217 \text{ kg}} = \underline{-0.929 \ \frac{\text{m}}{\text{sec}^2}}$$

c. To get the tensions in the strings, we just use the equations we developed:

$$T_1 = (0.0617) \cdot a + 0.605 \text{ N} = \underline{0.548 \text{ N}}$$

$$T_2 = 0.400 \text{ N} + (0.0867) \cdot a = \underline{0.319 \text{ N}}$$

SOLUTIONS TO THE TEST FOR MODULE #4

1. a. The weight is actually the force of gravity pushing down on the box. To lift the box at a constant velocity, then, the person doing the work must lift the box with a force of 50.0 N. The force must be directed straight up, which is parallel to the displacement. Thus:

$$W = F \cdot x \cdot \cos\theta = (50.0 \text{ N}) \cdot (1.20 \text{ m}) \cdot \cos(0.00) = \underline{6.00 \times 10^1 \text{ J}}$$

b. When force is constant and velocity is constant,

$$P = F \cdot v$$

$$45.0 \text{ Watts} = (50.0 \text{ N}) \cdot v$$

$$\underline{v = 0.900 \text{ m/sec}}$$

2. Initially, the car has this much kinetic energy:

$$KE = \frac{1}{2} \cdot m \cdot v^2 = \frac{1}{2} \cdot (5.0 \text{ kg}) \cdot (1.5 \frac{m}{sec})^2 = 5.6 \text{ J}$$

Afterward, the car has this much kinetic energy:

$$KE = \frac{1}{2} \cdot m \cdot v^2 = \frac{1}{2} \cdot (5.0 \text{ kg}) \cdot (3.5 \frac{m}{sec})^2 = 31 \text{ J}$$

Since the potential energy is not changing, this increase in energy must be due to the work being done on the car. Thus, the difference in the energy is the work done:

$$W = 31 \text{ J} - 5.6 \text{ J} = \underline{25 \text{ J}}$$

3. a. Since they are traveling at equal speeds, the first has three times the momentum. This means that the sum of the two momenta is pointed to the east. Thus, after the collision, the momentum of the combined system must also be pointed <u>to the east</u>.

b. If the two cars come to a halt after the collision, then the final momentum is zero. That means the sum of the initial momenta must also be zero. That means each car had equal and opposite momenta. As a result, <u>the lighter car was traveling with three times the speed of the heavier car.</u>

4. <u>Work is being done on the object. To move at a constant velocity, a force must be pushing the car so as to overcome friction, air resistance, etc.</u> Since the force and the displacement will be oriented in the same direction, **F•x** is not zero.

5. <u>They all have equal speeds the instant before they hit the ground.</u> You can think about this in many ways. In terms of energy, they are all given the same amount of initial kinetic energy,

because they all have the same speed. They are all launched from the same height, so they all have the same potential energy. Thus, they all have the same total energy. The instant before they hit the ground, they all have no potential energy. Thus, all of their total energy has been converted to kinetic energy. That means they all have the same kinetic energy and, since they all have the same mass, they all have the same speed.

6. No, the velocity is not necessarily zero. If a particle has negative potential energy and just enough kinetic energy so that the total energy adds to zero, it will still have a nonzero velocity, because it has kinetic energy.

7. No, it is not possible. Since there are no external forces, momentum is conserved. Initially, the sum of the momenta equals the momentum of the moving ball. Thus, after the collision, there must be equal momentum. That would not happen if both balls did not move.

8. Yes, it is possible. The sum of the momenta before must equal the sum of the momenta after. That can easily happen while both balls are moving.

9. Prior to release, the mass/spring system has potential energy:

$$U_{spring} = \frac{1}{2} \cdot k \cdot x^2$$

$$U_{spring} = \frac{1}{2} \cdot (123 \frac{N}{m}) \cdot (0.150 \text{ m})^2 = 1.38 \text{ J}$$

Since the target is sitting on the mass, it has that potential energy, too. There is no kinetic energy, thus, the total energy is 1.38 J. When the system is released, the potential energy will be converted into kinetic energy, and then it will be converted back into potential energy as the ball rises. In the end, the maximum height will be the point at which all of the energy is converted into gravitational potential energy:

$$1.38 \text{ J} = m \cdot g \cdot h$$

$$1.38 = (0.1000 \text{ kg}) \cdot (9.81 \frac{m}{\sec^2}) \cdot h$$

$$h = 1.41 m$$

This is *not quite* the answer. After all, we said that the only potential energy the target had came from the mass/spring system. Thus, we implicitly defined the depth at which the spring was compressed (15.0 cm below ground) as the point of zero kinetic energy. In the equation PE = m·g·h, the h is relative to the zero point of kinetic energy. Thus, the height relative to the ground is 1.41 m - 0.150 m = 1.26 m. If the student forgets this, count off only ¼ credit.

10. When the target reaches maximum height, it is actually at rest. Thus, its velocity and momentum are both zero. The bullet is traveling horizontally ($\theta = 0.00$), so this is really just a one-dimensional problem. Momentum must be conserved, so:

$$m_{bullet} \cdot v_{bullet} + m_{target} \cdot v_{target} = (m_{bullet} + m_{target}) \cdot v_{system}$$

$$(0.0150 \text{ kg}) \cdot (155 \frac{m}{sec}) = (0.0150 \text{ kg} + 0.1000 \text{ kg}) \cdot v_{system}$$

$$v_{system} = \underline{20.2 \frac{m}{sec}}$$

Notice that I defined motion in the direction of the bullet's initial velocity as positive. Thus, the 20.2 m/sec is in the same direction as the bullet's initial velocity.

11. Relative to the ground, the bullet/target system has both potential energy and kinetic energy. It is at a height of 1.26 m and a total mass of 0.115 kg.

$$TE = PE + KE = m \cdot g \cdot h + \frac{1}{2} \cdot m \cdot v^2$$

$$TE = (0.1150 \text{ kg}) \cdot (9.81 \frac{m}{sec^2}) \cdot (1.26 \text{ m}) + \frac{1}{2} \cdot (0.1150 \text{ kg}) \cdot (20.2 \frac{m}{sec})^2 = 24.9 J$$

When it reaches the ground, it will have converted all of that energy into kinetic energy:

$$24.9 \text{ J} = \frac{1}{2} \cdot m \cdot v^2$$

$$24.9 \text{ J} = \frac{1}{2} \cdot (0.1150 \text{ kg}) \cdot v^2$$

$$v = \underline{20.8 \frac{m}{sec}}$$

Please note that if the student used 1.41 m for the height (getting a v of 20.9 m/sec), do not count anything wrong. You already should have taken off for that in problem #9.

12. At first, the block has only potential energy. Thus, the total energy is:

$$TE = KE + PE = 0 + m \cdot g \cdot h = (m) \cdot (9.81 \frac{m}{sec^2}) \cdot (1.50 \text{ m}) = 14.7 \cdot m \ J$$

If there were no friction, then the block would have 14.7·m J at the end of the journey. However, there is friction, at least for most of the way. Thus, we must calculate the work that friction does and remove that energy from the total energy of the object. The frictional force on the ramp is:

$$f = \mu_k \cdot F_n = (0.250) \cdot m \cdot g \cdot \cos\theta = (0.250) \cdot (m) \cdot (9.81 \frac{m}{sec^2}) \cdot \cos(35.0) = 2.01 \cdot m \ N$$

Okay, that's the frictional force while the block is on the incline. To get the work done by friction, we multiply the force by the distance and by the cosine of the angle between force and displacement. What is that angle? Well, the frictional force works *along* the surface of the incline. We can calculate the distance down the incline using trigonometry:

$$\sin\theta = \frac{opposite}{hypotenuse}$$

$$\sin(35.0) = \frac{1.50 \ m}{length \ of \ incline}$$

$$length \ of \ incline = 2.62 \ m$$

Of course, the block slides *down* the incline, so that's the direction of the displacement. The frictional force works *up* the incline, so the angle between force and displacement is 180.0°. The work done by friction while sliding down ramp, then, is:

$$W_{f\_ramp} = (2.01 \cdot m \ N) \cdot (2.62 \ m) \cdot \cos(180.0) = -5.27 \cdot m \ J$$

Work is negative because it is *removing* energy from the system. The total energy at the bottom of the ramp, then, is

$$TE = 14.7 \cdot m \ J - 5.27 \cdot m \ J = 9.4 \cdot m \ J$$

The block then slides with no friction, so no more energy is lost. Thus, when it launches straight up, it will reach a maximum height determined by the total energy of 9.4·m J:

$$9.4 \cdot \cancel{m} \ J = \cancel{m} \cdot g \cdot h$$

$$9.4 \ J = (9.81 \frac{m}{sec^2}) \cdot h$$

$$\underline{h = 0.96 \ m}$$

13. In an elastic collision between balls of equal mass when one is at rest, the relative angle between the final velocities must be 90.0. That means that relative to the initial velocity of the moving ball, the ball initially at rest has an angle of 48.8°. However, that is not defined properly. The proper definition is 360.0 - 48.8 = $\underline{311.2°}$ relative to the moving ball's initial velocity. You could also say -48.8°.

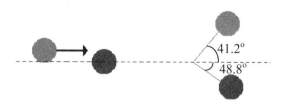

14. a. First, we need to determine the total energy in the system as well as the velocity of the ball when it hits the block. That will allow us to conserve both energy and momentum.

$$TE = KE + PE = 0 + m \cdot g \cdot h = (5.00 \text{ kg}) \cdot (9.81 \frac{m}{\sec^2}) \cdot (0.350 \, m) = 17.2 \text{ J}$$

When the ball falls to the point at which it would hang, all of that potential energy has been converted to kinetic energy. Thus, right before the collision:

$$17.2 \text{ J} = \frac{1}{2} \cdot m \cdot v^2$$

$$17.2 \text{ J} = \frac{1}{2} \cdot (5.00 \text{ kg}) \cdot v^2$$

$$v = 2.62 \, \frac{m}{\sec}$$

Next, let's conserve momentum:

$$m_{ball} \cdot v_{balli} + m_{block} \cdot v_{blocki} = m_{ball} \cdot v_{ballf} + m_{block} \cdot v_{blockf}$$

$$(5.00 \text{ kg}) \cdot (2.62 \, \frac{m}{\sec}) = (5.00 \text{ kg}) \cdot v_{ballf} + (20.0 \text{ kg}) \cdot v_{blockf}$$

$$v_{ballf} = \frac{(5.00 \text{ kg}) \cdot (2.62 \, \frac{m}{\sec}) - (20.0 \text{ kg}) \cdot v_{blockf}}{5.00 \text{ kg}} = 2.62 \frac{m}{\sec} - (4.00) \cdot v_{blockf}$$

Now let's conserve energy:

$$\frac{1}{2} \cdot m_{ball} \cdot v_{balli}{}^2 + \frac{1}{2} \cdot m_{block} \cdot v_{blocki}{}^2 = \frac{1}{2} \cdot m_{ball} \cdot v_{ballf}{}^2 + \frac{1}{2} \cdot m_{block} \cdot v_{blockf}{}^2$$

$$(5.00 \text{ kg}) \cdot (2.62 \frac{m}{sec})^2 = (5.00 \text{ kg}) \cdot v_{ballf}{}^2 + (20.0 \text{ kg}) \cdot v_{blockf}{}^2$$

Substituting the equation from momentum conservation:

$$(5.00 \text{ kg}) \cdot (2.62 \frac{m}{sec})^2 = (5.00 \text{ kg}) \cdot (2.62 \frac{m}{sec} - (4.00) \cdot v_{blockf})^2 + (20.0 \text{ kg}) \cdot v_{blockf}{}^2$$

$$34.3 \text{ J} = 34.3 \text{ J} - 105 \cdot v_{blockf} + (80.0 \text{ kg}) \cdot v_{blockf}{}^2 + (20.0 \text{ kg}) \cdot v_{blockf}{}^2$$

$$(100.0 \text{ kg}) \cdot v_{blockf}{}^2 - 105 \cdot v_{blockf} = 0$$

$$v_{blockf} \cdot (100.0 \cdot v_{blockf} - 105) = 0$$

$$v_{blockf} = 0, \ 1.05 \frac{m}{sec}$$

The first answer just gives us our original condition, so the second answer must refer to after the collision. Of course, we're still not done, because I write mean tests. What we really need to know is how far the block travels. That's not a problem, because we can determine its energy, and it will travel until friction works that energy out.

$$KE = \frac{1}{2} \cdot m \cdot v^2 = \frac{1}{2} \cdot (20.0 \text{ kg}) \cdot (1.05 \frac{m}{sec})^2 = 11.0 \text{ J}$$

The work done by friction, then, must be -11.0 J to stop the block:

$$W_f = f \cdot x \cdot \cos\theta = \mu_k \cdot m \cdot g \cdot x \cdot \cos\theta$$

$$-11.0 \text{ J} = (0.250) \cdot (20.0 \text{ kg}) \cdot (9.81 \frac{m}{sec^2}) \cdot x \cdot \cos(180.0)$$

$$x = \underline{0.224 \text{ m}}$$

b. To answer this question, we need the speed of the ball after the collision. We can get that from the speed of the block (already determined) and the momentum conservation equation:

$$\mathbf{v}_{ballf} = 2.62 \frac{m}{sec} - (4.00) \cdot \mathbf{v}_{blockf} = 2.62 \frac{m}{sec} - (4.00) \cdot (1.05 \frac{m}{sec}) = -1.58 \frac{m}{sec}$$

The negative sign means it is traveling in the opposite direction as it was originally traveling, which was what we defined as positive. Thus, its kinetic energy is:

$$KE = \frac{1}{2} \cdot m \cdot v^2 = \frac{1}{2} \cdot (5.00 \text{ kg}) \cdot (1.58 \frac{m}{sec})^2 = 6.24 \text{ J}$$

The maximum height will correspond to the point at which all of that kinetic energy has been converted into potential energy:

$$6.24 \text{ J} = m \cdot g \cdot h$$

$$6.24 \text{ J} = (5.00 \text{ kg}) \cdot (9.81 \frac{m}{sec^2}) \cdot h$$

$$h = \underline{0.127 \text{ m}}$$

15. Let's start by conserving momentum in the y-dimension, recognizing that the proper definition of the angle for the second ball is $314.5°$:

$$\cancel{m_1} \cdot v_{1i} \cdot \sin \theta_{1i} + \cancel{m_2} \cdot v_{2i} \cdot \sin \theta_{2i} = \cancel{m_1} \cdot v_{1f} \cdot \sin \theta_{1f} + \cancel{m_2} \cdot v_{2f} \cdot \sin \theta_{2f}$$

$$(0) \cdot \sin \theta_{1i} + (3.55 \frac{m}{sec}) \cdot \sin(0.00) = (v_{1f}) \cdot \sin(314.5) + v_{2f} \cdot \sin(41.2)$$

$$v_{1f} = (0.924) \cdot v_{2f}$$

Now if we look at the x-dimension, we can get a second equation:

$$v_{1i} \cdot \cos \theta_{1i} + v_{2i} \cdot \cos \theta_{2i} = v_{1f} \cdot \cos \theta_{1f} + v_{2f} \cdot \cos \theta_{2f}$$

$$(0) \cdot \cos \theta_{1i} + (3.55 \frac{m}{sec}) \cdot \cos(0.00) = (v_{1f}) \cdot \cos(314.5) + (v_{2f}) \cdot \cos(41.2)$$

Plugging the equation from the y-dimension into this equation gives us:

$$(3.55 \frac{m}{sec}) \cdot \cos(0.00) = ((0.924) \cdot v_{2f}) \cdot \cos(314.5) + (v_{2f}) \cdot \cos(41.2)$$

$$3.55 \frac{m}{sec} = (1.40) \cdot v_{2f}$$

$$v_{2f} = 2.54 \frac{m}{sec}$$

We can now get the speed of the first ball:

$$v_{1f} = (0.924) \cdot v_{2f} = 2.35 \frac{m}{sec}$$

The percentage of energy lost would be

$$\frac{\frac{1}{2} \cdot m_2 \cdot v_{2i}^2 - (\frac{1}{2} \cdot m_1 \cdot v_{1f}^2 + \frac{1}{2} \cdot m_2 \cdot v_{2f}^2)}{\frac{1}{2} \cdot m_2 \cdot v_{2i}^2} = \frac{(3.55 \frac{m}{sec})^2 - [(2.35 \frac{m}{sec})^2 + (2.54 \frac{m}{sec})^2]}{(3.55 \frac{m}{sec})^2} = 0.0499$$

Thus, <u>4.99% of the energy was lost</u>.

SOLUTIONS TO THE TEST FOR MODULE #5

1. Summing up the torques is all you have to do if you choose the axis correctly. The problem asks nothing about the force that the wall applies, so let's choose that as the axis of rotation. That way, the force applied by the wall drops out. There are two torques. The first is caused by the weight of the rod. That is positioned at the center of mass, which is the middle of the rod. Thus, it has a radius of $\frac{1}{2} \cdot L$. The weight, however, pulls straight down. Based on the geometry theorem given in the hint, the weight makes an angle θ with the radius vector. The other torque is caused by the tension on the string. It has a radius of L and also makes an angle θ with the radius.

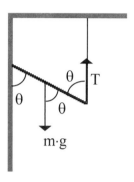

Since $\tau = r \cdot F \cdot \sin\theta$, we get the following for the sum of the torques (clockwise rotation is positive):

$$(\frac{1}{2}L) \cdot (m \cdot g) \cdot \sin\theta - (L) \cdot T \cdot \sin\theta = 0$$

$$(\frac{1}{2}\cancel{L}) \cdot (m \cdot g) \cdot \cancel{\sin\theta} = (\cancel{L}) \cdot T \cdot \cancel{\sin\theta}$$

$$\underline{T = \frac{1}{2} \cdot m \cdot g}$$

2. If the sphere is rotating at a constant speed, it must not have any net torque acting on it. The only way a single force leads to no torque is when <u>the force acts at the center of the sphere</u>.

3. <u>Once the bicycle is moving, the wheels develop angular momentum. You must then exert a large torque to tilt the wheels. Without the motion of the wheels, there is no angular momentum and thus very little torque is needed.</u> The faster the wheels turn, the larger the angular momentum and thus the larger the torque needed to tilt the bicycle.

4. After the child hits the ball, angular momentum will be conserved. Since the moment of inertia is $m \cdot r^2$ for a mass rotating about a fixed point, the angular momentum is:

$$L = I \cdot \omega = (m \cdot r^2) \cdot \frac{v}{r} = m \cdot r \cdot v$$

As the rope wraps around the ball, the radius of the ball's rotation decreases. Since the mass cannot change, in order to keep L constant, <u>the speed of the ball will increase</u>.

5. <u>No</u>. The net torque could be non zero if the two equal and opposite forces acted at different radii. The sum of the forces would be zero, but the sum of the torques would not be.

6. a. When the ball is at the top of the bowl, it has potential energy (m·g·h). When it is at the bottom of the bowl, the potential energy is gone, and it is replaced by translational kinetic energy ($\frac{1}{2}$·m·v²) and rotational kinetic energy ($\frac{1}{2}$·I·ω²). Thus:

$$m \cdot g \cdot h = \frac{1}{2} \cdot m \cdot v^2 + \frac{1}{2} \cdot I \cdot \omega^2$$

$$\cancel{m} \cdot g \cdot h = \frac{1}{2} \cdot \cancel{m} \cdot v^2 + \frac{1}{2} \cdot (\frac{2}{5} \cdot \cancel{m} \cdot \cancel{r}^2) \cdot (\frac{v}{\cancel{r}})^2$$

$$v = \sqrt{\frac{g \cdot h}{(\frac{1}{5} + \frac{1}{2})}} = \sqrt{\frac{(9.81 \frac{m}{sec^2}) \cdot (0.100 \text{ m})}{(\frac{1}{5} + \frac{1}{2})}} = 1.18 \underline{\frac{m}{sec}}$$

b. The only difference here is that there is now still some potential energy.

$$m \cdot g \cdot h = m \cdot g \cdot (\frac{1}{2} \cdot h) + \frac{1}{2} \cdot m \cdot v^2 + \frac{1}{2} \cdot I \cdot \omega^2$$

$$\frac{1}{2} \cdot \cancel{m} \cdot g \cdot h = \frac{1}{2} \cdot \cancel{m} \cdot v^2 + \frac{1}{2} \cdot (\frac{2}{5} \cdot \cancel{m} \cdot \cancel{r}^2) \cdot (\frac{v}{\cancel{r}})^2$$

$$v = \sqrt{\frac{g \cdot h}{2 \cdot (\frac{1}{5} + \frac{1}{2})}} = \sqrt{\frac{(9.81 \frac{m}{sec^2}) \cdot (0.100 \text{ m})}{2 \cdot (\frac{1}{5} + \frac{1}{2})}} = 0.837 \underline{\frac{m}{sec}}$$

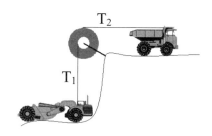

7. To raise the vehicle up at a constant velocity, the sum of the forces on the vehicle must be zero. Looking at the vehicle:

$$T_1 - m{\cdot}g = 0$$

$$T_1 = m{\cdot}g = 24600 \text{ N}$$

Illus. from the MasterClips collection

The pulley must rotate at constant angular velocity, so the sum of the torques must be zero:

$$T_2{\cdot}(2.00 \text{ m}) - T_1{\cdot}(0.750 \text{ m}) = 0$$

$$T_2{\cdot}(2.00 \text{ m}) - (24600 \text{ N}){\cdot}(0.750 \text{ m}) = 0$$

$$T_2 = 9230 \text{ N}$$

Since the sum of the forces on the truck must be zero as well, the truck must be exerting a <u>9230 N</u> force.

8. a. The second hand on the clock makes a full revolution (2π radians) in 60.0 seconds. Thus, the angular velocity is:

$$\omega = \frac{2\pi \text{ rad}}{60.0 \text{ sec}} = \underline{0.105 \ \frac{\text{rad}}{\text{sec}}}$$

b. Since it moves with constant angular velocity (2π radians every 60.0 seconds), the angular acceleration is <u>0</u>.

9. The easiest way to do this is recognize that since all of the bars that make up the square are the same, the center of mass of the square is in the center of the square (2.50 m to the right and 2.50 m above the bottom, left-hand corner). Since the square is made up of 4 bars, the total mass is 180.0 kg. Also, the two bars that make up the "X" are the same, so the center of mass of the "X" is at the center of the "X." That is 2.50 m to the right and 4.00 m above the bottom left-hand corner. The total mass there is 24.0 kg. Now we can calculate the overall center of mass:

$$X_{cm} = \frac{m_1 \cdot x_1 + m_2 \cdot x_2 + m_3 \cdot x_3 \dots m_n \cdot x_n}{m_1 + m_2 + m_3 \dots m_n}$$

$$X_{cm} = \frac{(180.0 \text{ kg}) \cdot (2.50 \text{ m}) + (24.0 \text{ kg}) \cdot (2.50 \text{ m})}{180.0 \text{ kg} + 24.0 \text{ kg}} = 2.50 \text{ m}$$

$$y_{cm} = \frac{m_1 \cdot y_1 + m_2 \cdot y_2 + m_3 \cdot y_3 \dots m_n \cdot y_n}{m_1 + m_2 + m_3 \dots m_n}$$

$$y_{cm} = \frac{(180.0 \text{ kg}) \cdot (2.50 \text{ m}) + (24.0 \text{ kg}) \cdot (4.00 \text{ m})}{180.0 \text{ kg} + 24.0 \text{ kg}} = 2.68 \text{ m}$$

The center of mass is <u>2.50 m to the right and 2.68 m above the bottom, left-hand corner of the square.</u>

10. a. The glue will increase the moment of inertia. Since the angular momentum must be the same, <u>the disk will rotate more slowly.</u>

b. Based on the number of revolutions per second, the disk has an angular velocity of 18.8 rad/sec. Since the moment of inertia of the disk is $\frac{1}{2} \cdot m \cdot r^2$, the angular momentum is:

$$L = I \cdot \omega = \frac{1}{2} \cdot (1.00 \text{ kg}) \cdot (0.0300 \text{ m})^2 \cdot (18.8 \frac{\text{rad}}{\text{sec}}) = 0.00846 \frac{\text{kg} \cdot \text{m}^2}{\text{sec}}$$

That must stay the same. As the glue hardens, it makes a hoop around the disk, with a moment of inertia of $M \cdot r^2$. Thus:

$$L = I_1 \cdot \omega + I_2 \cdot \omega = (\frac{1}{2} \cdot m \cdot r^2) \cdot \omega + (M \cdot r^2) \cdot \omega$$

$$0.00846 \frac{\text{kg} \cdot \text{m}^2}{\text{sec}} = \frac{1}{2} \cdot (1.00 \text{ kg}) \cdot (0.0300 \text{ m})^2 \cdot \omega + (0.2500 \text{ kg}) \cdot (0.0300 \text{ m})^2 \cdot \omega$$

$$\omega = 12.5 \frac{\text{rad}}{\text{sec}}$$

Since each revolution is 2π radians, dividing by 2π gives us the number of revolutions each second, which is <u>1.99 rev/sec</u> .

11. a. The sum of the forces on the heavy mass (rightward motion positive) give us:

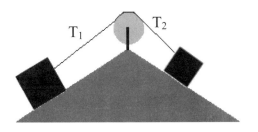

$$T_1 - m_1 \cdot g \cdot \sin\theta = m_1 \cdot a$$

$$T_1 = m_1 \cdot a + m_1 \cdot g \cdot \sin\theta$$

The sum of the forces on the lighter mass gives us:

$$m_2 \cdot g \cdot \sin\theta \ - \ T_2 \ = \ m_2 \cdot a$$

$$T_2 \ = m_2 \cdot g \cdot \sin\theta \ - \ m_2 \cdot a$$

The pulley's rotation ($I = \frac{1}{2} \cdot M \cdot R^2$) gives us the last equation we need:

$$T_2 \cdot R \ - \ T_1 \cdot R \ = \ I \cdot \alpha$$

Plugging in the two equations for tension as well as a/R for α:

$$(m_2 \cdot g \cdot \sin\theta - m_2 \cdot a) \cdot R - (m_1 \cdot g \cdot \sin\theta + m_1 \cdot a) \cdot R = \frac{1}{2} \cdot M \cdot R^2 \cdot \frac{a}{R}$$

$$a = \frac{m_2 \cdot g \cdot \sin\theta \ - \ m_1 \cdot g \cdot \sin\theta}{m_1 + m_2 + \frac{1}{2} \cdot M} = \frac{(10.0 \text{ kg} - 15.0 \text{ kg}) \cdot (9.81 \frac{m}{\sec^2}) \cdot \sin(30.0)}{15.0 \text{ kg} + 10.0 \text{ kg} + \frac{1}{2} \cdot (2.00 \text{ kg})} = -0.94 \frac{m}{\sec^2}$$

The minus just means that the system moves to the left.

b. The tension in the string attached to the heavier mass is T_1.

$$T_1 \ = m_1 \cdot a \ + m_1 \cdot g \cdot \sin\theta$$

$$T_1 = (15.0 \text{ kg}) \cdot (-0.94 \frac{m}{\sec^2}) + (15.0 \text{ kg}) \cdot (9.81 \frac{m}{\sec^2}) \cdot \sin(30.0) = 6.0 \times 10^1 \text{ N}$$

SOLUTIONS TO THE TEST FOR MODULE #6

1. When the acceleration is at its maximum, the mass is at the amplitude. Thus, <u>the speed is at its minimum</u>. Because springs exert a restoring force, <u>the acceleration is opposite of the displacement</u>.

2. When the amplitude is A, the total energy is given by the initial potential energy:

$$TE = U_{initial} = \frac{1}{2} \cdot k \cdot A^2$$

If the energy is evenly split between kinetic and potential, then each will get half of that. Thus, $U = \frac{1}{4} \cdot k \cdot A^2$. Thus:

$$U = \frac{1}{2} \cdot k \cdot x^2$$

$$\frac{1}{4} \cdot k \cdot A^2 = \frac{1}{2} \cdot k \cdot x^2$$

$$\underline{x = \frac{A}{\sqrt{2}}}$$

3. When the pendulum gets started, it has all potential energy, which is given by $U = m \cdot g \cdot h$, where h is the height relative to the equilibrium position. When energy is evenly split between kinetic and potential, that means the potential energy will be $\frac{1}{2} \cdot m \cdot g \cdot h$. Thus, this will happen when the bob on the pendulum is half as high as it was when the pendulum was released, or $\frac{1}{2} \cdot h$. Notice that this is different than the answer in problem #2 because the potential energy in a pendulum depends linearly on h rather than on the square of h.

4. The period is <u>T</u>. The acceleration due to gravity does not affect the period. The period is determined by mass and k only.

5. The period of a simple pendulum on earth is:

$$T_{earth} = 2\pi \cdot \sqrt{\frac{L}{g}}$$

On the moon, the only difference is that the acceleration due to gravity is one-sixth of g:

$$T_{moon} = 2\pi \cdot \sqrt{\frac{L}{\frac{1}{6} \cdot g}} = 2\pi \cdot \sqrt{\frac{6 \cdot L}{g}}$$

The period on the moon, then, is simply $\underline{\sqrt{6}\cdot T}$.

6. To determine the position at any time, we must determine the equation of motion.

$$\mathbf{x} = A \cdot \cos(\omega \cdot t + \delta)$$

We know A (15.0 cm), but we must calculate ω:

$$\omega = \frac{2\pi}{T} = \frac{2\pi}{2\pi\sqrt{\dfrac{5.00 \text{ kg}}{315\dfrac{N}{m}}}} = 7.94 \frac{\text{rads}}{\text{sec}}$$

We must also determine δ. Since the block is displaced to the left, I would call that a negative displacement. Thus, at t = 0, $\mathbf{x}$ = -0.150 m.

$$\mathbf{x} = A \cdot \cos(\delta)$$

$$-0.150 \text{ m} = (0.150 \text{ m}) \cdot \cos(\delta)$$

$$\delta = \cos^{-1}(-1) = \pi$$

Now we have the equation:

$$\mathbf{x} = (0.150 \text{ m}) \cdot \cos\left[(7.94 \frac{\text{rads}}{\text{sec}}) \cdot t + \pi\right]$$

To get the position, we now just have to put in the time:

$$\mathbf{x} = (0.150 \text{ m}) \cdot \cos\left[(7.94 \frac{\text{rads}}{\text{sec}}) \cdot (0.555 \text{ sec}) + \pi\right] = 0.0449 \text{ m}$$

Since the answer is positive, we say that the mass is 0.0449 m to the right of equilibrium.

7. The period of the simple pendulum is just:

$$T = 2\pi \cdot \sqrt{\frac{L}{g}}$$

However, the period of a physical pendulum with a moment of inertia of $I = \frac{1}{3} \cdot M \cdot L^2$ is:

$$T = 2\pi \cdot \sqrt{\frac{I}{m \cdot g \cdot d}} = 2\pi \cdot \sqrt{\frac{\frac{1}{3} \cdot m \cdot L^2}{m \cdot g \cdot \frac{1}{2} L}} = 2\pi \cdot \sqrt{\frac{\frac{2}{3} L}{g}}$$

Remember, d = ½·L because d is the distance from the pivot point to the center of mass of the rod. To get these equations to be identical, <u>the length of the rod must be 1.5 times the length of the simple pendulum.</u>

8. Since the wave formed by interference has a lower amplitude than the initial wave, <u>the two waves must have interfered destructively. The other wave must have had an amplitude of 4.0 cm</u> so that, when subtracted from 13.0 cm, you get 9.0 cm.

9. We know the frequency and wavelength. From that, we can get the speed:

$$f = \frac{v}{\lambda}$$

$$v = f \cdot \lambda = (60.0 \; \frac{1}{sec}) \cdot (0.0550 \; m) = 3.30 \; \frac{m}{sec}$$

The speed can now give us the tension:

$$v = \sqrt{\frac{T}{\mu}}$$

$$T = v^2 \cdot \mu = (3.30 \; \frac{m}{sec})^2 \cdot (0.350 \; \frac{kg}{m}) = 3.81 \; \frac{kg \cdot m}{sec^2} = \underline{3.81 \; N}$$

10. The wavelength is the distance from crest to crest. The trough is half the wavelength away. Thus, the wave must travel 5.00 m to get to the position. Thus, <u>it will take 1.00 seconds.</u>

11. According to the equation, $\lambda = 0.150$ m and v = 35.0 m/sec. The frequency, then, is:

$$f = \frac{v}{\lambda} = \frac{35.0 \; \frac{m}{sec}}{0.150 \; m} = \underline{233 \; Hz}$$

12. In a longitudinal wave, the oscillations are parallel to the propagation. In a transverse wave, the oscillations are perpendicular to the propagation.

13. It is inverted. See Figure 6.7.

14. If the wave has 5 antinodes, it is the fifth harmonic. Thus, n = 5:

$$\lambda = \frac{2 \cdot L}{n}$$

$$65.0 \text{ cm} = \frac{2 \cdot L}{5}$$

$$\underline{L = 163 \text{ cm}}$$

15. To figure out the number of nodes, I need to figure out the wavelength. I can do that with the frequency, as long as I can get the speed.

$$v = \sqrt{\frac{T}{\mu}} = \sqrt{\frac{50.0 \text{ N}}{0.550 \frac{\text{kg}}{\text{m}}}} = 9.53 \frac{\text{m}}{\text{sec}}$$

Now I can get the wavelength:

$$\lambda = \frac{v}{f} = \frac{9.53 \frac{\text{m}}{\text{sec}}}{1.27 \frac{1}{\text{sec}}} = 7.50 \text{ m}$$

Now we can get n:

$$\lambda = \frac{2 \cdot L}{n}$$

$$7.50 \text{ m} = \frac{2 \cdot (15.0 \text{ m})}{n}$$

$$n = 4$$

When n = 4, there are 5 nodes.

SOLUTIONS TO THE TEST FOR MODULE #7

1. First, we need to know the speed of the wave:

$$v = (331.5 + 0.606 \cdot T) \frac{m}{sec} = (331.5 + 0.606 \cdot 28.0) \frac{m}{sec} = 348.5 \frac{m}{sec}$$

Now we can get the wavelength:

$$f = \frac{v}{\lambda}$$

$$\lambda = \frac{v}{f} = \frac{348.5 \frac{m}{sec}}{295 \frac{1}{sec}} = \underline{1.18 \ m}$$

2. The person is hearing beats, and beats occur at the difference in the frequency between the two waves. Since the first wave has a frequency of 295 Hz, the other wave has a frequency of either 293 Hz or 297 Hz.

3. The intensity of a sound wave diminishes as $1/r^2$. If you were standing 20 cm away and then moved to 200 m away, you increased the distance by a factor of 1000. Thus, the intensity diminished by a factor of $(1000)^2$, or 10^6. That's a decrease of 6 bels, or 60 dB. Thus, the mower's loudness will now be only 35 dB.

4. We know the relationship between length of a tube and the wavelength of the sound waves produced. However, to deal with frequency, we must first know speed:

$$v = (331.5 + 0.606 \cdot T) \frac{m}{sec} = (331.5 + 0.606 \cdot 20.0) \frac{m}{sec} = 343.6 \frac{m}{sec}$$

Now we can get wavelength:

$$f = \frac{v}{\lambda}$$

$$\lambda = \frac{v}{f} = \frac{343.6 \frac{m}{sec}}{736 \frac{1}{sec}} = 0.467 \ m$$

Now we can determine the harmonic. This is a tube closed on one end, so:

$$\lambda = \frac{4 \cdot L}{n} \quad n = 1,3,5,\ldots$$

$$0.467 \ \cancel{m} = \frac{4 \cdot (0.350 \ \cancel{m})}{n}$$

$$n = 3.00$$

The air is vibrating at the <u>third harmonic</u>.

5. <u>No, he will not hear the same pitch. The relative motion is the same, but the Doppler shift</u>
<u>equation is different depending on whether it is the source or the observer that is moving. If you</u>
work out the equation for any given speed, you will see that the observed frequency is slightly
different if the source is moving as compared to the observed frequency when the observer is
moving.

6. <u>When the air density changes, the wave encounters a new medium. Thus, part of the wave is</u>
<u>reflected. When it is reflected, it is Doppler shifted as if it originated in the moving air mass.</u>
<u>Using the Doppler shift equation, then, the amount of the shift tells you the speed of the air mass.</u>

7.   In this case, the source is moving and the observer is stationary. The source is moving
towards the observer, which will increase the frequency. Thus, we subtract the speed of the
source so that the observed frequency is higher than that of the true frequency:

$$f_{observed} = \left(\frac{V_{sound} \pm V_{observer}}{V_{sound} \pm V_{source}} \right) \cdot f_{true}$$

$$f_{observed} = \left(\frac{345 \ \frac{\cancel{m}}{\cancel{sec}}}{345 \ \frac{\cancel{m}}{\cancel{sec}} - 25.0 \ \frac{\cancel{m}}{\cancel{sec}}} \right) \cdot (500.0 \ \text{Hz}) = \underline{539 \ \text{Hz}}$$

8. Now both source and observer are moving. In this case, the observer is moving away, which
will lower the frequency. Thus, his speed must be subtracted in the numerator:

$$f_{observed} = \left(\frac{345 \ \frac{\cancel{m}}{\cancel{sec}} - 6 \ \frac{\cancel{m}}{\cancel{sec}}}{345 \ \frac{\cancel{m}}{\cancel{sec}} - 25.0 \ \frac{\cancel{m}}{\cancel{sec}}} \right) \cdot (500.0 \ \text{Hz}) = \underline{5.30 \times 10^2 \ \text{Hz}}$$

9. Since the light must reflect at the same angle at which it hit the glass, we can use geometry to tell us the angle of refraction:

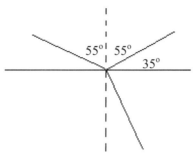

Since the angle between the reflected ray and the horizontal is 35°, and since the angle between the reflected ray and the refracted ray is 90°, the angle between the refracted ray and the horizontal must be 55°. That means the refracted ray must have an angle of 35° relative to the vertical:

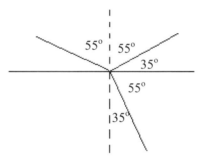

Snell's Law, then, becomes:

$$n_1 \cdot \sin \theta_1 = n_2 \cdot \sin \theta_2$$

$$n_2 = \frac{n_1 \cdot \sin \theta_1}{\sin \theta_2} = \frac{(1.00) \cdot \sin(55)}{\sin(35)} = \underline{1.4}$$

10. This goes back to the definition of index of refraction:

$$n = \frac{c}{v_{\text{light in medium}}}$$

$$v_{\text{light in medium}} = \frac{c}{n} = \frac{2.998 \times 10^8 \ \frac{m}{sec}}{1.428} = \underline{2.099 \times 10^8 \ \frac{m}{sec}}$$

11. As we learned in the course, the higher the energy, the slower light travels in a dense medium. Orange light is lower in energy (ROY G. BIV is in the order of *increasing* energy), so orange light will be faster than blue light.

12. Following the rules of ray tracing, we get:

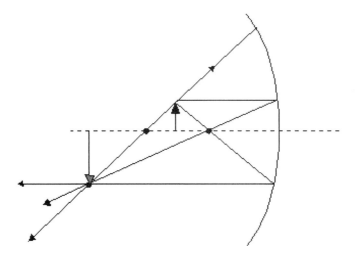

The image is real and inverted.

13. The radius of curvature is twice the focal length, and for concave mirrors, the focal length is positive in the equation:

$$\frac{1}{s_o} + \frac{1}{s_i} = \frac{1}{f}$$

$$\frac{1}{15.0\,\text{cm}} + \frac{1}{s_i} = \frac{1}{10.0\,\text{cm}}$$

$$s_i = 30.0\ \text{cm}$$

The image is 30.0 cm away from the mirror on the same side of the object. The magnification is:

$$m = -\frac{s_i}{s_o} = -\frac{30.0\ \text{cm}}{15.0\ \text{cm}} = -2.00$$

The image is 2.00 times as large as the object.

14. Using the ray tracing rules, we get:

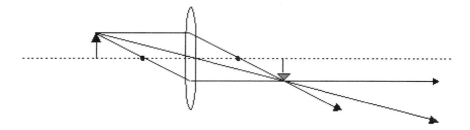

The image is real and inverted.

15. The focal length of a converging lens is positive.

$$\frac{1}{s_o} + \frac{1}{s_i} = \frac{1}{f}$$

$$\frac{1}{20.0 \text{ cm}} + \frac{1}{s_i} = \frac{1}{10.0 \text{ cm}}$$

$$s_i = 20.0 \text{ cm}$$

The image is 20.0 cm away from the mirror on the opposite side as compared to the object. The magnification is:

$$m = -\frac{s_i}{s_o} = -\frac{20.0 \text{ cm}}{20.0 \text{ cm}} = -1.00$$

The image is the same size as the object.

16. The light rays are not being bent strongly enough. Thus, converging lenses should be used to bend the rays more.

SOLUTIONS TO THE TEST FOR MODULE #8

1. When you set centripetal force equal to gravitational force, you get this equation:

$$\frac{m_{sat} \cdot v_{sat}^2}{R} = \frac{G \cdot m_{sat} \cdot m_e}{R^2}$$

$$v = \sqrt{\frac{G \cdot m_e}{R}}$$

The second satellite has a speed equal to:

$$v_{second} = \sqrt{\frac{G \cdot m_e}{2 \cdot R}}$$

This means

$$v_{second} = v \cdot \sqrt{\frac{1}{2}}$$

2. The mass is easy, as it doesn't change. Thus, the mass is m. The weight depends on the force due to gravity:

$$weight = F_g = \frac{G \cdot m \cdot m_{planet}}{R^2}$$

The mass of the object does not change. However, the mass of the planet decreases by a factor of ½, which decreases the weight by ½. The radius of the planet decreases by ½ as well, and that *increases* the gravitational force by 2^2, or 4. This means that overall, gravitational force at the surface of the planet changed by a factor of ½·4 = 2. Thus, at the surface of the planet, the weight will be 2·w.

3. Gravitational force is mutual. If object one exerts a force of F, object two exerts a force of -F, because it will exert an equal but opposite force.

4. Each object exerts the same force on the other. However, since the object of mass 2m is twice as massive, it experiences half the acceleration. Thus, acceleration is ½·a.

5. When the object is at an altitude of 1120 km (1.12×10^6 m), the distance from the center of the moon is 1.74×10^6 m + 1.12×10^6 = 2.86×10^6 m. At that distance from the center of the moon, it has a potential energy of:

$$U_{grav} = -\frac{G \cdot m_1 \cdot m_2}{r} = -\frac{(6.67 \times 10^{-11} \, \frac{N \cdot m^2}{kg^2}) \cdot (7.36 \times 10^{22} \, kg) \cdot (m_2)}{2.86 \times 10^6 \, m} = -(1.72 \times 10^6 \, \frac{J}{kg}) \cdot m_2$$

When it hits the surface, the potential energy is:

$$U_{grav} = -\frac{G \cdot m_1 \cdot m_2}{r} = -\frac{(6.67 \times 10^{-11} \, \frac{N \cdot m^2}{kg^2}) \cdot (7.36 \times 10^{22} \, kg) \cdot (m_2)}{1.74 \times 10^6 \, m} = -(2.82 \times 10^6 \, \frac{J}{kg}) \cdot m_2$$

This is a difference in potential energy of:

$$\Delta PE = (-2.82 \times 10^6 \, \frac{J}{kg}) \cdot m_2 - (-1.72 \times 10^6 \, \frac{J}{kg}) \cdot m_2 = -(1.10 \times 10^6 \, \frac{J}{kg}) \cdot m_2$$

This means PE decreased by $(1.10 \times 10^6 \, J/kg) \cdot m_2$. That all must have gone into kinetic energy, so KE = $(1.10 \times 10^6 \, J/kg) \cdot m_2$.

$$\frac{1}{2} \cdot m_2 \cdot v^2 = (1.10 \times 10^6 \, \frac{J}{kg}) \cdot m_2$$

$$v = \sqrt{2 \cdot 1.10 \times 10^6 \, \frac{J}{kg}} = 1.48 \times 10^3 \, \underline{\frac{m}{sec}}$$

6. <u>The object feels the most gravitational force in (c), because it has some mass below it. The object feels the same gravitational force in (a) and (b), because inside a ring of mass, the mass exerts no net gravitational pull.</u>

7. There are several ways to do this, but the easiest is with Kepler's Third Law, which says T^2/a^3 is constant for all planets. Thus, if a increases by a factor of 9.53, T^2 will also have to increase by $(9.53)^3$ in order to keep T^2/a^3 constant. Thus, the orbital period for Saturn is $\sqrt{(9.53)^3}$ times that of earth, or <u>29.4 years.</u>

8. Escape velocity is determined by energy arguments:

$$TE_{before} = TE_{after}$$

$$\frac{1}{2} \cdot m \cdot (1.568 \times 10^4 \, \frac{m}{sec})^2 - \frac{G \cdot m \cdot m_{planet}}{R} = 0$$

$$\frac{m_{planet}}{R} = \frac{(1.568 \times 10^4 \ \frac{m}{sec})^2}{2 \cdot (6.67 \times 10^{-11} \ \frac{N \cdot m^2}{kg^2})} = 1.84 \times 10^{18} \ \frac{kg}{m}$$

9. When dealing with a roughly circular orbit, we know that:

$$\frac{m_{Venus} \cdot v_{Venus}^2}{R} = \frac{G \cdot m_{Venus} \cdot m_{sun}}{R^2}$$

$$m_{sun} = \frac{v_{venus}^2 \cdot R}{G}$$

To get the mass of the sun, then, I need the G (which I have), R (which I have), and the speed of Venus. I can get that, however. I know that the orbital period of the earth is 1.000 years, which is 31,557,600 sec. I also know that from Kepler's Third Law, T^2/a^3 must be constant. Thus if a decreases by a factor of 0.722, T^2 will also have to decrease by $(0.722)^3$ in order to keep T^2/a^3 constant. Thus, the orbital period for Venus is $\sqrt{(0.722)^3}$ times that of earth, or 19,400,000 sec. In that amount of time, Venus travels $2 \cdot \pi \cdot r$:

$$m_{sun} = \frac{\left(\frac{2 \cdot \pi \cdot R}{19,400,000 \ sec}\right)^2 \cdot R}{G} = \frac{\left(\frac{2 \cdot \pi}{19,400,000 \ sec}\right)^2 \cdot R^3}{G}$$

$$m_{sun} = \frac{\left(\frac{2 \cdot \pi}{19,400,000 \ sec}\right)^2 \cdot (1.08 \times 10^{11} \ m)^3}{6.67 \times 10^{-11} \ \frac{N \cdot m^2}{kg^2}} = 1.98 \times 10^{30} \ kg$$

10. The total energy is the sum of the potential plus the kinetic energy. The potential energy is:

$$U_{grav} = -\frac{G \cdot m_{sat} \cdot m_e}{r}$$

The kinetic energy is:

$$\frac{m_{sat} \cdot v_{sat}^2}{r} = \frac{G \cdot m_{sat} \cdot m_e}{r^2}$$

$$v = \sqrt{\frac{G \cdot m_e}{r}}$$

$$KE = \frac{1}{2} \cdot m_{sat} \cdot v^2 = \frac{1}{2} \cdot (m_{sat}) \cdot (\sqrt{\frac{G \cdot m_e}{r}})^2 = \frac{G \cdot m_{sat} \cdot m_e}{2 \cdot r}$$

The total energy, then, is:

$$TE = PE + KE = -\frac{G \cdot m_{sat} \cdot m_e}{r} + \frac{G \cdot m_{sat} \cdot m_e}{2 \cdot r} = -\frac{G \cdot m_{sat} \cdot m_e}{2 \cdot r}$$

$$-1.23 \times 10^{10} \text{ J} = -\frac{(6.67 \text{x} 10^{-11} \frac{N \cdot m^2}{kg^2} \cdot (1,456 \text{ kg}) \cdot (5.98 \text{x} 10^{24} \text{ kg})}{2 \cdot r}$$

$$r = \frac{(6.67 \text{x} 10^{-11} \frac{N \cdot m^2}{kg^2} \cdot (1,456 \text{ kg}) \cdot (5.98 \text{x} 10^{24} \text{ kg})}{2 \cdot (1.23 \text{x} 10^{10} \text{ J})} = 2.36 \text{x} 10^7 \frac{N \cdot m^2}{J}$$

Since (by $W = F \cdot x$) a Joule is a N·m, the unit works out to meters. Thus, the radius is 2.36x10^7 m.

11 a. The speed of light is the same in all inertial reference frames. Thus, the defensive tracking systems see the light approaching the ship at c.

b. The speed of light is the same in all inertial reference frames. Thus, the offensive tracking systems see the light traveling away from the ship at c.

12. a. The person on earth also sees the light traveling at c. Thus, if the light took $3.45 \text{x} 10^{-4}$ seconds to travel from one ship to another, the laser light traveled:

$$x = v_o \cdot t$$

$$x = (2.998 \text{x} 10^8 \frac{m}{sec}) \cdot (3.45 \text{x} 10^{-4} \text{ sec}) = 103,000 \text{ m}$$

b. The first space ship is in a different reference frame, so it will measure a different time (t') as compared to the person at rest relative to the ships:

$$t' = (3.45 \times 10^{-4} \text{ sec}) \cdot \sqrt{1 - (\frac{0.750c}{c})^2}$$

$$t' = 2.28 \times 10^{-4} \text{ sec}$$

c. The space ship also sees light traveling at c. Thus, if it took 2.28×10^{-4} seconds to travel from one ship to another, the distance it travels must be:

$$x = v_o \cdot t$$

$$x = (2.998 \times 10^8 \ \frac{m}{sec}) \cdot (2.28 \times 10^{-4} \ sec) = \underline{68,400 \ m}$$

d. The other ship is traveling at the same speed relative to the earth. Thus, it experiences the same time dilation and length contraction relative to an observer on earth, so it also measures that the laser light travels 68,400 m.

SOLUTIONS TO THE TEST FOR MODULE #9

1. It is more proper to say that you are cold because of the heat, <u>because heat is energy that is transferred. You get cold because energy is transferred from you to the outside.</u> Thus, you are cold because of energy exchange, which is heat.

2. When you heat a substance, its temperature does not change during the phase change. Thus, the flat part at the start of the graph corresponds with the melting of the substance. The substance then warms to its boiling point and begins to boil. The second flat portion of the graph corresponds to that boiling, so the substance boils at <u>55 °C.</u> Your number can be slightly different than that, because you are reading from a graph. It should be between 50 and 60, however.

3. Energy, temperature, and mass are related by the equation:

$$q = m \cdot c \cdot \Delta T = (150.0 \text{ g}) \cdot (0.236 \frac{J}{g \cdot °C}) \cdot (10.0\,°C - 25.0\,°C) = -531 \text{ J}$$

The negative sign just means energy is released. Thus, the metal must lose <u>531 J</u>.

4. The energy related to a phase change is given by:

$$q = m \cdot L$$

$$L = \frac{q}{m} = \frac{7850 \text{ J}}{50.0 \text{ g}} = 157 \frac{J}{g}$$

5. We know what will happen. The hot water will lose energy to the ice cube. The ice cube will warm up, melt, and then the water produced will warm up more. How much energy will be lost by the water?

$$q_{lost} = m \cdot c \cdot \Delta T = (300.0 \text{ g}) \cdot (4.19 \frac{J}{g \cdot °C}) \cdot (2.1\,°C - 95.0\,°C) = -117,000 \text{ J}$$

What will happen to that energy? Well, the energy will be gained by the ice cube, warming it to 0.00 °C, melting it, and then warming it more:

$$q_{gained} = m_{ice} \cdot c_{ice} \cdot \Delta T_{ice} + m_{ice} \cdot L_{fus} + m_{ice} \cdot c_{water} \cdot (T_{final} - 0.0 \text{ C})$$

$$q_{gained} = m_{ice} \cdot (2.02 \frac{J}{g \cdot °C}) \cdot (0.0\,°C - -9.1\,°C) + m_{ice} \cdot (334 \frac{J}{g}) + m_{ice} \cdot (4.19 \frac{J}{g \cdot °C}) \cdot (2.1\,°C - 0.0\,°C)$$

Now remember, $q_{lost} = -q_{gained}$.

$$-117{,}000 \text{ J} = -m_{ice} \cdot (2.02 \frac{\text{J}}{\text{g} \cdot {}^\circ\text{C}}) \cdot (0.0\,{}^\circ\text{C} - -9.1\,{}^\circ\text{C}) - m_{ice} \cdot (334 \frac{\text{J}}{\text{g}}) - m_{ice} \cdot (4.19 \frac{\text{J}}{\text{g} \cdot {}^\circ\text{C}}) \cdot (2.1\,{}^\circ\text{C} - 0.0\,{}^\circ\text{C})$$

$$m_{ice} = \frac{-117{,}000 \text{ J}}{-361 \frac{\text{J}}{\text{g}}} = \underline{324 \text{ g}}$$

6. We are given the coefficient of volume expansion, but we need to calculate length. Thus, we need to use the relationship:

$$\beta \approx 3 \cdot \alpha$$

Thus, $\alpha = 9.0 \times 10^{-6}$ 1/°C. Now we can calculate the length:

$$\Delta L = \alpha \cdot L_o \cdot \Delta T = (9.0 \times 10^{-6} \frac{1}{{}^\circ\text{C}}) \cdot (1.000 \text{ m}) \cdot (150.0\,{}^\circ\text{C} - 25.0\,{}^\circ\text{C}) = 0.0011 \text{ m}$$

The glass rod, then, is 1.001 m long at 150.0 °C.

7. We do not know the volumes, but we can get the ratio:

$$\Delta V = \beta \cdot V_o \cdot \Delta T$$

$$\frac{\Delta V}{V_o} = \beta \cdot \Delta T = (2.7 \times 10^{-5} \frac{1}{{}^\circ\text{C}}) \cdot (150.0\,{}^\circ\text{C} - 25.0\,{}^\circ\text{C}) = 0.0034$$

This is the ratio of the *change* in volume to the original volume. The ratio of the final volume to the original volume is 1.0034.

8. Since the pressure is the same on both sides, we can say:

$$P_{left} = P_{right}$$

$$\frac{F_{left}}{A_1} = \frac{F_{right}}{A_2}$$

$$F_{right} = \frac{F_{left}}{A_1} \cdot A_2 = \frac{1 \text{ N}}{A_1} \cdot (100 \cdot A_1) = \underline{100 \text{ N}}$$

9. There are 6.02×10^{23} molecules in a mole. Thus:

$$\text{\# moles} = (1.8 \times 10^{24} \, \cancel{\text{molecules}} \cdot \frac{1 \, \cancel{\text{mole}}}{6.02 \text{x} 10^{23} \, \cancel{\text{molecules}}}) = \underline{3.0 \text{ moles}}$$

10. Since the Maxwell-Boltzmann distribution is not symmetric, the average is to the right of the peak. I would say that the average is 650 m/sec, but any answer in the range of 580 - 750 m/sec is acceptable.

11. To relate speed and temperature, we must get the mass of an individual molecule. Right now, we have the mass of a *mole*. Thus:

$$m = (\frac{0.0320 \text{ kg}}{6.02 \text{x} 10^{23}}) = 5.32 \text{x} 10^{-26} \text{ kg}$$

Now we can relate temperature to speed:

$$\overline{v^2} = \frac{3kT}{m}$$

$$T = \frac{m \cdot \overline{v^2}}{3k} = \frac{(5.32 \text{x} 10^{-26} \text{ kg}) \cdot (417 \, \frac{m}{\sec})^2}{3 \cdot (1.38 \text{x} 10^{-23} \, \frac{J}{K})} = \underline{223 \text{ K}}$$

12. We can solve this using the ideal gas law:

$$PV = nRT$$

$$P = \frac{nRT}{V} = \frac{(3.45 \, \cancel{\text{moles}}) \cdot (8.31 \, \frac{J}{\cancel{\text{mole}} \cdot \cancel{K}}) \cdot (298.2 \, \cancel{K})}{(0.234 \text{ m}^3)} = 36,500 \, \frac{J}{\text{m}^3} = 36,500 \, \frac{N \cdot m}{\text{m}^3} = \underline{36,500 \text{ Pa}}$$

That sounds like a lot of pressure, but remember, atmospheric pressure is 101.3 kPa, or 101,300 Pa. Thus, this is about 1/3 of atmospheric pressure.

13. We relate heat to temperature in a gas with the following:

$$q = n \cdot C_p \cdot \Delta T$$

$$C_p = \frac{q}{n \cdot \Delta T} = \frac{(345.0 \text{ J})}{(2.50 \text{ mole}) \cdot (5.7 \, ^\circ C)} = \underline{24 \, \frac{J}{\text{mole} \cdot ^\circ C}}$$

Remember, since we are dealing with ΔT here, you could also use K for temperature.

14. The molar heat capacities are related by:

$$C_p = C_v + R$$

$$C_v = C_p - R = 24 \; \frac{J}{mole \cdot K} - 8.31 \; \frac{J}{mole \cdot K} = \underline{16 \; \frac{J}{mole \cdot K}}$$

15. Now that we have the molar heat capacity at constant volume, we can determine the temperature if volume were held constant:

$$q = n \cdot C_v \cdot \Delta T$$

$$\Delta T = \frac{q}{n \cdot C_p} = \frac{(345.0 \; \cancel{J})}{(2.50 \; \cancel{mole}) \cdot (16 \; \frac{\cancel{J}}{\cancel{mole} \cdot {}^\circ C})} = \underline{8.6 \; {}^\circ C}$$

SOLUTIONS TO THE TEST FOR MODULE #10

1. a. <u>The second brick has a positive q</u>, since it is cooler and will therefore absorb heat. As a result, <u>the first will have a negative q</u>.

b. We used the <u>Zeroth Law of Thermodynamics</u>.

c. Since Equation (10.7) tells us that the sign of ΔS is the same as the sign for q, <u>the second brick will have a positive ΔS, while the first brick has a negative ΔS</u>.

d. <u>This is consistent with the Second Law of Thermodynamics because although one brick has a negative ΔS, the other brick has a positive ΔS. The second law says only that the total entropy of the universe must increase or stay the same.</u> Thus, the loss of entropy in one brick is offset by a gain in entropy in the other brick.

2. a. <u>The internal energy of the gas stays the same.</u> Isothermal means no change in temperature, which also means no change in internal energy.

b. Since the expansion is isothermal, $\Delta U = 0$, which means q = W. Since this is an expansion, W is positive. Thus, q is positive, which means it is <u>greater than zero</u>.

3. a. Since this is adiabatic, q = 0. This means that $\Delta U = -W$. The gas is compressed, so W is negative. That makes ΔU positive, so <u>the internal energy increases</u>.

b. If the internal energy increases, <u>the temperature increases</u>.

c. Since q is zero, ΔS is also zero by Equation (10.7). Thus, <u>entropy stays the same</u>.

4. a. Isothermal means that $\Delta U = 0$, so q = W. If entropy increases, then q is positive. Since q = W, <u>W is positive</u>.

b. <u>The gas expanded</u>, because W is positive for expansions and negative for compressions.

5. a. Calculating the work is easy since this is an isobaric process:

$$W = P \cdot \Delta V = (4.5 \times 10^5 \text{ Pa}) \cdot (0.0359 \text{ m}^3 - 0.0205 \text{ m}^3) = \underline{6,900 \text{ J}}$$

b. If we could get q, we could determine ΔU from the first law. Well, we can get q, because we have C_p, and we can calculate the temperatures. Initially:

$$PV = nRT$$

$$T = \frac{PV}{nR} = \frac{(4.5 \times 10^5 \text{ Pa}) \cdot (0.0205 \text{ m}^3)}{(5.0 \text{ moles}) \cdot (8.31 \frac{\text{Pa} \cdot \text{m}^3}{\text{mole} \cdot \text{K}})} = 220 \text{ K}$$

At the end:

$$PV = nRT$$

$$T = \frac{PV}{nR} = \frac{(4.5 \times 10^5 \ \text{Pa}) \cdot (0.0359 \ \text{m}^3)}{(5.0 \ \text{moles}) \cdot (8.31 \ \frac{\text{Pa} \cdot \text{m}^3}{\text{mole} \cdot \text{K}})} = 390 \ \text{K}$$

Now we can calculate q.

$$q = n \cdot C_p \cdot \Delta T = (5.0 \ \text{moles}) \cdot (20.8 \ \frac{\text{J}}{\text{mole} \cdot \text{K}}) \cdot (390 \ \text{K} - 220 \ \text{K}) = 18,000 \ \text{J}$$

Getting ΔU is now easy:

$$\Delta U = q - W = 18,000 \ \text{J} - 6,900 \ \text{J} = \underline{11,000 \ \text{J}}$$

6. This is a simple application of Equation (10.9):

$$e_{\text{Carnot}} = 1 - \frac{T_c}{T_h} = 1 - \frac{298}{789} = \underline{0.622}$$

7. a. Since the compression is isothermal $\Delta U = 0$ and therefore $q = W$. Thus, $q = -5,160$ J. Remember, q is negative because working on a gas (compression) means W is negative. Now that we know q, we can determine ΔS:

$$\Delta S_{\text{rev}} = \frac{q}{T} = \frac{-5,160 \ \text{J}}{516 \ \text{K}} = \underline{-10.0 \ \frac{\text{J}}{\text{K}}}$$

b. Since the system decreased in entropy, the surroundings must have an equal or greater increase in entropy, or this could not happen. Thus, the minimum ΔS for the surroundings is 10.0 J/K.

8. In the Carnot engine, the gas exchanges energy during the isothermal steps. Since the gas is doing work, this must be the isothermal expansion.

9. The gas does not exchange energy with the surroundings during the two adiabatic steps of the Carnot cycle. Since $\Delta U = -W$ during adiabatic processes, W must be negative for the heat to increase. That means the gas is compressed. Thus, this is the adiabatic compression.

10. No work is done from 1 to 2, since the volume does not change. The problem tells us that 27,000 J of work is done from 2 to 3. Going from 3 back to 1 is an isobaric step, so work is easy to calculate:

$$W = P \cdot \Delta V = (1.0 \times 10^5 \text{ Pa}) \cdot (0.20 \text{ m}^3 - 0.40 \text{ m}^3) = -2.0 \text{x} 10^4 \text{ J}$$

The total work is just the sum of the work in each step:

$$W_{total} = 0 + 27{,}000 \text{ J} - 2.0 \text{x} 10^4 \text{ J} = \underline{7{,}000 \text{ J}}$$

11. Since $\Delta U = 0$ for a cyclic process, $q = W$. Thus, $\underline{7{,}000 \text{ J of energy are absorbed.}}$

12. We know that the total q is 7,000 J. We can figure out the q of the other two steps, since the step from 1 to 2 is isochoric and the step from 3 to 1 is isobaric. We just need temperatures:

$$\text{State 1: } T = \frac{PV}{nR} = \frac{(1.0 \times 10^5 \text{ Pa}) \cdot (0.20 \text{ m}^3)}{(5.0 \text{ moles}) \cdot (8.31 \frac{\text{Pa} \cdot \text{m}^3}{\text{mole} \cdot \text{K}})} = 480 \text{ K}$$

$$\text{State 2: } T = \frac{PV}{nR} = \frac{(2.0 \times 10^5 \text{ Pa}) \cdot (0.20 \text{ m}^3)}{(5.0 \text{ moles}) \cdot (8.31 \frac{\text{Pa} \cdot \text{m}^3}{\text{mole} \cdot \text{K}})} = 960 \text{ K}$$

$$\text{State 3: } T = \frac{PV}{nR} = \frac{(1.0 \times 10^5 \text{ Pa}) \cdot (0.40 \text{ m}^3)}{(5.0 \text{ moles}) \cdot (8.31 \frac{\text{Pa} \cdot \text{m}^3}{\text{mole} \cdot \text{K}})} = 960 \text{ K}$$

Since going from 1 to 2 is isochoric, we must use C_v to calculate q for this step:

$$q = n \cdot C_v \cdot \Delta T = (5.0 \text{ moles}) \cdot (12.5 \frac{\text{J}}{\text{mole} \cdot \text{K}}) \cdot (960 \text{ K} - 480 \text{ K}) = 3.0 \times 10^4 \text{ J}$$

Since going from 3 to 1 is isobaric, we must use C_p to calculate q for this step:

$$q = n \cdot C_p \cdot \Delta T = (5.0 \text{ moles}) \cdot (20.8 \frac{\text{J}}{\text{mole} \cdot \text{K}}) \cdot (480 \text{ K} - 960 \text{ K}) = -5.0 \text{x} 10^4 \text{ J}$$

The total q has already been determined to be 7,000 J. Thus,

$$q_{total} = q_1 + q_2 + q_3$$

$$7{,}000 \text{ J} = 3.0 \text{x} 10^4 \text{ J} + q_2 + -5.0 \text{x} 10^4 \text{ J}$$

$$\underline{q_2 = 27,000 \text{ J}}$$

13. By either noticing that the temperature of 2 and 3 are the same, or by recognizing that q from problem #12 equals the W given for the step from 2 to 3, you should see that this is an <u>isothermal</u> expansion.

SOLUTIONS TO THE TEST FOR MODULE #11

1. The acceleration will decrease as the particles get farther apart because the electrostatic force will decrease. Thus, only curves A and B are possibilities. However, the force (and thus the acceleration) depends on the *square* of the distance. Thus, the curve will not be linear, as it is in A. The curve will look like a $1/x^2$ curve, as does <u>B</u>.

2. The electric fields of each will add, since the negative will pull a positive charge towards it while the positive will push a positive charge away from it. Thus, the total is just the sum of the two:

$$E_{tot} = E_1 + E_2$$

$$E_{tot} = \frac{(8.99 \times 10^9 \; \frac{N \cdot m^2}{C^2}) \cdot (5.00 \times 10^{-6} \, C)}{(0.375 \; m)^2} + \frac{(8.99 \times 10^9 \; \frac{N \cdot m^2}{C^2}) \cdot (5.00 \times 10^{-6} \, C)}{(0.375 \; m)^2}$$

$$E_{tot} = 6.39 \times 10^5 \; \frac{N}{C}$$

3. a. The particles will all have equal numbers of lines coming from them, and the lines will be pushed away from each other:

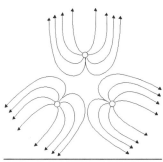

b. The electric field is zero <u>in the center of the triangle</u>, because all three particles push on a positive particle equally and in opposite directions at that point.

c. We need to work out the geometry first, but its not too complicated:

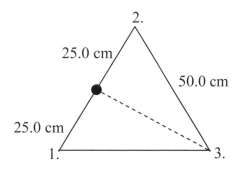

The distances are easy. The point is in the center of the left leg. Thus, the distances to particle 1 and 2 are both 25.0 cm. A line drawn from particle 3 to the point makes a 90 degree angle, since any altitude of an equilateral triangle is perpendicular to its base. Thus, it forms the leg of a right triangle with a 50.0 cm hypotenuse and another leg of 25.0 cm. Thus, it is 43.3 cm long, and that's the distance to particle 3.

Now you can recognize something. The electric fields from particles 1 and 2 will cancel, as the point is right in between them. Thus, they form *zero* electric field. The only electric field remaining, then, comes from particle 3. We just need to calculate that electric field, then:

$$E = \frac{k \cdot Q}{r^2} = \frac{(8.99 \times 10^9 \; \frac{N \cdot m^2}{C^2}) \cdot (5.00 \times 10^{-6} C)}{(0.433 \; m)^2} = 2.40 \times 10^5 \; \frac{N}{C}$$

Thus, the electric field is 2.40 x 10⁵ N/C directly away from particle 3. Note that you could have plugged through the vector addition if you did not notice that particles 1 and 2 cancel each other out. Had you done that you would have gotten the same magnitude at an angle of 150°, which is directly away from particle 3.

4. a. We can use the electric field equation to determine the ratio:

$$\frac{E_1}{E_2} = \frac{\frac{k \cdot Q}{(5.0 \; cm)^2}}{\frac{k \cdot Q}{(9.0 \; cm)^2}} = \frac{81}{25} = 3.2$$

b. Since the charge tripled, the electric field will triple. However, the sign of the charge changed, which reverses the electric field. Thus, the new one will be -3E₁. Take ½ off if you do not have the negative.

5. a. Since we are only interested in the -1.2 mC charge, we only need concern ourselves with forces which act on that charge. The +1.2 mC charge exerts an attractive force on it:

$$F = \frac{k \cdot q_1 \cdot q_2}{r^2}$$

$$F = \frac{(8.99 \times 10^9 \; \frac{Newtons \cdot m^2}{C^2}) \cdot (1.2 \times 10^{-3} \; C) \cdot (1.2 \times 10^{-3} \; C)}{(0.40 \; m)^2} = 8.1 \times 10^4 \; Newtons$$

The +2.4 mC charge also exerts an attractive force on it:

$$F = \frac{k \cdot q_1 \cdot q_2}{r^2}$$

$$F = \frac{(8.99 \times 10^9 \; \frac{\text{Newtons} \cdot \text{m}^2}{\text{C}^2}) \cdot (1.2 \times 10^{-3} \; \text{C}) \cdot (2.4 \times 10^{-3} \; \text{C})}{(0.20 \; \text{m})^2} = 6.5 \times 10^5 \; \text{Newtons}$$

Our force diagram, then, looks like this:

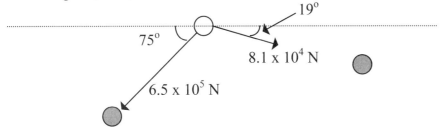

Since these vectors do not point in the same dimension, we will have to add them with trig. First, however, let's define the angles properly. Vector angles are always defined counterclockwise from the +x axis. This means that the first angle is 341°, and the angle for the vector on the left is 255°. Now we can add these vectors:

$$A_x = (8.1 \times 10^4 \; \text{Newtons}) \cdot \cos(341°) = 7.7 \times 10^4 \; \text{Newtons}$$

$$A_y = (8.1 \times 10^4 \; \text{Newtons}) \cdot \sin(341°) = -2.6 \times 10^4 \; \text{Newtons}$$

$$B_x = (6.5 \times 10^5 \; \text{Newtons}) \cdot \cos(255°) = -1.7 \times 10^5 \; \text{Newtons}$$

$$B_y = (6.5 \times 10^5 \; \text{Newtons}) \cdot \sin(255°) = -6.3 \times 10^5 \; \text{Newtons}$$

$$C_x = A_x + B_x = 7.7 \times 10^4 \; \text{Newtons} + -1.7 \times 10^5 \; \text{Newtons} = -9 \times 10^4 \; \text{Newtons}$$

$$C_y = A_y + B_y = -2.6 \times 10^4 \; \text{Newtons} + -6.3 \times 10^5 \; \text{Newtons} = -6.6 \times 10^5 \; \text{Newtons}$$

All that's left to do now is convert these x and y components into vector magnitude and direction:

$$\text{Magnitude} = \sqrt{C_x{}^2 + C_y{}^2} = \sqrt{(-9 \times 10^4 \; \text{Newtons})^2 + (-6.6 \times 10^5 \; \text{Newtons})^2} = 6.7 \times 10^5 \; \text{Newtons}$$

$$\theta = \tan^{-1}\left(\frac{C_y}{C_x}\right) = \tan^{-1}\left(\frac{-6.6 \times 10^5 \; \text{Newtons}}{-9 \times 10^4 \; \text{Newtons}}\right) = 82°$$

Since both the x and y components of the vector are negative, we know that the vector is in quadrant III. This means that we need to add $180°$ to the angle above to properly define the vector angle. The instantaneous electrostatic force on the -1.2 mC charge, then, is 6.7 x 10^5 N at 262°.

b. The force and electric field are related by Equation (11.4)

$$F = q \cdot E$$

$$E = \frac{F}{q} = \frac{6.7 \times 10^5 \text{ N}}{-0.0012 \text{ C}} = -5.6 \times 10^8 \frac{\text{N}}{\text{C}}$$

The negative means that the electric field is directed opposite the force. Thus, the electric field is 5.6 x 10^8 N/C at 82°.

6. a. Particle 1 is negative, because force lines point into it.
b. Particle 2 is positive, because force lines point out of it.
c. There are 8 lines going into particle 1. There are 29 lines coming out of particle 2. Since the number of lines is proportional to charge, the magnitude of particle 2's charge is $\frac{29}{8} \cdot Q$.

7. The charge on the plastic ball will attract a charge of +5.00 mC to the inner surface of the spherical shell.

8. Since the spherical shell is neutral, there must be a charge of -5.00 mC on the outer surface.

9. At 20.0 cm from the center, you see the charge on the plastic ball, but it is as if it is concentrated at the center:

$$E = \frac{k \cdot Q}{r^2} = \frac{(8.99 \times 10^9 \ \frac{\text{N} \cdot \text{m}^2}{\text{C}^2}) \cdot (0.00500 \ \text{C})}{(0.200 \ \text{m})^2} = 1.12 \times 10^9 \ \frac{\text{N}}{\text{C}}$$

10. At 53.0 cm from the center, you are in the conductor. Thus, the field is 0.

11. At 60.0 cm, you are outside of the conductor. The only thing you see is the -5.00 mC on the outer surface of the conductor, but it is as if it is concentrated at the center:

$$E = \frac{k \cdot Q}{r^2} = \frac{(8.99 \times 10^9 \ \frac{\text{N} \cdot \text{m}^2}{\text{C}^2}) \cdot (0.00500 \ \text{C})}{(0.600 \ \text{m})^2} = 1.25 \times 10^8 \ \frac{\text{N}}{\text{C}}$$

SOLUTIONS TO THE TEST FOR MODULE #12

1. Nothing happens to the capacitance. The capacitance depends only on the size of the plates, the distance between the plates, and the presence of a dielectric. An increased potential increases the *charge* on the capacitor, but not the capacitance.

2. The easiest thing to do here is look at the change in potential. It starts out 3.0 cm from the charge and ends up 5.0 cm from the charge. The change in potential, then, is:

$$\Delta V = V_{final} - V_{initial} = \frac{k \cdot Q}{r_{final}} - \frac{k \cdot Q}{r_{initial}}$$

$$\Delta V = \frac{(8.99 \times 10^9 \ \frac{N \cdot m^2}{C^2}) \cdot (0.0122 \ C)}{0.050 \ m} - \frac{(8.99 \times 10^9 \ \frac{N \cdot m^2}{C^2}) \cdot (0.0122 \ C)}{0.030 \ m} = -1.5 \times 10^9 \ \text{Volts}$$

The potential energy, then, changed by

$$\Delta U = q \cdot \Delta V$$

$$\Delta U = (4.56 \times 10^{-5} \ C) \cdot (-1.5 \times 10^9 \ \frac{J}{C}) = -6.8 \times 10^4 \ J$$

Since the change in potential is the negative of the work [Equation (12.3)], then the work done is 6.8 x 10⁴ J.

3. The particle is positively charged. Think about the work. It is positive. That means potential energy is decreasing. If potential energy is decreasing, the particle is moving in the direction that the electric field accelerates it. Positive particles are accelerated in the same direction as the electric field, so this particle must be positive. Negative work means it is being pushed against the electric field.

4. This problem is really rather easy. Remember, the electric field in between the plates of a parallel plate capacitor is uniform, with the arrows pointing directly from the positive plate to the negative plate. Also, the path does not matter. So let's choose this path:

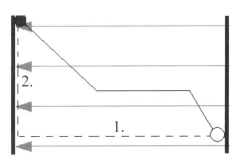

In path 2, no work is done, because the motion is perpendicular to the electric field. Thus, the only work done is in path 1, where the motion is parallel to the field.

$$W = q \cdot E \cdot x \cdot \cos\theta = (-2.36 \times 10^{-6} \ \text{C}) \cdot (78.2 \ \frac{\text{N}}{\text{C}}) \cdot (0.0346 \ \text{m}) \cdot \cos(0) = \underline{-6.39 \times 10^{-6} \ \text{J}}$$

The negative sign simply means that work was done against the electric field. Please note that you could solve this another way. You could use the electric field and the distance between the plates to calculate ΔV, and then use that and the charge to calculate ΔU, which is the negative of the work done.

5. a. Remember, positive charges are accelerated towards lower potentials, and negative charges are accelerated towards higher potentials. If these charges were positive, they would accelerate to the right. Thus, particle (a) would have the highest potential. If the charges were negative, they would accelerate to the left, so once again, particle (a) would have the highest potential. Either way, then, particle (a) has the highest potential.

b. The two particles have equal potential because they are at the same left/right position in the electric field. Thus, if particle (c) has twice the potential energy, it must have twice the charge. That means the ratio of the charge of particle (c) to that of particle (b) is 2.

6. a. It is moving towards a lower potential. As Equation (12.6) says, the potential is inversely proportional to the distance between the moving particle and the fixed ones. As the particle moves towards the midpoint, the distance decreases. This raises the *magnitude* of the potential, but since the charges are negative, it makes the potential *more negative*, which means lower. You could also think of it this way: when negative particles are accelerated by the electric field, they move to higher potentials. This negative particle is moving opposite the acceleration, so it is moving to a lower potential.

b. First, we have to figure out how much energy the particle must lose in order to come to a complete stop. It starts out with this much kinetic energy:

$$KE = \frac{1}{2} \cdot m \cdot v^2$$

$$KE_{initial} = \frac{1}{2} \cdot (1.45 \, \text{kg}) \cdot (607 \, \frac{\text{m}}{\text{sec}})^2$$

$$KE_{initial} = 2.67 \times 10^5 \ \text{J}$$

All of that must be converted into potential energy before the particle stops. Thus, the change in potential energy will be 2.67 x 10⁵ J. Now we can figure out the change in potential:

$$\Delta U = q \cdot \Delta V$$

$$\Delta V = \frac{\Delta U}{q} = \frac{2.67 \times 10^5 \text{ J}}{-0.00634 \text{ C}} = -4.21 \times 10^7 \text{ V}$$

Since it is initially shot far from the midpoint, its initial potential is 0. Thus, its final potential must be 4.21 x 10⁷ V. Both particles exert a potential on the charge, but they will always be equidistant from the charge, since the charge is traveling straight down towards the center.

$$V_{final} = \frac{k \cdot q_1}{r} + \frac{k \cdot q_2}{r}$$

$$-4.21 \times 10^7 \text{V} = \frac{(8.99 \times 10^9 \frac{\text{N} \cdot \text{m}^2}{\text{C}^2}) \cdot (-0.00912 \text{ C})}{r} + \frac{(8.99 \times 10^9 \frac{\text{N} \cdot \text{m}^2}{\text{C}^2}) \cdot (-0.00912 \text{ C})}{r}$$

$$r = 2 \cdot \frac{(8.99 \times 10^9 \frac{\text{N} \cdot \text{m}^2}{\text{C}^2}) \cdot (-0.00912 \text{ C})}{-4.21 \times 10^7 \frac{\text{N} \cdot \text{m}}{\text{C}}} = 3.89 \text{ m}$$

That's not quite the answer, however. We need to figure out the vertical distance from the midpoint. We can figure that out with geometry:

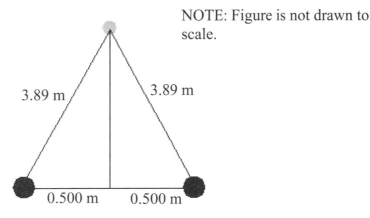

NOTE: Figure is not drawn to scale.

3.89 m   3.89 m

0.500 m   0.500 m

The vertical distance, then, is one leg of a right triangle whose hypotenuse is 3.89 m and whose other leg is 0.500 m. The vertical distance, then, is 3.86 m.

c. The particle will be traveling at 607 m/sec again. When the particle accelerates back, the electric field will restore all of the kinetic energy it initially took away.

7. a. The capacitance, charge, and potential difference are related by Equation (12.9). If the charge is left the same but the capacitance is doubled, the potential difference decreases by a factor of 2. Thus, the new potential is ½·ΔV_1.

b. Any of the equations for energy will work to analyze this. Equation (12.13) says that the energy is proportional to Q^2 and inversely proportional to the capacitance. Since Q stayed the same, the only thing that changed was the capacitance, which doubled. That would halve the energy. Thus, the new energy is ½·E_1.

8. a. The physicist would have to <u>increase the length of each side by a factor of $\sqrt{2}$</u>. Remember, the capacitance depends on *area*. The area of a plate is the length times the width. To double the area, you increase length and width by $\sqrt{2}$.

b. The capacitance is inversely proportional to the distance between the plates. Thus, <u>he would have to decrease the distance between the plates by a factor of 2</u>.

9. The charge and energy give us enough information to determine the capacitance:

$$U_{cap} = \frac{1}{2} \cdot \frac{Q^2}{C}$$

$$C = \frac{Q^2}{2 \cdot U_{cap}} = \frac{(4.56 \times 10^{-5} \text{ C})^2}{2 \cdot 1{,}090 \text{ J}} = 9.54 \times 10^{-13} \frac{C}{V}$$

Now that we know the capacitance, we can get the distance between the plates:

$$C = \frac{\varepsilon_o \cdot A}{d}$$

$$d = \frac{\varepsilon_o \cdot A}{C} = \frac{8.85 \times 10^{-12} \frac{C^2}{N \cdot m^2} \cdot (0.0341 \text{ m}) \cdot (0.0341 \text{ m})}{9.54 \times 10^{-13} \frac{C}{V}} = 0.0108 \frac{V \cdot C}{N} = 0.0108 \frac{J}{N} = \underline{0.0108 \text{ m}}$$

Notice that since a Volt is a J/C, and since a Joule is a N·m, the units work out to meters.

10. a. We are given enough information to calculate the potential difference between the plates:

$$\Delta V = \frac{Q}{C}$$

$$\Delta V = \frac{9.66 \times 10^{-5} \text{ C}}{1.34 \times 10^{-6} \frac{\text{C}}{\text{V}}} = 72.1 \text{ V}$$

That's the potential difference that the electron experiences. The change in potential energy, then, is:

$$\Delta U = q \cdot \Delta V = (-1.6 \times 10^{-19} \text{ C}) \cdot (72.1 \frac{\text{J}}{\text{C}}) = -1.2 \times 10^{-17} \text{ J}$$

All of that potential energy loss turns into kinetic energy gain. Since the electron started at rest, the kinetic energy it gains is all of the kinetic energy it has.

$$KE = \frac{1}{2} \cdot m \cdot v^2$$

$$v = \sqrt{\frac{2 \cdot KE}{m}} = \sqrt{\frac{2 \cdot (1.2 \times 10^{-17} \text{ J})}{(9.31 \times 10^{-31} \text{ kg})}} = \underline{5.1 \times 10^6 \ \frac{\text{m}}{\text{sec}}}$$

b. The electric field of a parallel plate capacitor is given by Equation (12.12):

$$\Delta V = E \cdot d$$

$$E = \frac{\Delta V}{d} = \frac{72.1 \text{ V}}{0.0035 \text{ m}} = 21,000 \ \frac{\text{V}}{\text{m}}$$

A V/m is the same as a N/C, so the electric field has a magnitude of 21,000 N/C.

SOLUTIONS TO THE TEST FOR MODULE #13

1. We know the power and the current, so we can get the resistance:

$$P = I^2 \cdot R$$

$$R = \frac{P}{I^2} = \frac{15.0 \, \dfrac{J}{\sec}}{(1.43 \, \dfrac{C}{\sec})^2} = 7.34 \, \frac{\dfrac{J}{\sec}}{\dfrac{C^2}{\sec^2}} = 7.34 \, \frac{J \cdot \sec}{C^2} = 7.34 \, \frac{V \cdot \sec}{C} = 7.34 \, \frac{V}{A} = = 7.34 \ \Omega$$

2. Only the resistors in parallel can break without causing current to stop flowing in the rest of the circuit. Thus, the 4.00 Ω, 8.00 Ω, or 9.00 Ω resistor could break without stopping current flow in the rest of the circuit.

3. Three things affect resistance: resistivity (determined by the material), length, and cross-sectional area. The first two are the same in all resistors, so it must be the cross-sectional area that is different. The 9.00 Ω resistor is $9.00/5.00 = 1.80$ times more resistive. That must mean its cross-sectional area is 1.80 times *smaller*. Thus, the cross-sectional area is A/1.80.

4. Since we are just dealing with the total current, we can replace all of the resistors with one equivalent resistor. The 4.00 Ω, 8.00 Ω, and 9.00 Ω resistors are all in parallel, so they have an equivalent resistance of:

$$\frac{1}{R_{eff}} = \frac{1}{R_1} + \frac{1}{R_2} + \frac{1}{R_3} = \frac{1}{4.00 \ \Omega} + \frac{1}{8.00 \ \Omega} + \frac{1}{9.00 \ \Omega} = 0.486 \, \frac{1}{\Omega}$$

$$R_{eff} = \frac{1}{0.486 \, \dfrac{1}{\Omega}} = 2.06 \ \Omega$$

When we replace the three parallel resistors with this one, we have three resistors (5.00 Ω, 2.06 Ω, and 7.00 Ω) in series, which gives a total resistance of 14.06 Ω. Thus, this circuit is equivalent to a battery hooked up to one 14.06 Ω resistor.

$$V = I \cdot R = (1.00 \ A) \cdot (14.06 \ \Omega) = 14.1 \ V$$

5. We can get the power from the current and voltage:

$$P = I \cdot V = (1.00 \ A) \cdot (14.1 \ V) = (1.00 \, \frac{\text{C}}{\sec}) \cdot (14.1 \, \frac{J}{\text{C}}) = 14.1 \ \text{Watts}$$

We can now use the time to calculate the work (energy dissipated):

$$P = \frac{W}{\Delta t}$$

$$W = P \cdot \Delta t = (14.1 \ \frac{J}{\text{sec}}) \cdot (3.60 \times 10^3 \ \text{sec}) = \underline{50{,}800 \ J}$$

6. a. When no current flows, the emf is the same as the potential difference, <u>9.00 V</u>.

b. When current flows, the internal resistance of the battery must be taken into account. Thus, we have a circuit like that drawn to the right. The two resistors are in series, so the total resistance of the circuit is 27.0 Ω. The current, then, is:

$$V = I \cdot R$$

$$I = \frac{V}{R} = \frac{9.00 \ V}{27.0 \ \Omega} = 0.333 \ A$$

The 2.0 Ω resistor is in the battery, however. Thus, the voltage drop across that resistor lowers the potential difference between the two sides of the battery:

$$V = I \cdot R = (0.333 \ A) \cdot (2.0 \ \Omega) = 0.67 \ V$$

The battery, then, has a potential difference of <u>8.33 V</u> in this circuit.

7. a. The capacitor will charge until its potential difference is equal to that of the battery, <u>1.5 V</u>.

b. <u>Current will not immediately stop flowing, because the charged capacitor will act like a battery until its charge is drained.</u>

8. This will take an application of Kirchhoff's Rules, so we might as well choose a loop. In this loop, the current (I_1) starts from the battery and goes through the 15.0 Ω resistor. Then, it can split and go to the 30.0 Ω resistor or the 25.0 Ω resistor. Only part of it (I_2) will go through the 25.0 Ω resistor. Then, the current recombines with the rest and encounters the 9.00 V battery, negative side first. Thus:

$$9.00 \ V \ - \ I_1 \cdot (15.0 \ \Omega) - I_2 \ (25.0 \ \Omega) = 0$$

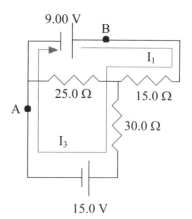

Now we need another loop. In this loop, I_1 leaves the battery and goes through the 15.0 Ω resistor. The part that did not go through the 25.0 Ω resistor goes through the 30.0 Ω resistor, and we will call it I_3. It also encounters the 15.0 V battery positive side first, and then encounters the 9.00 V battery negative side first.

$$9.00 \text{ V} - 15.0 \text{ V} - I_1 \cdot (15.0 \text{ Ω}) - I_3 \cdot (30.0 \text{ Ω}) = 0$$

From the junction rule, we also know that:

$$I_1 = I_2 + I_3$$

Putting I_2 in terms of I_1:

$$9.00 \text{ V} - I_1 \cdot (15.0 \text{ Ω}) - I_2 \cdot (25.0 \text{ Ω}) = 0$$

$$I_2 = \frac{9.00 \text{ V} - I_1 \cdot (15.0 \text{ Ω})}{25.0 \text{ Ω}}$$

Putting I_3 in terms of I_1:

$$-6.00 \text{ V} - I_1 \cdot (15.0 \text{ Ω}) - I_3 \cdot (30.0 \text{ Ω}) = 0$$

$$I_3 = \frac{-6.00 \text{ V} - I_1 \cdot (15.0 \text{ Ω})}{30.0 \text{ Ω}}$$

Now we can put those expressions into the final equation:

$$I_1 = I_2 + I_3$$

$$I_1 = \frac{9.00 \text{ V} - I_1 \cdot (15.0 \text{ Ω})}{25.0 \text{ Ω}} + \frac{-6.00 \text{ V} - I_1 \cdot (15.0 \text{ Ω})}{30.0 \text{ Ω}}$$

$$(30.0 \text{ Ω}) \cdot I_1 = 10.8 \text{ V} - I_1 \cdot (18.0 \text{ Ω}) - 6.00 \text{ V} - I_1 \cdot (15.0 \text{ Ω})$$

$$I_1 = \frac{4.8 \text{ V}}{63.0 \text{ Ω}} = 0.076 \text{ A}$$

To answer the question, we need I_3:

$$I_3 = \frac{-6.00\ \text{V} - I_1 \cdot (15.0\ \Omega)}{30.0\ \Omega} = \frac{-6.00\ \text{V} - (0.076\ \text{A}) \cdot (15.0\ \Omega)}{30.0\ \Omega} = -0.24\ \text{A}$$

The negative just means we got the direction wrong in our drawings. Thus, <u>0.24 A flow through the 30.0 Ω resistor</u>.

9. To get the current flow, we need to evaluate I_2. We know I_1 is drawn correctly in problem #8 and that I_3 is drawn backwards in problem #8. What about I_2?

$$I_2 = \frac{9.00\ \text{V} - I_1 \cdot (15.0\ \Omega)}{25.0\ \Omega} = \frac{9.00\ \text{V} - (0.076\ \text{A}) \cdot (15.0\ \Omega)}{25.0\ \Omega} = 0.32\ \text{A}$$

Since this number is positive, we know that we had it drawn correctly originally. Thus, we can take our diagrams from problem #8 and just reverse I_3.

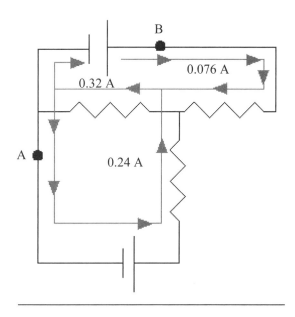

10. To figure out the potential difference between the two points, we just start at point A and follow the current to point B. The current starts at point A and crosses the 15.0 V battery, negative side first. Then, 0.238 A crosses over the 30.0 Ω resistor. Then, we have to take a right, passing across the 15.0 Ω resistor *against* the current. That raises the potential. Thus:

$$15.0\ \text{V} - (0.238\ \text{A}) \cdot (30.0\ \Omega) + (0.0762\ \text{A}) \cdot (15.0\ \Omega) = 9.00\ \text{V}$$

This means that the current *gained* 9.00 V going from point A to point B. Thus, <u>point A is at a potential that is 9.00 V lower than point B</u>. You could also just start at point B and go backwards to point A. To do that, you encounter the positive side of the battery first. Thus, the change in potential going from B to A is -9.00 V (which is the same conclusion).

11. Don't let this diagram fool you. The middle resistor is tilted, but it is simply in parallel with the other two. After all, as current enters, it can move through *any three* of the resistors. Thus, this is a really simply problem:

$$\frac{1}{R_{eff}} = \frac{1}{R_1} + \frac{1}{R_2} + \frac{1}{R_3} = \frac{1}{25.0\ \Omega} + \frac{1}{15.0\ \Omega} + \frac{1}{20.0\ \Omega} = 0.1567\ \frac{1}{\Omega}$$

$$R_{eff} = \frac{1}{0.1567\ \frac{1}{\Omega}} = \underline{6.382\ \Omega}$$

12. To get the equivalent capacitance, we need to get rid of the parallel capacitors first. That's easy, since they just add to one equivalent capacitor equal to 40.0 μF. Thus, the circuit is really three capacitors (10.0 μF, 40.0 μF, 15.0 μF) in series.

$$\frac{1}{C_{eff}} = \frac{1}{C_1} + \frac{1}{C_2} + \frac{1}{C_3} = \frac{1}{10.0\ \mu F} + \frac{1}{40.0\ \mu F} + \frac{1}{15.0\ \mu F}$$

$$C_{eff} = \underline{5.22\ \mu F}$$

13. First we can calculate the charge stored on the effective capacitor:

$$\Delta V = \frac{Q}{C}$$

$$Q = \Delta V \cdot C = (9.00\ \cancel{V}) \cdot (5.22 \times 10^{-6}\ \frac{C}{\cancel{V}}) = 4.70 \times 10^{-5}\ C$$

Now, the three capacitors which are in series to make up this capacitor must all have the same charge. Thus, the charge on the 10.0 μF capacitor will be 4.70 x 10⁻⁵ C.

SOLUTIONS TO THE TEST FOR MODULE #14

1. The force exerted by the magnetic field on the wire is clearly pointing up, because the wire is moving up when the current flows through it. Since the current flows to the right along the connecting wire, if I point the fingers of my right hand in that direction, I must curl them *into* the paper in order to get my thumb to point up. Thus, the magnetic field is pointing into the page.

2. When the connecting wire moves in the magnetic field, a motional emf is generated in the wire which opposes the voltage that is causing the current. Thus, the voltage must be increased to counteract the motional emf. You can see that the emf opposes the voltage that makes the current, because the right hand rule tells us that **v** x **B** points to the left. That means the left hand side of the connecting wire will be positive. That opposes the current.

3. To get the wire to float without traveling up or down, the magnetic force must equal the gravitational force:

$$F_b = m \cdot g$$

$$I \cdot \ell \cdot B \cdot \sin\theta = m \cdot g$$

$$I = \frac{m \cdot g}{B \cdot \ell \cdot \sin\theta} = \frac{(0.0150 \text{ kg}) \cdot (9.81 \frac{m}{\sec^2})}{(0.367 \text{ T}) \cdot (0.500 \text{ m})} = 0.802 \frac{N}{T \cdot m} = 0.802 \frac{\cancel{N}}{\frac{\cancel{N}}{A \cdot \cancel{m}} \cdot \cancel{m}} = \underline{0.802 \text{ A}}$$

4. The emf is zero. There is no emf unless the flux changes. The magnetic field is not changing, because the wire's current is not changing, and the surface area is not changing. Thus, the flux does not change and no emf is generated.

5. The charged particle will move in a circle, with a radius given by Equation (14.5). The time it takes to travel that circle is the circumference of the circle ($2\pi r$) divided by the speed:

$$T = \frac{2\pi r}{v}$$

We can plug Equation (14.5) in for "r" to get:

$$T = \frac{2\pi \cdot \frac{m \cdot \cancel{v}}{q \cdot B}}{\cancel{v}} = \underline{2\pi \cdot \frac{m}{q \cdot B}}$$

6. a. The current depends on the emf, which depends on the change in flux. Initially, the flux is:

$$\Phi_o = \mathbf{B} \bullet \mathbf{A} = B \cdot A \cdot \cos(0) = (0.654 \text{ T}) \cdot (0.250 \text{ m}) \cdot (0.250 \text{ m}) = 0.0409 \text{ Wb}$$

When the magnetic field reaches zero, the flux will be zero as well.

$$\frac{\Delta\Phi}{\Delta t} = \frac{0 \text{ T} \cdot \text{m}^2 - 0.0409 \text{ T} \cdot \text{m}^2}{1.00 \text{ sec}} = -0.0409 \frac{\frac{N}{A \cdot m} \cdot m^2}{\text{sec}} = -0.0409 \frac{\frac{J \cdot sec}{C}}{sec} = -0.0409 \text{ V}$$

That's the emf. It is negative because the flux decreased. We will deal with that when we determine direction. For now, let's just determine the current:

$$V = I \cdot R$$

$$I = \frac{V}{R} = \frac{0.0409 \text{ V}}{0.00341 \text{ }\Omega} = \underline{12.0 \text{ A}}$$

b. The magnetic field lines point into the page. The flux *decreases*. To oppose that decrease, the current's magnetic field must also point into the page. Thus, <u>the current flows clockwise</u>.

7. a. <u>The wires are repelled from one another</u>. Consider the top wire. It "feels" the magnetic field from the bottom wire, which the right hand rule tells us goes into the page in the vicinity of the top wire. To determine the force that the wire experiences, we do the cross product between *ℓ* and **B**. The top wire's current goes to the right, so that is the direction of *ℓ*. When we cross it with **B**, which goes into the page, we get a force pointed up, which is away from the other wire.

b. The strength of the magnetic field from a current-carrying wire is given by:

$$B = \frac{\mu_0 \cdot I}{2\pi \cdot r}$$

The force that another current-carrying wire experiences due to a magnetic field is:

$$\mathbf{F} = I \cdot (\ell \times \mathbf{B})$$

Thus, the force that the top wire experiences due to the bottom wire is:

$$F = I \cdot \ell \cdot B \cdot \sin\theta$$

The magnetic field is into the page and the current is flowing to the right, so $\theta = 90$. Thus:

$$F = I \cdot \ell \cdot \frac{\mu_0 \cdot I}{2\pi \cdot r}$$

The force per unit length is this force divided by the length of the wire, which is ℓ:

$$\frac{F}{\ell} = \frac{I \cdot \ell \cdot \frac{\mu_0 \cdot I}{2\pi \cdot r}}{\ell} = \frac{\mu_0 \cdot I^2}{2\pi \cdot r}$$

8. a. <u>No, the bar will not move.</u> The constant magnetic field cannot exert a force unless the bar is *already* moving.

b. <u>The bar will slow down and eventually come to a halt.</u> If the bar is shoved to the left, the electrons in the bar will move to the left. Crossing **v** with **B** gives us a direction of down. Since the electrons move the opposite way due to their negative charge, the top of the conductor becomes negative and the bottom becomes positive. Current, therefore, will travel counterclockwise. The bar, then, is a portion of a current-carrying wire in which current travels down the bar. The magnetic force that such a current-carrying wire will experience points to the right, according to ℓ x **B**. Thus, the force experienced as a result of the current is opposite of the motion, so the bar will slow down and eventually stop.

c. The magnetic flux into the page increases. To oppose that increase, the current will have to develop a magnetic field that points out of the page inside the rectangle. Thus, once again, <u>the current travels counterclockwise.</u>

d. As the magnetic field is being changed, current flows counterclockwise, or *down* the conductor. According to ℓ x **B**, then, it experiences a force pointed to the right. Thus, <u>the bar will begin to accelerate to the right.</u>

e. When the magnetic field is held constant again, the flux will still be changing, because the bar will still be in motion from when the magnetic field was changing. However, as the bar moves to the right, *the flux will decrease*, because the rectangle will be getting smaller. This will set up a clockwise current. That current will experience a force to the left, which will begin to slow the bar down. Thus, <u>the bar will slow down and come to a halt.</u>

9. <u>There is no way to adjust the magnetic and electric fields so that they are nonzero and the particle travels straight.</u> If the particle is positive, the electric field will push it down. The magnetic field will also push it down, because the right hand rule says **v** x **B** is pointed down. If the particle is negative, the electric field will push it up. Well, **v** x **B** is pointed down, but a negative particle experiences a force opposite of **v** x **B**, so the magnetic force on the negatively-charged particle will still be up. Either way, then, the particle will be deflected.

SOLUTIONS TO THE TEST FOR MODULE #15

1. <u>Nothing will happen</u>. Remember, if the electron cannot absorb just the energy it needs to get to the next orbit, it cannot move, because it cannot be anywhere except in one of the allowed orbits. Since absorbing 15 eV of energy would put the electron between the next two orbits, it cannot absorb the energy.

2. To get photoelectrons, the light must give the electrons enough energy to escape the metal. The energy required is given by the work function.

$$E = h \cdot f$$

$$f = \frac{E}{h} = \frac{4.70 \ \cancel{eV}}{4.14 \times 10^{-15} \ \cancel{eV} \cdot sec} = \underline{1.14 \times 10^{15} \ \frac{1}{sec}}$$

3. <u>Equation (b) represents Bohr's quantum assumption</u>, because it restricts the value of the orbit radius.

4. Once the electron got up to the fourth orbit, there are *many* ways it could get down. First, it could jump straight from the fourth orbit back to the first. That would result in one wavelength of light. It could also jump from the fourth to the third (another wavelength of light for a total of 2 so far), from the third to the second (another wavelength for a total of 3), and then from the second to the first (yet another wavelength for a total of 4). However, it could jump from the fourth to the third (we already considered that wavelength), and *then* jump straight from the third to the first (that's a new wavelength, so the total is now 5). Also, it could jump from the fourth to the second (another new one for a total of 6) and then from the second to the first (we already considered that one, however). Thus, there are a total of <u>6 possible wavelengths</u> of light that can be emitted when the electron decays from the fourth orbit back to the first one.

5. <u>This is atomic absorption spectroscopy</u>. If the scientist is looking at what light didn't pass through, then that light must have been absorbed.

6. The radius is given by Equation (15.18):

$$r = (0.529 \ \text{Å}) \cdot \frac{n^2}{Z}$$

The radius, then, is inversely proportional to the atomic number. Thus, the radius is three times larger for the hydrogen as compared to the lithium ion. Thus, <u>r = 3a</u>.

7. The amount of energy needed for an electronic transition is governed by Equation (15.15):

$$\Delta E = (13.6 \text{ eV}) \cdot Z^2 \cdot \left[\left(\frac{1}{n_{final}}\right)^2 - \left(\frac{1}{n_{initial}}\right)^2\right]$$

$$\Delta E = (13.6 \text{ eV}) \cdot 1^2 \cdot \left[\left(\frac{1}{4}\right)^2 - \left(\frac{1}{2}\right)^2\right] = \underline{-2.55 \text{ eV}}$$

The negative sign just means that the electron absorbed the energy.

8. We first need to get the energy difference:

$$\Delta E = (13.6 \text{ eV}) \cdot Z^2 \cdot \left[\left(\frac{1}{n_{final}}\right)^2 - \left(\frac{1}{n_{initial}}\right)^2\right]$$

$$\Delta E = (13.6 \text{ eV}) \cdot 2^2 \cdot \left[\left(\frac{1}{2}\right)^2 - \left(\frac{1}{4}\right)^2\right] = 10.2 \text{ eV}$$

Now we can get the frequency:

$$E = h \cdot f$$

$$10.2 \text{ eV} = (4.14 \times 10^{-15} \text{ eV} \cdot \text{s}) \cdot f$$

$$f = 2.46 \times 10^{15} \frac{1}{s}$$

Now we can get the wavelength:

$$f = \frac{v}{\lambda}$$

$$2.46 \times 10^{15} \frac{1}{s} = \frac{2.998 \times 10^8 \frac{m}{s}}{\lambda}$$

$$\lambda = \underline{1.22 \times 10^{-7} \text{ m}}$$

9. The energy difference will tell us the final Bohr orbit:

$$\Delta E = (2.18 \times 10^{-18} \text{ J}) \cdot Z^2 \cdot \left[\left(\frac{1}{n_{final}} \right)^2 - \left(\frac{1}{n_{initial}} \right)^2 \right]$$

$$4.09 \times 10^{-19} \text{ J} = (2.18 \times 10^{-18} \text{ J}) \cdot 1^2 \cdot \left[\left(\frac{1}{n_{final}} \right)^2 - \left(\frac{1}{4} \right)^2 \right]$$

$$\frac{4.09 \times 10^{-19} \text{ J}}{(2.18 \times 10^{-18} \text{ J}) \cdot 1^2} = \left(\frac{1}{n_{final}} \right)^2 - \frac{1}{16}$$

$$0.188 + \frac{1}{16} = \left(\frac{1}{n_{final}} \right)^2$$

$$\frac{1}{n_{final}} = 0.500$$

$$n_{final} = 2$$

The electron lands in the <u>second Bohr orbit</u>.

10. The energy will tell us the orbit number:

$$E = -R_h \cdot Z^2 \cdot \left(\frac{1}{n} \right)^2$$

$$-30.6 \text{ eV} = -(13.6 \text{ eV}) \cdot 3^2 \cdot \left(\frac{1}{n} \right)^2$$

$$\left(\frac{1}{n} \right)^2 = \frac{-30.6 \text{ eV}}{(-13.6 \text{ eV}) \cdot 9} = 0.250$$

$$\frac{1}{n} = 0.500$$

$$n = 2$$

Now that we know the orbit number, we can calculate the distance:

$$r = (0.529 \text{ Å}) \cdot \frac{n^2}{Z}$$

$$r = (0.529 \text{ Å}) \cdot \frac{2^2}{3}$$

$$r = \underline{0.705 \text{ Å}}$$

11. a. The ground state is the lowest energy state. Thus, it is -34.5 eV.

b. To get free of the atom, its energy must no longer be negative (bound energies are negative). Thus, it must absorb at least 34.5 eV of energy.

c. If it goes from the lowest energy to the highest energy state, it must absorb the difference between the two states:
$$-10.1 \text{ eV} - -34.5 \text{ eV} = 24.4 \text{ eV}$$

This would require light of frequency:

$$E = h \cdot f$$

$$f = \frac{E}{h} = \frac{24.4 \text{ eV}}{4.14 \times 10^{-15} \text{ eV} \cdot \text{s}} = \underline{5.89 \times 10^{15} \text{ Hz}}$$

12. The de Broglie wavelength will give us the speed:

$$\lambda = \frac{h}{p} = \frac{h}{m \cdot v}$$

$$v = \frac{h}{m \cdot \lambda} = \frac{6.63 \times 10^{-34} \text{ J} \cdot \text{sec}}{(9.11 \times 10^{-31} \text{ kg}) \cdot (8.12 \times 10^{-7} \text{ m})} = 896 \ \frac{\frac{\text{kg} \cdot \text{m}^2}{\text{sec}^2} \cdot \cancel{\text{sec}}}{\cancel{\text{kg} \cdot \text{m}}} = \underline{896 \ \frac{\text{m}}{\text{sec}}}$$

13. Based on the frequency, the maximum energy that the electron can get is:

$$E = h \cdot f = (4.14 \times 10^{-15} \text{ eV} \cdot \cancel{\text{sec}}) \cdot (1.92 \times 10^{15} \ \frac{1}{\cancel{\text{sec}}}) = 7.95 \text{ eV}$$

If the maximum kinetic energy is 3.22 eV, then the electrons lost 4.73 eV of energy escaping the metal. Thus, the work function is 4.73 eV.

SOLUTIONS TO THE TEST FOR MODULE #16

1. An ^{56}Fe nucleus has more binding energy than any other nucleus in Creation. That's why it is considered the most stable nucleus in Creation.

2. Pions are the particles that are exchanged between nucleons. This particle exchange is responsible for the strong nuclear force, which holds the nucleus together.

3. The first nucleus is more stable, as it has more binding energy per nucleon.

4. The only thing that can annihilate matter is antimatter. Thus, the electron must have collided with a positron.

5. A nucleus is stable if it lies in the valley of stable nuclei in Figure 16.2. ^{12}C, ^{145}Nd, and ^{65}Zn all lie in the valley and are thus stable. ^{75}Mg is above the valley, ^{80}Zr and ^{170}Pt lie below the valley.

6. ^{40}Ar is lighter than ^{56}Fe. This means it will produce energy only in nuclear fusion, not nuclear fission.

7. Since carbon's atomic number is 6, all carbon atoms have 6 protons. The mass number, which is the sum of the protons and neutrons in a nucleus, therefore indicates that a ^{12}C nucleus has 6 neutrons. The sum of the masses of 6 protons and 6 neutrons is:

$$6 \times (1.0073 \text{ amu}) + 6 \times (1.0087 \text{ amu}) = 12.0960 \text{ amu}$$

Since the mass of a ^{12}C nucleus is only 11.9967 amu, there is a mass deficit of 0.0993 amu. This mass deficit is converted to energy according to Equation (8.7). To use this equation, however, we must have consistent units. Since we have the speed of light in m/sec, then the energy will come out in Joules as long as the mass is in kilograms (remember, a Joule is a $(kg \cdot m^2)/sec^2$). Thus, we must first convert the mass deficit to kg:

$$\frac{0.0993 \text{ amu}}{1} \times \frac{1.6605 \times 10^{-27} \text{ kg}}{1 \text{ amu}} = 1.65 \times 10^{-28} \text{ kg}$$

Now we can use Equation (8.7):

$$E = m \cdot c^2 = (1.65 \times 10^{-28} \text{ kg}) \cdot (2.998 \times 10^8 \frac{m}{sec})^2 = 1.48 \times 10^{-11} \text{ J}$$

To get the binding energy per nucleon, we must divide by the number of nucleons (12):

$$\frac{1.48 \times 10^{-11} \text{ J}}{12 \text{ nucleons}} = 1.23 \times 10^{-12} \underline{\frac{\text{J}}{\text{nucleon}}}$$

8. Since we know that there are 3 protons and 3 neutrons in a ^{6}Li nucleus, we can figure out the mass of the nucleons:

$$3 \text{ x } (1.0073 \text{ amu}) + 3 \text{ x } (1.0087 \text{ amu}) = 6.0480 \text{ amu}$$

This isn't the mass of the nucleus, however, because the nucleons always lose some mass when they form a nucleus. How much mass do these nucleons lose? We can calculate it from the binding energy:

$$E = m \cdot c^2$$

$$5.16 \times 10^{-12} \text{ J} = m \cdot (2.998 \times 10^8 \frac{m}{\text{sec}})^2$$

$$m = 5.74 \times 10^{-29} \text{ kg}$$

We can convert that to amu:

$$\frac{5.74 \times 10^{-29} \text{ kg}}{1} \times \frac{1 \text{ amu}}{1.6605 \times 10^{-27} \text{ kg}} = 0.0346 \text{ amu}$$

Now remember, this is the mass that the nucleons *lose* when they make a nucleus. Thus, the mass of the nucleus is:

$$6.0480 \text{ amu} - 0.0346 \text{ amu} = \underline{6.0134 \text{ amu}}$$

9. In beta decay, the nucleus emits a beta particle $_{-1}^{0}e$ so that a neutron can turn into a proton. ^{248}Np has 93 protons and 155 neutrons. When a neutron turns into a proton, the result will be a nucleus with 94 protons and 154 neutrons. That is ^{248}Pu. The reaction, then, is:

$$\underline{_{93}^{248}\text{Np} \rightarrow _{94}^{248}\text{Pu} + _{-1}^{0}e}$$

10. In alpha decay, the nucleus loses 2 protons and 2 neutrons in the form of an alpha particle. ^{218}Po has 84 protons and 134 neutrons. When it loses 2 protons and 2 neutrons, the result will be a nucleus with 82 protons and 132 neutrons, which is ^{214}Pb. The reaction is:

$$\underline{_{84}^{218}\text{Po} \rightarrow _{82}^{214}\text{Pb} + _{2}^{4}\text{He}}$$

11. In this problem, the elapsed time is an integral multiple of the half-life. Thus, the easiest way to solve the problem is to realize that after 14.3 days, the 44.0 grams will decay to 22.0 grams. After the second 14.3 days (for a total of 28.6 days), the remaining 22.0 grams will decay to 11.0 grams.

12. In this case, the elapsed time is not an integral multiple of the half-life. Thus, we must use the equations:

$$10.76 \text{ yrs} = \frac{0.693}{k}$$

$$k = \frac{0.693}{10.76 \text{ yrs}} = 0.0644 \ \frac{1}{yr}$$

Now we can use Equation (16.5). Remember, "N" can refer to number of grams or number of nuclei.

$$N = N_o \cdot e^{-kt}$$

$$N = (15.0 \text{ grams}) \cdot e^{-(0.0644\frac{1}{yr}) \cdot (20.0 \text{ yrs})} = \underline{4.14 \text{ grams}}$$